CHEMISTRY

Counts

THIRD EDITION

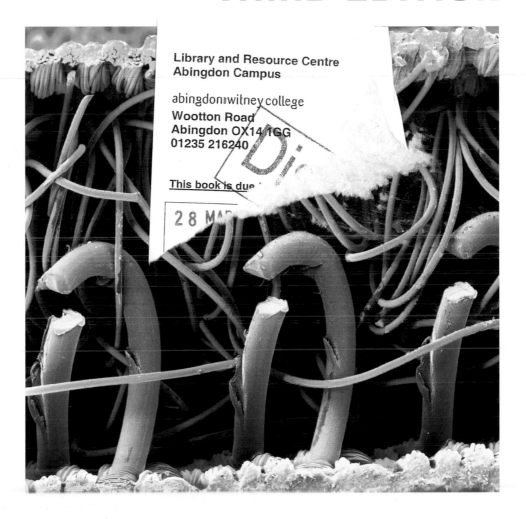

GRAHAM HILL

Hodder & Stoughton

A MEMBER OF THE HODDER HEADLINE GROUP

Acknowledgements

The publishers would like to thank the following companies and individuals who have given permission to reproduce photographs in this book. Every effort has been made to trace and acknowledge ownership of copyright. The publishers will be glad to make suitable arrangements with any copyright holder whom it has not been possible to contact.

Aluminium Federation (73 top; 125), Andrew Lambert (9 all; 130), Associated Press (117 right), AutoExpress Picture Library (229 bottom), Bruce Coleman Collection (22 top; 39; 108; 182), Burton McCall/Mag-Lite (83), Corbis (2; 3; 4; 5 all; 7 bottom left; 8; 11; 21 bottom; 22 bottom; 26 top right; 30all; 35; 36; 37; 38; 48; 50; 56 bottom; 59 all; 61; 62; 70 top; 80 top; 82 right; 99; 107 bottom; 113; 116; 119; 120; 122 bottom; 124; 128; 132 all; 137; 139 bottom; 142 bottom; 156; 158 top; 159; 172 right; 178; 184; 188; 193; 215 middle left; 227; 233; 249 bottom; 261; 268; 269; 274), Empics (21 top), FLPA (34), Geosciences Photo Library (285 top), GSF Picture Library (122 top; 160 bottom; 170 right; 279; 281; 283 top; 284; 285 all but top; 286; 291 bottom; 295 all), Hodder & Stoughton (1; 26 top left; 32; 46 right; 51 bottom right; 56 top; 66; 69; 79 top; 80 bottom; 81; 82 left and middle; 104 top; 118 bottom; 140 top; 142 top; 148; 149; 158 bottom; 169; 175; 176; 199 all; 200 all; 202 all; 211; 212; 214 all but far left; 218; 237 all; 242 right; 262; 263; 291 top), Holt Studios (79 bottom; 100; 246 all; 247; 248; 249 top), James Davis Photography (174), Life File (12; 14; 46 left; 58; 60 all; 89; 98; 102; 104 bottom; 117 top; 131; 144 all; 145; 160 top; 172 left; 186 left and middle; 204; 205; 206; 210 right; 214 far left; 215 all but middle left; 221; 229 top; 234; 238 all; 239; 240 all), Mary Evans (26 bottom), Norman Conquest (118 top), Photofusion (90 top), R D Battersby (210 left), Robert Brook Environmental Images (195 all), Science Photo Library (7 all but bottom left; 13; 24; 45; 51 top and bottom left; 70 bottom; 71; 73 bottom; 78; 84; 90 bottom; 92; 105; 107 top; 114; 127; 138; 139 top; 140 bottom; 141 all; 151; 152; 170 left; 171 all; 173 all; 179; 186 right; 196; 203; 208 all; 228; 232; 242 left; 257; 258; 259; 260; 264; 265; 266; 273; 283 bottom), TopFoto (181), Topham Picturepoint (97; 180), QA Photos (31)

Cover photo
An electronmicroscope photo of a velcro fastening for clothes and footwear. The velcro material is nylon polymer made in two separate parts. One part has a hooked surface (blue in the photo) and the other part has a smoother surface with loose strands (green in the photo).
When the two surfaces are brought together, they form a strong bond which can be peeled apart.
Magnification is ×35

Orders: please contact Bookpoint Ltd, 130 Milton Park, Abingdon, Oxon OX14 4SB.
Telephone: (44) 01235 827720. Fax: (44) 01235 400454. Lines are open from 9.00–6.00, Monday to Saturday, with a 24 hour message answering service. Email address: orders@bookpoint.co.uk

British Library Cataloguing in Publication Data
A catalogue record for this title is available from the British Library

ISBN 0 340 79050 4

This edition published 2002
Second edition published 1995
First edition published 1986
Impression number   10 9 8 7 6 5 4 3 2 1
Year   2007   2006   2005   2004   2003   2002

Copyright © 2002 Graham Hill

Typeset by J&L Composition Ltd, Filey, North Yorkshire.
Printed in Italy for Hodder & Stoughton Educational, a division of Hodder Headline Ltd, 338 Euston Road, London NW1 3BH.

Preface

This book is about chemistry and the part that chemistry plays in our everyday lives, in industry and in society. I hope that you will find it lively, colourful and interesting.

The Third Edition
This third edition of the book has been fully revised and updated to meet the requirements of the new specifications (syllabuses) for GCSE Chemistry and the Chemistry Component of GCSE Double Science in Key Stage 4 of the National Curriculum. The content of the book has been very carefully matched to the GCSE Chemistry requirements of all four awarding bodies – AQA, Edexcel, OCR and WJEC. This includes an extension of the topics related to Ideas and Evidence and to opportunities to practise and use ICT skills.

Sections in Chemistry Counts
Chemistry Counts is divided into twelve major sections. These sections are themselves divided into several two, three or four-page units, each of which ends with several short questions to help you to understand the topic you have just studied.

The first one or two units in most of the twelve sections revise key ideas and crucial facts from your studies in Key Stage 3. These units link with KS3 and provide a smooth introduction to KS4.

At the end of each section, there are Activities, a Summary and Exam Questions.

The Activities are related to different aspects of chemistry and include creative writing, text-related exercises, data response questions, ICT and problem-solving exercises. They will enable you to practise different skills and help you appreciate the wider social, environmental, economic and technological aspects of chemistry.

The Summaries will help you to focus on the important facts and ideas in each section, providing a structure to your studies.

The Exam Questions are taken from recent examinations and specimen papers provided by the awarding bodies.

Safety considerations have been given the highest priority throughout the book and in this respect I have appreciated the experienced advice of Dr. Peter Burrows, Past-Chairman of the Safeguards in Science Committee of the Association for Science Education.

Acknowledgements
Many people have influenced the planning and writing of *Chemistry Counts* and the revision for this new edition. I am particularly grateful to:

- Elisabeth Tribe, Director of Schools Publishing, Hodder and Stoughton Educational,

- Ruth Hughes, Editor of *Chemistry Counts* up to the production of page proofs,

- Kate Fowler (Editor) and Helena Ingham (Editorial Assistant) who ensured the final stages of production went through smoothly and successfully,

- John Payne, Senior Examiner with OCR for detailed advice and recommendations,

- Phil Hills, past Senior Examiner with AQA and Andrew Watts, St Benedict's School, Bury St. Edmunds for initial advice and suggestions,

- Paul Richards, Dr. Challoner's Grammar School, for help with ICT exercises,

- Countless students at Dr. Challoner's Grammar School and

- my wife, Elizabeth for typing and art work in the initial stages of production and proof reading.

It has been a privilege to continue working on a successful project with such able, enthusiastic and supportive colleagues.

Graham Hill
Amersham

May 2002

To Jennifer, Matthew, Rebecca, George and Elizabeth

How to get the most from Chemistry Counts

I hope that *Chemistry Counts* will interest and inspire you in your studies. At the same time, I want the book to help you to get the best possible grades in your GCSE studies.

Although you are probably using the book under the direction of your teacher, you may be using it on your own or doing some of both. Whichever way you are using *Chemistry Counts*, make sure you get the most from it.

How the book is structured
Chemistry Counts is divided into 12 sections, each covering a major theme of the National Curriculum. Each of these sections is divided into bite-sized units of two, three or four pages.

In most sections, the first one or two units revise key ideas and important facts from your Key Stage 3 studies and provide a smooth introduction to the Key Stage 4 material.

Finding what you want
If you are looking for information on a particular topic, look it up in the <u>Contents</u> list at the front of the book and in the <u>Index</u> at the back of the book.

Using the book in class, for homework or revision
Chemistry Counts will help you to use homework time effectively and to revise successfully for class tests and exams.

During most of your GCSE course, you will be helped and guided by your teacher. He or she will ask you to read various sections and answer specific questions from the book as you work through the GCSE course.

At other times, you will be expected to revise for topic tests and prepare for exams. This will require a good deal of self motivation on your part, particularly as the GCSE exams approach and you have study leave.

In preparing for exams and even for shorter topic tests, it is important to have a schedule.

The following suggestions will help you to get the most from *Chemistry Counts*, whether you are studying a topic for the first time or preparing for a test or exam.

- Decide which topic you wish to study.

- Use the <u>Contents</u> list and the <u>Index</u> in the book to identify the units which cover your chosen topic.

- Read the units you have identified, making brief notes or adding to the notes you already have on the topic. Words which are written in bold in *Chemistry Counts* and the <u>Summary</u> which covers your chosen topic will help you to identify the key points in each unit.

- Answer the short questions at the end of each unit which you study. You should be able to answer all these short questions fairly easily from what you have read and studied in that unit. Try to get into the habit of answering the end-of-unit questions every time you read a unit, even when your teacher does not ask you to do this.

- When you have completed the units in most of a section in *Chemistry Counts*, try to answer some of the <u>Exam Questions</u> at the end of the section. Answering these longer past exam questions is one of the best ways of preparing for an exam.

- Don't be afraid to ask your teacher if you don't understand something or you can't answer a question. Your teacher will be pleased to see your enthusiasm and commitment. Your teacher is as keen for you to do well as you are.

Finally, good luck in all your studies.

Graham Hill

Contents

A From Raw Materials to Pure Substances   1

1 Raw Materials to Useful Substances   2
2 Elements – the Simplest Materials   5
3 Elements, Mixtures and Compounds   8
4 Separating Materials   10
5 Pure Substances   14
Activities   16
Summary   19
Exam Questions   20

B Our Environment – Air and Water   21

1 The Air   22
2 Oxygen   24
3 Burning and Breathing   26
4 Rusting   28
5 Oxidation and Reduction   30
6 How Pure is Our Air?   32
7 Water Supplies   35
8 The Properties of Water   38
Activities   40
Summary   42
Exam Questions   43

C Particles, Reactions and Equations   45

1 Evidence for Particles   46
2 Particles in Motion   48
3 Atoms, Molecules and Ions   51
4 Measuring Atoms   54
5 Using Relative Atomic Masses   56
6 Particles in Reactions – Equations   58
7 Formulas and Equations   60
Activities   62
Summary   64
Exam Questions   66

D Electricity and Electrolysis   69

1 Electricity in Everyday Life   70
2 Which Substances Conduct Electricity?   72
3 Investigating Electrolysis   74
4 Charges on Ions   76
5 Electrolysis in Industry   80
6 Electroplating and Anodizing   82
Activities   84
Summary   86
Exam Questions   87

E Patterns and Properties   89

1 Looking for Patterns   90
2 Patterns of Elements   92
3 Modern Periodic Tables   94
4 The Alkali Metals   96
5 The Transition Metals   98
6 The Halogens   100
7 Reactions of Chlorine and the Halogens   102
8 The Uses of Chlorine   104
9 The Noble Gases   106
Activities   108
Summary   110
Exam Questions   111

F Metals   113

1 The Properties of Metals   114
2 Alloys   116
3 The Reactions of Metals   118
4 Extracting Metals   122
5 Extracting Iron from Iron Ore   126
6 Metal Compounds   128
7 Identifying Cations   130
Activities   132
Summary   134
Exam Questions   135

G Acids, Bases and Salts 137

1	Introducing Acids	138
2	Acids in Everyday Life	140
3	Properties of Acids	142
4	Neutralisation	145
5	Sulphuric Acid	148
6	Bases and Alkalis	150
7	Salts	152
8	Preparing Salts	154
9	Limestone for Industry	156
10	Hard Water	158
11	Softening Hard Water	160
	Activities	162
	Summary	164
	Exam Questions	166

H The Structure of Materials 169

1	Studying Structures	170
2	The Structure of Substances	172
3	Diamond and Graphite: Giant Covalent Structures	174
4	Simple Molecular Substances	177
5	Carbon Dioxide	180
6	Giant Ionic Structures	182
7	Salt – an Important Ionic Compound	184
8	From Sand to Glass	186
	Activities	188
	Summary	190
	Exam Questions	191

I Useful Products from Oil 193

1	Energy from Fuels	194
2	Crude Oil	196
3	Alkanes from Oil and Gas	199
4	Cracking – More Petrol from Crude Oil	202
5	Ethene	204
6	Polymers from Alkenes	206
7	Plastics	209
8	Alcohol from Ethene or Sugar	212
9	Ethanoic Acid and Carboxylic Acids	215
10	Energy Changes and Chemical Bonds	217
	Activities	220
	Summary	222
	Exam Questions	224

J Reaction Rates 227

1	How Fast?	228
2	Studying Reaction Rates	230
3	Making Reactions Go Faster	232
4	Temperature and Reaction Rates	234
5	Catalysts and Reaction Rates	236
6	Reversible Reactions	240
7	Manufacturing Ammonia – the Haber Process	242
8	From Ammonia to Fertilisers	245
9	The Nitrogen Cycle	248
	Activities	250
	Summary	252
	Exam Questions	253

K Atomic Structure and Chemical Bonding 257

1	Inside Atoms	258
2	The Structure of Atoms	260
3	Atomic Number and Mass Number	262
4	Isotopes	264
5	Arranging Electrons in Atoms	266
6	Chemical Bonding	270
	Activities	273
	Summary	275
	Exam Questions	276

L Earth and Atmosphere 279

1	Origins of the Earth and Atmosphere	280
2	Rocks in the Earth	284
3	Earth Movements	289
	Activities	293
	Summary	296
	Exam Questions	298
	Table of Relative Atomic Masses	301

Index 302

From Raw Materials to Pure Substances

This photograph shows crude oil which is one of the most important raw materials. Crude oil is sometimes called 'Black Gold'

By the end of this section you should:
- Appreciate the variety of useful substances that can be made from raw materials, such as metal ores, rocks and crude oil.
- Know that there are approximately 100 elements and that all materials are composed of one or more of them.
- Appreciate that there are different types of chemical reactions, such as thermal decomposition and synthesis, and that chemical reactions are used to make new materials.
- Understand the classification of materials as elements, mixtures and compounds.
- Be able to describe and explain the separation of mixtures using processes such as filtration for purifying our water supplies, evaporation for extracting sea salt and fractional distillation for separating the fractions in crude oil.

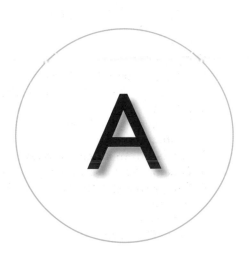

Raw Materials to Useful Substances

Mining iron ore

Iron ore, like that being mined in the photograph above, is useless. You can't eat it, wear it or grow things in it. But, if we heat it with limestone, coke and air we can turn it into iron, and from iron we can make steel.

These different materials like iron, iron ore, limestone, coke and air are called **substances**.

- The study of materials and substances is called **chemistry**.
- Chemists and chemical engineers study materials and try to change useless materials, like iron ore, into useful substances, like iron and steel.

Raw materials from the Earth

Materials that occur naturally, like iron ore, limestone, water and air, are called **raw materials** or **naturally occurring materials**. They are found in the Earth, in the sea and in the air. On the other hand, materials like steel do not occur naturally, but we can make it from iron ore. Because of this, steel is called a **man-made** material. Every year, the chemical industry produces millions of tonnes of important man-made materials from raw materials. Table 1 shows the five most important raw materials and the useful substances we make from them.

Table 1

	Raw material	Useful substances obtained from the raw material
1	Metal ores	Metals (e.g. iron, copper, gold and aluminium) Alloys (e.g. steel, brass)
2	Rocks	Limestone for building and construction and for making quicklime, cement, iron and glass Sand for making glass
3	Crude oil	Fuels such as petrol (gasoline) for cars, diesel (for cars and larger vehicles), kerosene (for aircraft) Polymers such as polyethene, polypropene, PVC and polyester
4	Air	Nitrogen for making ammonia, nitric acid and fertilisers Oxygen for breathing equipment, steel manufacture Argon in electric light bulbs
5	Sea water and salt beds	Salt for treating icy roads Brine (concentrated sodium chloride) for making sodium hydroxide, chlorine and hydrogen

As you read this book, you will study further the processes involved in converting these five raw materials into useful products.

Materials and their properties

Look at the variety of different materials in this room

Look around the lab in which you are working or around your home. Notice the variety of different materials and their uses.

- **Metals** are used to make cutlery, taps, pans, ornaments and tools. Metals have been used for these items because they are hard, strong, shiny and can be made into different shapes.

3

● Curtains, carpets and your own clothes are made from **fibres** which are soft and comfortable. Some fibres like cotton and wool occur naturally as part of plants and animals, but others like polyester and nylon are made from the chemicals in crude oil.

● **Plastics** such as polythene, polypropene and PVC are used for clingfilm, washing-up bowls, combs and toys. Plastics are used because they are fairly cheap, flexible (bendy) and easily moulded into different shapes.

● Window frames, doors, chairs and tables are often made of **wood**. Why is wood used for doors and furniture?

● Windows, bottles, jars, and crockery are made of **glass** or **ceramics**. Why is glass used for windows?

If you have tried to answer the last two questions, you will see that we choose different materials for different uses because they have different **properties**.

> The properties of a material tell you what it is like and what it can be used for.

Study Questions

1 How would you explain to a friend what 'chemistry' is?
2 Make a list of five substances used in cooking and give the chemical name of their main constituent (e.g. salt – sodium chloride). Say which materials occur naturally and which are man-made.
3 a) What does the word 'ore' mean?
   b) Which metals are obtained from the following ores: *bauxite; copper pyrites; haematite; galena; tinstone?*
4 Look at today's newspaper. What news or adverts does it contain about raw materials for the chemical industry?
5 At one time, gutters and drainpipes were made of iron. Today they are made of plastics like PVC (polyvinyl chloride).
   a) What properties of iron made it useful for gutters and drainpipes?
   b) What were the disadvantages of iron?
   c) Why has iron been replaced by plastics?

Most of the outside of this building is glass. What are the advantages of using glass? What are the disadvantages?

Classifying materials

Properties show clearly that one material is different from another. They also help us to put similar materials into groups or sets. For example, it is useful to put household materials into the five groups listed above – metals, fibres, plastics, wood and glass/ceramics. There is a special word for grouping things which have similar properties. It is called **classification**.

Scientists classify materials in several ways. One of the most useful is as **solids**, **liquids** and **gases**. These are sometimes called the **three states of matter**.

In the next two units, we will look at the classification of materials as elements, mixtures and compounds.

Elements – the Simplest Materials

Robert Boyle was the first scientist to use the word 'element', in 1661. Boyle said that elements could not be broken down into simpler substances. This is still a useful definition of an element.

When bread is well-toasted, it gets covered in a black solid which is carbon. Smoke, containing water vapour and carbon dioxide, also rises from the burnt toast.

> Changes like this, that result in new materials, are called **chemical reactions** and the new substance is called the **product** of the reaction.

The chemical reaction which produced carbon from bread is caused by heat from the cooker. Many foods are prepared by chemical reactions caused by heat.

We can summarise the reaction which takes place when bread is heated strongly by writing a word equation.

$$\text{bread} \xrightarrow{\text{heat}} \text{carbon} + \text{carbon dioxide} + \text{water}$$

No matter how the black carbon is treated, it cannot be broken down into a simpler substance.

> Substances that cannot be broken down into simpler substances are called **elements**. Elements are the simplest possible materials.

Carbon is an element. But substances like water and carbon dioxide are not elements because they can be broken down into simpler substances. Substances like water and carbon dioxide, which contain two or more elements, are called **compounds**.

When electricity is passed through water containing a little sulphuric acid, the water breaks down into hydrogen and oxygen (Figure 1).

$$\text{water} \xrightarrow{\text{electricity}} \text{hydrogen} + \text{oxygen}$$

The hydrogen and oxygen cannot be broken down into anything simpler: they are elements. Other elements include aluminium, iron, copper, nitrogen and carbon.

Gold is an element which occurs in the Earth's crust. This photograph shows the gold in Tutankhamun's funeral mask

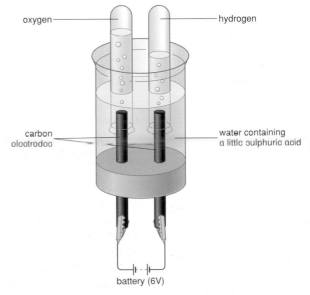

Figure 1 *When electricity is passed through water containing a little sulphuric acid, it breaks down into hydrogen and oxygen*

There are approximately 100 elements that we know of, but scientists are still discovering new ones. Although there are millions and millions of different substances in the universe, they are all composed of one or more of these elements.

For example, grass is made of carbon, hydrogen and oxygen. Sand is made of silicon and oxygen and salt contains sodium and chlorine. So, *elements are the building blocks for all substances*. In the same way, bricks are the building blocks for houses. Using a few different types of brick it is possible to build millions of different houses.

When a compound is split into simpler substances, the reaction is an example of **decomposition**.

> Decomposition is the breaking up of more complex substances into simpler substances.

So, the breakdown of bread into carbon, carbon dioxide and water is an example of decomposition. Another example of decomposition occurs when electricity is passed through molten sodium chloride. The sodium chloride splits up to form sodium and chlorine.

$$\text{sodium chloride} \xrightarrow{\text{electricity}} \text{sodium} + \text{chlorine}$$

When decomposition is brought about by heating, the process is described as **thermal decomposition**.

An important example of thermal decomposition is the manufacture of quicklime (calcium oxide). This is produced by heating limestone (calcium carbonate). The products are quicklime and carbon dioxide.

$$\begin{array}{c} \text{calcium carbonate} \\ \text{(limestone)} \end{array} \xrightarrow{\text{heat}} \begin{array}{c} \text{calcium oxide} \\ \text{(quicklime)} \end{array} + \text{carbon dioxide}$$

Water can be decomposed into hydrogen and oxygen, but hydrogen can be exploded with oxygen to form water again. A reaction like this in which two or more substances join together is called **synthesis**.

> Synthesis is the building up of more complex substances by joining together simpler substances.

Notice that synthesis is the reverse of decomposition. Synthesis is 'building up', whereas decomposition is 'breaking up'.

$$\text{water} \underset{\text{synthesis}}{\overset{\text{decomposition}}{\rightleftarrows}} \text{hydrogen} + \text{oxygen}$$

The 'pop' test for hydrogen

The reaction between hydrogen and oxygen is used as a test for hydrogen. When hydrogen is produced, it can be collected over water or in an inverted test tube. When a lighted splint is brought to the mouth of the inverted tube, the hydrogen reacts immediately with oxygen in the air. A small explosion occurs and a 'pop' is heard (Figure 2).

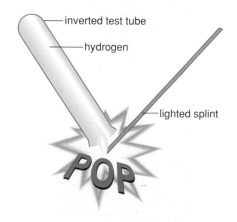

inverted test tube

hydrogen

lighted splint

POP

Figure 2 *The 'pop' test for hydrogen*

When chemical reactions occur, no matter is lost. All the mass of the reactants goes into forming the products. We say that all the mass is conserved. This is summarised in the **Law of Conservation of Mass**.

> This states that: in any chemical change, the total mass of the products equals the total mass of the reactants.

Sulphur deposits in a volcanic vent. Sulphur is an element and an important raw material. It is used to manufacture sulphuric acid

Study Questions

1 Write a short article for 12 year olds explaining what elements are. Your article should include diagrams and photos if these will help.

2 Write down the names of all the elements mentioned in this unit.

3 A gas was produced when a solid was heated. How would you test to see if the gas is (a) hydrogen, (b) water vapour, (c) oxygen?

4 a) Is it possible to decompose an element? Explain your answer.
   b) Is it possible to decompose a compound? Explain your answer.
   c) Which of the following can be decomposed:
      sugar; zinc; hydrogen; salt?
   d) Explain why a synthesis reaction *always* produces a compound.

5 A colourless gas **A** relights a glowing splint.
   i) **A** reacts with copper to give a black solid **B**.
   ii) **A** reacts with a hot dark grey solid **C** to give a colourless gas **D**.
   iii) **D** turns limewater milky.
   iv) **B** and **D** are produced when the green powder **E** decomposes on heating.
      a) Identify the substances **A** to **E**.
      b) Write word equations for the reactions in (i), (ii) and (iv).

6 Elements have been named after two of the four scientists shown in the photographs on the right and below.
   a) Which two scientists are they?
   b) Choose one of the four scientists and write a few paragraphs to describe his/her life and work.

John Dalton

Fritz Haber

Marie Curie

Dmitri Mendeleev

Elements, Mixtures and Compounds

The bands of rocks in the Grand Canyon are mainly sandstones and limestones. The main elements in sandstones are silicon and oxygen. The elements in limestone are calcium, carbon and oxygen

When copper coins are first made, they look orange and shiny. Gradually, the coins become dull as a layer of black copper oxide forms on the surface. The two elements, copper and oxygen, have not just *mixed* together. They have **reacted** (**combined**) to form copper oxide. The copper oxide is an entirely new substance. A chemical reaction has occurred.

$$\text{copper} \ + \ \text{oxygen} \ \rightarrow \ \text{copper oxide}$$

Copper and oxygen are elements. They have combined to form a **compound** called copper oxide.

> A compound is a substance which contains two or more elements combined together.

Many other elements can combine through chemical reactions to form compounds (Figure 1).

When *two* elements react to form a compound, the name of the compound ends in **–ide**. For example,

$$\begin{array}{lclcl} \text{copper} & + & \text{oxygen} & \rightarrow & \text{copper ox} \textbf{ide} \\ \text{sodium} & + & \text{chlorine} & \rightarrow & \text{sodium chlor} \textbf{ide} \\ \text{carbon} & + & \text{oxygen} & \rightarrow & \text{carbon diox} \textbf{ide} \end{array}$$

When a metal reacts with a non-metal, the non-metal forms the **–ide** part in the name of the compound. When two non-metals react, the more reactive non-metal forms the **–ide** part in the name.

Most materials are mixtures. They may be:

● *mixtures of elements*, like **alloys**, which are metals mixed with other elements (e.g. mild steel is mainly iron with about 0.15% carbon)

● *mixtures of compounds*, like seawater which contains salt (sodium chloride) and water

● *mixtures of elements and compounds*, like air, which contains the elements nitrogen and oxygen plus the compounds carbon dioxide and water vapour.

> A mixture is two or more substances which are *not* combined together chemically.

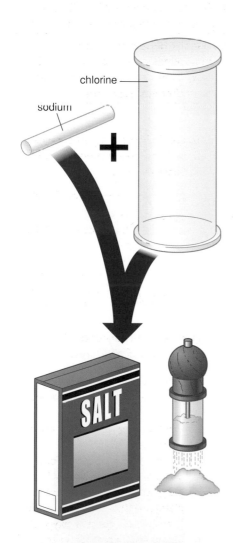

chlorine

sodium

Figure 1 *Sodium and chlorine are elements. They combine (react) to form salt (sodium chloride). Sodium chloride is a compound*

Mixtures and compounds

The important differences between mixtures and compounds are summarised in Table 1. These differences can be illustrated using iron filings and sulphur as in the photos on the left. If you try this experiment, **wear eye protection**.

Making a mixture. Mix some iron filings with powdered sulphur. In the mixture, you can still see the yellow sulphur. Iron can be separated from the mixture with a magnet

Table 1 *The differences between mixtures and compounds*

When a mixture forms	When a compound forms
• Elements or compounds just mix together.	• Elements or compounds combine (react).
• There is no new substance.	• A new substance forms.
• The composition of the mixture can vary.	• The composition of the new compound is always the same.
• No chemical reaction occurs.	• A chemical reaction occurs.
• The mixture has properties like the original substances.	• The new compound has different properties from the elements in it.
• The constituents can be separated fairly easily by processes such as filtration, distillation and magnetic attraction.	• The constituent elements in compounds cannot be separated easily. They can only be separated using chemical reactions.

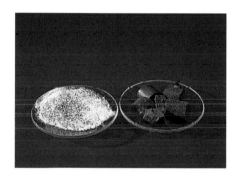

Making a compound. Heat a mixture of iron filings and sulphur. The mixture gets red hot and iron sulphide forms

Study Questions

1 Prepare a short talk on alloys. In your talk:
   a) explain what an alloy is,
   b) give some examples of alloys,
   c) show some uses of alloys,
   d) say why alloys are important.
2 Mercury is a liquid at room temperature. It has a high boiling point, a high density and it is a good conductor. Why do these properties make mercury very useful in thermometers?
3 When water is added to white (anhydrous) copper sulphate in a test tube, a blue substance is produced. At the same time, the test tube gets hot.
   a) Is the blue product a compound or a mixture?
   b) Give two pieces of evidence to support your answer.
4 Write word equations for the reactions which occur when:
   a) coke (carbon) burns in air (oxygen),
   b) a thin, dark layer of copper oxide forms on copper coins,
   c) hydrogen explodes with air (oxygen).

5 Figure 2 shows the percentages of the commonest five elements in the Earth's crust.

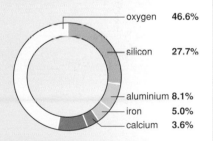

oxygen	46.6%
silicon	27.7%
aluminium	8.1%
iron	5.0%
calcium	3.6%

Figure 2 *The abundance of elements in the Earth's crust*

   a) What total percentage do these five elements make up?
   b) What percentage of the Earth's crust do all the other elements make up?
   c) What is the most abundant metal in the Earth's crust?
   d) Oxygen is the most abudant element. What materials in the Earth's crust contain oxygen?
   e) Name one substance in the Earth's crust that contains (i) silicon, (ii) iron, (iii) calcium, (iv) aluminium.

4 Separating Materials

Most naturally-occurring materials are mixtures. Very often, these mixtures have to be separated before we can use the materials in them. Just imagine what might happen if we used untreated, muddy water for cooking or if we tried to run our cars on crude oil rather than petrol!

The methods that we choose to separate mixtures depend on the different properties of the substances in them.

Separating an insoluble solid from a liquid

1 Filtration

Usually, it is easy to separate an insoluble solid from a liquid by **filtering**. This method is used to make filter coffee by separating the **residue** (coffee grains) from the **filtrate** (filter coffee). Notice how the equipment used to make filter coffee in Figure 1 is similar to that which you would use for filtration in the lab.

Figure 1 *Filtering coffee. The filter bag is made of filter paper. It has tiny holes that let the liquid through, but these holes are too small for the solid particles to pass through. The liquid that runs out of the filter bag is called the* **filtrate**. *The solid left behind is called the* **residue**.

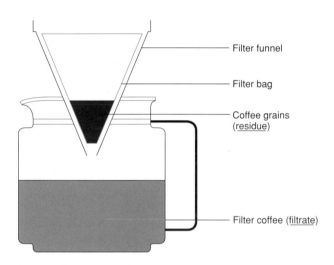

Filter funnel

Filter bag

Coffee grains (residue)

Filter coffee (filtrate)

Clean water for our homes

Filtration plays an important part in obtaining clean water for our homes. Figure 2 shows the main stages in the purification of our water supplies.

1 The water is first stored in reservoirs where most of the solid particles can settle out.

2 As the water is needed, it is filtered through clean sand and gravel which trap smaller particles of mud and suspended solids (Figure 3).

3 After filtering, the water is treated with small amounts of chlorine to kill harmful bacteria in the water.

4 The purified water is finally pumped to storage tanks and water towers from which it flows to our homes.

Figure 2 *Stages in the purification of our water supplies*

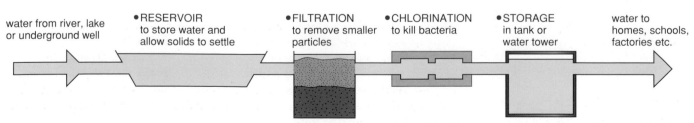

water from river, lake or underground well

- RESERVOIR to store water and allow solids to settle

- FILTRATION to remove smaller particles

- CHLORINATION to kill bacteria

- STORAGE in tank or water tower

water to homes, schools, factories etc.

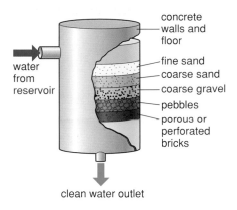

concrete
walls and
floor

water
from
reservoir

fine sand
coarse sand
coarse gravel
pebbles
porous or
perforated
bricks

clean water outlet

Figure 3 *Water is filtered through layers of sand and gravel, which trap small particles*

Filtration is also used to separate beer from its sediment (yeast) before bottling. The beer is filtered by forcing it through filter cloths to catch the sediment.

2 Centrifuging

Sometimes, solid particles in a liquid are so small that they can pass through a filter paper. In this case, filtration is useless. The tiny solid particles float in the liquid as a **suspension**. In this case, the solid can be separated by **centrifuging**. The mixture is poured into a tube and spun round very rapidly in a centrifuge. This forces the denser solid particles to the bottom of the tube and the liquid can be poured off easily. Centrifuging is used in hospitals to separate denser blood cells from blood plasma (liquid). It is also used in dairies to separate milk from cream.

Separating a soluble solid from a solution

Tap water is clean but *not* pure. It contains dissolved gases including oxygen from the air and dissolved solids from the soil and river beds over which it flowed. Tap water is a **solution**. Seawater (brine) is another example of a solution. It contains salt and many other substances dissolved in water. You can't see the salt in clear seawater, but it must be there because you can taste it. The salt has been broken up into tiny particles which are too small to be seen even with a microscope. These particles are so small that they can pass through the holes in filter paper during filtration.

> The mixture of dissolved salt and water forms a **solution**.
> The substance that dissolves is called the **solute**.
> The liquid in which the solute dissolves is the **solvent**.

Solids, such as salt and sugar, which dissolve are described as **soluble**. Solids, such as sand, which do not dissolve are **insoluble**.

The easiest way to obtain a soluble solid from its solution (such as the salt in seawater) is by **evaporation**.

Extracting salt from seawater

When seawater is left in the Sun, white salt is left behind as the water evaporates. Next time you are at the seaside, look for white rings of salt around the edges of rock pools.

> This process during which a liquid turns to a vapour is called **evaporation**.

If the solvent evaporates slowly from a solution, the solute is often left behind as large, well-shaped crystals.

> This process of obtaining crystals by evaporating the solvent from a solution is called **crystallisation**.

Usually, evaporation is carried out more rapidly by boiling the solution. In this case, the solute is left behind as small, poorly-shaped crystals.

In some hot countries, salt is obtained from seawater on a large scale by evaporation. The sea is allowed to flood large flat areas in shallow ponds called salt pans. As the water evaporates, sea salt is left behind as a clean white solid.

Evaporation is also an essential process in drying wet clothes and in producing concentrated evaporated milk.

Evaporation is used for the large-scale extraction of sea salt in hot countries

Separating a solvent from a solution

Sometimes, the part of a solution that you want is the liquid solvent and *not* the solute. In this case, **distillation** can be used to collect the solvent. Distillation can be used to separate pure water from seawater (Figure 4).

When the seawater is boiled, water evaporates off as steam. The steam then passes into a water-cooled sloping tube called a **condenser**. Here the steam turns back to water.

The process during which vapour changes to liquid is called **condensation**.

Figure 4 *Separating pure water from seawater by distillation. The pure water which collects after distillation is called the* **distillate**

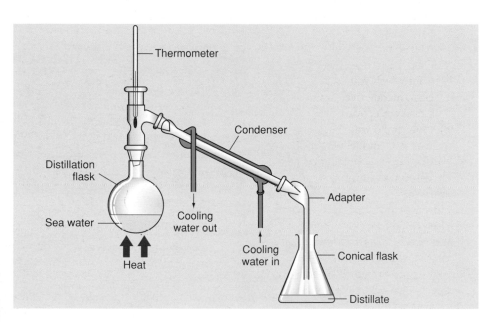

Notice from the process of distillation in Figure 4 that:

distillation = evaporation + condensation

Distillation is an important process in:

- obtaining pure drinking water from seawater in parts of the Middle East where fuel is cheap,

- making 'spirits' such as whisky, gin and vodka from weaker alcoholic liquids.

Separating liquids which mix completely

If alcohol is added to water, the two liquids mix completely to form a single layer. Liquids like these which mix completely are described as **miscible**. Miscible liquids can be separated by a special form of distillation called **fractional distillation**. The method works because the different liquids have different boiling points. When the mixture is heated, different liquids boil off at different temperatures as each one reaches its boiling point. The liquid with the lowest boiling point is collected first, then the one with the next lowest boiling point and so on.

Whisky is made by distilling a liquid called wort in copper vessels. Wort is like weak beer. It is made by fermenting barley

Fractional distillation is important in:

● separating the different fractions in crude oil (Unit I2),

● separating the different gases from liquid air (Unit B1).

Separating similar substances

Chromatography can sometimes be used to separate very similar substances. For example, it is used to separate dyes in ink, different sugars in urine and drugs in blood.

Figure 5 shows how dyes in ink can be separated by chromatography. As the solvent moves up the paper, the dyes separate. Some dyes stick to the paper strongly, other dyes tend to dissolve in the solvent. The dyes that dissolve more readily in the solvent will travel further up the paper.

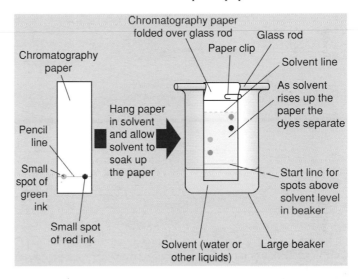

Figure 5 *Separating the dyes in inks by chromatography. How many dyes are there in (i) the green ink, (ii) the red ink?*

This method was initially used to separate mixtures of coloured substances. So, the method was called chromatography from the Greek word 'khroma' meaning colour.

Nowadays, chromatography is also used to separate colourless substances. After the solvent has soaked up the paper, it is dried and then sprayed with **locating agent**. The locating agent reacts with each of the colourless substances to form a coloured product.

This scientist is using chromatography to study new dyes

5 Pure Substances

How pure is 'Pure Orange Juice'?

The label in the photo says that the orange juice is *pure*. This means that it has had nothing added to it or taken out of it. The so-called 'pure orange juice' contains many different substances. The proportions of these different substances give different juices a slightly different flavour.

> When chemists say that something is pure, they mean that it is a single substance and not a mixture of substances.

The orange juice is not pure to a chemist because it contains many substances. As we have seen in earlier units, most materials that occur naturally are mixtures, *not* pure substances.

Testing for pure substances

> There are two general methods of testing to see if a substances is pure:
>
> 1   checking its melting point,
> 2   checking its boiling point.

If a substance is pure it contains only one kind of material and only *one* particular substance. So, all the material should melt or boil at the same temperature. Figure 1 shows how you can check the purity of water by measuring its boiling point.

However, the boiling point of a liquid changes as the atmospheric pressure rises or falls. On top of Mount Everest, where the pressure is much lower than at sea level, water boils at about 70°C. But, if the atmospheric pressure stays constant, *a pure substance will always boil at the same temperature*. In the same way, a pure substance always melts at the same temperature if the pressure is constant.

Because of this, we must choose a **standard pressure** and measure all boiling points and melting points at this standard. Scientists have chosen the pressure exerted by a column of mercury 760 mm high as standard atmospheric pressure. This pressure is called 1 atmosphere (atm).

Pure water always boils at 100°C and pure ice always melts at 0°C at 1 atm pressure. Other substances melt and boil at different temperatures. So, measuring the melting point or the boiling point of a substance at 1 atm pressure is the best way to decide if it is pure.

If the substance is impure, its melting point and boiling point will differ from those of the pure substance. The impure substance will also melt or boil over a range of temperatures. For example, salty water boils above 100°C. As the water boils away and the solution gets more concentrated, the boiling point slowly rises.

Hazard symbols

Different chemicals and different materials have very different properties. Some materials and chemicals can cause hazards. For example, concentrated sulphuric acid will burn (corrode) your skin. Chlorine is toxic (poisonous) and ethanol is very flammable. Hazardous chemicals are found in many widely used materials, such as petrol and lavatory bleach. So, it is very important that anyone using these dangerous substances is aware of the possible hazards.

Many of these substances are transported around the country. Because of this, it is important to have a system of labelling the containers of dangerous substances.

0-110°C thermometer

boiling water

small Bunsen burner

Figure 1 *Checking the purity of some water by measuring its boiling point*

A series of **hazard symbols** are used to label chemicals that might cause problems. These are shown in Figure 2 with examples of the substances to which they apply. The symbols have been chosen so that everyone can understand them and know what they mean. Figure 3 shows the hazard label for Pentel correcting fluid.

Figure 2 *The main hazard symbols*

Hazard symbol					
What does the symbol mean?	Oxidising — These substances provide oxygen. This allows other materials to burn more strongly.		Toxic — These substances can cause death. They may cause problems when swallowed or breathed.		Harmful — These are similar to toxic substances, but less dangerous.
Examples	Potassium manganate(VII) Sodium nitrate		Chlorine Sulphur dioxide		Aspirin Iodine Ethanol (alcohol)
What does the symbol mean?	Corrosive — These substances attack and destroy living tissues including eyes and skin.		Irritant — These substances are not corrosive, but can redden or blister the skin.		Highly flammable — These substances easily catch fire.
Examples	Concentrated sulphuric acid Sodium hydroxide		Dilute sulphuric acid Iodine solution Sodium hydroxide		Petrol Ethanol (alcohol) Magnesium

Study Questions

1 What is a 'pure' substance?
2 Describe how you could use chromatography to test whether some red ink contains a single pure dye or a mixture of dyes.
3 Which of the following are pure substances and which are mixtures: *seawater; petrol; iron; steel; steam; soil; milk; salt?*
4 Look at the hazard symbols in Figure 2 and what they mean. What is the difference between:
 i) toxic and harmful substances,
 ii) oxidising and highly flammable substances?

Figure 3 *The hazard label for Pentel correcting fluid. What is the highly flammable substance in it?*

Section A   Activities

Keep out of reach of children ¥ Irritating to eyes, skin and the respiratory system ¥ In case of contact with eyes, rinse immediately with plenty of water and seek medical advice. If swallowed, seek medical advice immediately and show this container or label. ¥ Do not inhale spray ¥ Use only in well ventilated areas ¥ Do not mix with other cleaning agents or acids as this could give rise to dangerous fumes (chlorine)

1 What's in a label?

Look closely at the labels on the left which come from a container of '*Flash Spray with Bleach*'.

1 What does the hazard symbol on the label mean?

2 Why should '*Flash*' be kept out of the reach of children?

3 What chemical in '*Flash*' can cause possible harm?

4 Why does the safety warning say '*Use only in well ventilated areas*'?

5 Why is it wise to allow hot surfaces to cool before using '*Flash*'?

2 Searching for the simplest substances

Three thousand years ago, the ancient Greeks had lots of ideas and theories about substances. They were the first to suggest there might be one simple substance from which all other substances and materials were made.

Some Greeks thought that the simple substance might be water because their crops could not grow without it. They thought their crops were made from water. Water could also be frozen to make ice and heated to make steam. 'Water', they said 'is the one simple substance from which all other substances can be made'.

Other Greeks thought that the simplest substance was air because everyone needed air to live. There were other ideas as well. Some Greeks thought that fire was the simplest substance because it could bring about dramatic changes – rocks to metals and clay into pots. Others thought that the simplest substance might be earth.

In time, these ideas developed into the theory of the four 'elements' – *Earth*, *Air*, *Fire* and *Water*. The Greeks believed that all substances could be made from these four 'elements'. Put the four 'elements' together in the right amounts and you could make anything – rocks, metals, wood and even living things.

Their four 'elements' could also be described in terms of the four important 'qualities' (properties) of substances (Figure 1). So, water is cold and wet, fire is hot and dry and so on. Their theory must be right, or so they thought.

Although the Greeks were good with ideas and theories, they were not so good at experiments. Their ideas rarely got tested.

But, in 330 BC, the Greek theory about their 'four elements' was put to the test. The Greek army, led by Alexander the Great, conquered Egypt and a new science of materials started. The new science was called 'alchemy' from the word 'chem' which was an old name for Egypt.

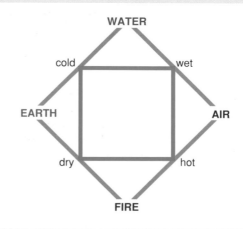

Figure 1 *The four 'elements'*

The theory about the 'four elements' could be tested by the metal workers and alchemists in Egypt. The Egyptian metal workers had made copper from rocks. They could change the colour of gold by alloying it with silver or copper. The alchemists were curious about new substances and greedy for wealth. Could they combine *Earth*, *Air*, *Fire* and *Water* in the right amounts to make gold?

The new Egyptian and Greek alchemists found lots of new substances but the 'theory of four elements' didn't help them. They tried hundreds of different mixtures of *Earth*, *Air*, *Fire* and *Water*, but they couldn't make any gold. When they tried and failed, they couldn't understand where they had gone wrong.

For hundreds of years, cheating alchemists pretended they had a recipe for making gold. Until the late 17th century, almost all scientists continued to believed in alchemy.

In 1677, Robert Boyle challenged the Greek theory of *Earth*, *Air*, *Fire* and *Water* as the four simplest substances. Boyle said that elements must be simple and unmixed (unreacted) substances. He said that *Earth*, *Air*, *Fire* and *Water* did not fit this description and that they were not elements at all.

1   Why did some ancient Greeks think that water might be the simplest substance from which everything is made?

2   Some ancient Greeks thought that Earth might be the simplest substance from which everything is made. What might have led them to this idea?

3   Which of the four ancient Greek 'qualities' would describe: (i) *Earth* (ii) *Air*?

4   Why did the ancient Greeks make very little progress with their scientific ideas?

5   Which of the 'four elements' of the ancient Greeks is: (i) not a substance, (ii) a pure substance?

6   Egyptian metal workers could change the colour of gold by alloying it. What do you think they mixed the gold with to make it: (i) lighter (whiter) in colour, (ii) darker (more orange) in colour?

7   How do you think the Egyptian metal workers obtained: (i) gold from rocks, (ii) copper from rocks containing substances such as copper oxide and copper sulphide?

8   Which substances in the passage above are in fact elements?

3 Word processing your own word quiz

1   Make a list of the important words in section A. After each key word, write down what it means. For example:

- **Chemistry** – The study of materials and substances.
- **Substances** – Materials like iron, iron ore, limestone, coke and air.
- **Raw materials** – Materials that occur naturally.

In the diagram on page 18, these three important words have been used to make a word quiz. Can you see that the missing word is AIR?

2   Now make up a word quiz of your own using important words from the whole of section A. Write clues to find your missing word as in the example.

3   Use a computer to design and develop a neat version of your word quiz. Try to use all the facilities of your computer including different sized letters, drawings (diagrams), shading, brushwork, etc.

4   Try out your word quiz on your friends.

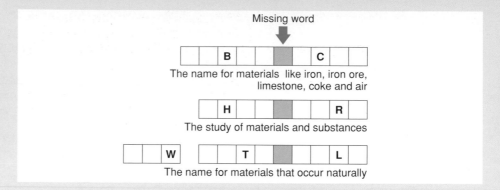

Missing word

| | B | | | | C | |

The name for materials like iron, iron ore,
limestone, coke and air

| | H | | | | R | |

The study of materials and substances

| | W | | | T | | | L | |

The name for materials that occur naturally

4 Using the web to obtain data about elements

- Log on to the internet and open the website www.pearl1.lanl.gov/periodic/.

- Choose a metal, a non-metal and a semi-metal by clicking them on the periodic table.

- Click the '**Edit**' icon on the toolbar and copy the data for each element.

- Save only the information on the history, uses, properties and costs of the elements chosen.

- Print off your data for presentation to your class. Personalise your presentation with WordArt, or in other ways if you wish.

5 Creating and using a database for elements

a) Using your textbook or a website, find the following data for 10 elements mentioned in Unit 2 of this section: *density*; *melting point*; *boiling point*; *percentage present in the Earth*.

b) Open a database and insert this data.

c) Set up queries to find those elements which are: (i) less dense than water; (ii) more dense than water; (iii) solids at room temperature; (iv) liquids at room temperature; (v) gases at room temperature.

1 What is the boiling point of the least dense element?
2 What is the boiling point of the most abundant element?

1 **Chemistry** is the study of materials and substances. Chemists and chemical engineers study materials and try to change useless raw materials, like metal ores, rocks and crude oil, into useful substances, like steel, glass and petrol.

2 **Chemical reactions**

- A **chemical reaction** always results in a new substance. The new substance is called the **product** of the reaction.
- **Decomposition** is the splitting up of one substance into two or more simpler substances. When decomposition is caused by heat, the process is called **thermal decomposition**.
- **Synthesis** is the reverse of decomposition. Synthesis is the joining together of two or more substances.

3 **Elements, mixtures and compounds**

- **Elements** are the simplest substances. They cannot be broken down into simpler substances.
- **Compounds** are substances containing two or more elements chemically *combined* together.
- **Mixtures** are two or more substances which are mixed together but *not* combined together chemically. An **alloy** is a mixture of a metal with one or more other elements.

4 **Methods of separation**

- The separation of a mixture depends on differences in a particular property of the substances being separated.
- An insoluble solid can be separated from a liquid by **filtering** or **centrifuging**.
- A soluble solid (solute) can be separated from its solution by **evaporating** off some of the solvent and allowing the solid to **crystallise**.
- A solvent can be separated from its solution by **distillation**.
- Miscible liquids can be separated by **fractional distillation**.
- Similar substances can sometimes be separated by fractional distillation or **chromatography**.

5 **Pure substances**

- When chemists say that a substance is *pure*, they mean that it contains only one substance.
- The purity of a substance can be tested by:
  checking its melting point or checking its boiling point.

Section A Exam Questions

1   The uses of *elements* depend on their properties.

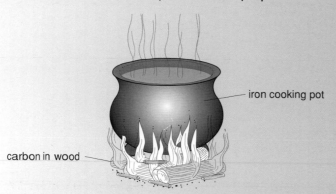

iron cooking pot

carbon in wood

(a) Carbon and iron are both *elements*. What is an *element*?

(b) Write out the statements below and then complete the sentences by crossing out the words that are wrong. The first one has been done for you.

Non-Metals	Metals	can be hammered into shape.
Non-Metals	Metals	often have low melting points.
Non-Metals	Metals	are good conductors of heat.

(c) In the box are the names of three metals.

| copper | iron | sodium |

Which **one** of these is **not** a good metal for making the cooking pot? Give a reason for your answer.

AQA 2000

2   Two students made the insoluble salt, lead sulphate, and wrote these notes about the experiment.

'We took 25 cm³ of lead nitrate solution and slowly added 25 cm³ of acid to it. The mixture turned cloudy white. We stirred the mixture and filtered it to obtain the solid lead sulphate.'

(a) Describe **one** safety precaution which the students should take during this experiment.

(b) (i)   Which acid was added to lead nitrate solution to make lead sulphate?
            A hydrochloric acid; **B** nitric acid; or **C** sulphuric acid

     (ii) Draw, and name, the piece of apparatus that should be used to measure 25 cm³ of the acid.

(c) Redraw and label the diagram top right, which shows the mixture being filtered to obtain solid lead sulphate.

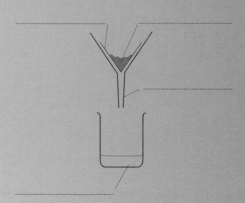

Edexcel (specimen paper, 2003)

3   (a) Use these salts to answer the following questions.
         A potassium iodide
         B silver bromide
         C sodium chloride
     Which one of the salts (**A**, **B** or **C**):
         (i)   can be made from the elements potassium and iodine;
         (ii)   has the formula NaCl;
         (iii) is used for de-icing roads;
         (iv)   is used in photography?

    (b) (i)   Sodium chloride can be made by the reaction shown in this word equation.

              sodium hydroxide + hydrochloric acid →
                     sodium chloride + water

              Name ONE reactant and ONE product in this equation.

         (ii) Zinc reacts with hydrochloric acid to form zinc chloride and hydrogen. Write the word equation for this reaction.

Edexcel 2000

4   (a) Water is essential for life. Two of the stages involved in the treatment of public water supplies are the use of filter beds and chlorination.
     State the purpose of
         (i)   filter beds,
         (ii) chlorination.

    (b) Describe how you would show that a colourless liquid is **pure** water. Include in your answer the result you would expect.

    (c) (i)   A small amount of soap solution was added to samples of soft water and hard water and the mixtures were shaken. How would you identify the hard water?

         (ii) What is dissolved in water which makes it hard?

         (iii) Give **one** advantage of hard water.

         (iv) Give **one** method of softening hard water other than by boiling.

WJEC 2000

Our Environment
– Air and Water

We need air every minute of our lives. We can survive for weeks without food, days without water, but only a few minutes without air

During the 1950s, there were no fish in the River Thames between London Bridge and the sea. During the 1960s, pollution controls were introduced and in 1974, salmon were caught in the Thames for the first time since 1835. Today, more than 70 species of fish have returned to the river

By the end of this section you should:
- Appreciate that both air and water are essential for life.
- Be able to recall the properties, reactions and uses of oxygen.
- Understand the part that oxygen plays in burning, breathing and rusting.
- Recognise oxidation and reduction reactions involving oxygen.
- Know about the importance of clean air and the sources of air pollution.
- Appreciate the importance of clean water supplies.
- Know about the solubility of substances in water and understand solubility curves.

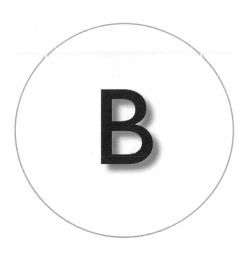

River water and sea water contain dissolved oxygen. Fish take in water through their mouths. This flows over their gills which extract oxygen from the water

Air is all around us. We need it to live. We need it to burn fuels and keep warm. We also obtain useful products from air. These products include oxygen and nitrogen. Air is a mixture, but the substance in it that we need for both breathing and burning is **oxygen**.

What percentage of the air is oxygen?

Figure 1 shows an experiment to find the volume of oxygen in air. Air is passed over heated copper. The hot copper reacts with oxygen in the air to form copper oxide.

$$\text{copper} \ + \ \text{oxygen} \ \rightarrow \ \text{copper oxide}$$

This removes oxygen from the air and its volume decreases.

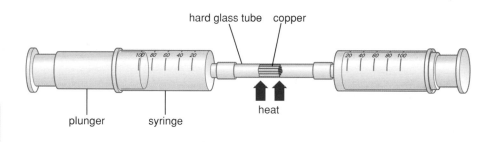

Figure 1 *Finding the percentage of oxygen in the air.* **Wear eye protection** *if you try this experiment*

Did you know?

If you rested all day, you would still need to breathe in about 15 000 litres of air.

At the beginning of the experiment, one syringe is empty and the other is filled with 100 cm³ of air. The silica tube is then heated strongly. When the copper is red hot, the syringes are used to push the air forwards and backwards over the heated copper, so that all the oxygen in the air reacts with the copper. The tube is now allowed to cool and the volume of gas in the syringe is measured. Finally, the heating and cooling are repeated until the volume of gas which remains in the syringe is constant. Table 1 shows the results from one experiment.

Table 1 *The results of an experiment to find the percentage of oxygen in air*

Volume of air in syringe before heating	100 cm³
Volume of gas after first heating and cooling	82 cm³
Volume of gas after second heating and cooling	79 cm³
Volume of gas after third heating and cooling	79 cm³

1 Has all the oxygen been used up after the first heating?

2 Has all the oxygen been used up after the second heating?

3 Why is the heating and cooling repeated three times?

4 How much oxygen did the copper remove?

5 What is the percentage of oxygen in the air?

Humans have no gills. They must carry a supply of air for underwater swimming

Gases in the air

Table 2 gives some information about the main gases in clean, dry air.

Table 2

Gas	% of air by volume	Boiling point/°C	Important uses
Nitrogen	78.1	−196	making ammonia for nitric acid and fertilisers
Oxygen	20.9	−182	steel making and welding (see Unit B2)
Argon	0.9	−186	filling electric light bulbs (Argon is very unreactive. It will not even react with the white hot filament.)

Clean, dry air also contains small percentages of carbon dioxide, neon, krypton and xenon. Together, these gases make up about 0.1% of clean, dry air. Although clean, dry air contains nitrogen, oxygen, argon and small percentages of the four gases just mentioned, ordinary air also contains some water vapour and waste gases from industry (Unit B6).

Obtaining gases from the air

The air is an important source of oxygen, nitrogen and argon. Figure 2 summarises how the gases are separated.

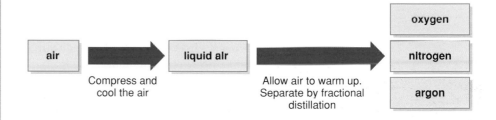

Figure 2 *Separating gases in the air by fractional distillation*

Look at the boiling points of the gases in Table 2.

1 Which gas forms a liquid first as the air is cooled?
2 Which gas boils off first when liquid air warms up?
3 Which gas boils off second when liquid air warms up?
4 Which gas boils off third when liquid air warms up?

Study Questions

1 In the syringe experiment to find the percentage of oxygen in the air, the hard-glass tube containing copper was weighed before and after the experiment.

Volume of oxygen in air   21 cm³
Mass of tube + contents at start
11.365 g
Mass of tube + contents finally
11.393 g

a) Why does the tube + contents increase in mass?
b) What volume of oxygen does the copper react with?
c) What mass of oxygen does the copper react with?
d) What is the density of this oxygen (i.e. the mass of 1 cm³ of oxygen)?

2 Discuss the following questions with two or three other people in your class. The percentage, by volume, of carbon dioxide in ordinary air is 0.03%. Would you expect the percentage of carbon dioxide to be higher, lower or about the same as this:
a) in a crowded classroom,
b) in a greenhouse full of plants on a sunny day,
c) in the centre of a busy city?

Oxygen

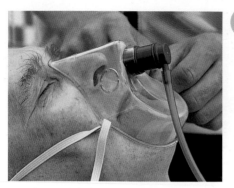

Oxygen being used to revive someone

The uses of oxygen

Oxygen is essential for burning and breathing, but the oxygen does not have to be pure. Pure oxygen is, however, required in large quantities for industrial and medical uses.

- **Manufacture of steel.** One tonne of pure oxygen is needed to produce every 10 tonnes of steel from impure pig iron. Oxygen is blown through the impure molten iron to remove carbon and sulphur impurities. The carbon and sulphur react with oxygen to form carbon dioxide and sulphur dioxide, which escape as gases.

- **Welding and cutting metals.** Pure oxygen is used in oxy-acetylene welding and cutting. When acetylene burns in oxygen, the temperature reaches 3200°C. This is hot enough to melt most metals which can then be cut or welded together.

- **Breathing apparatus.** Pure oxygen is used in life-support machines in hospitals. Oxygen helps patients with lung diseases, such as pneumonia, to breathe. It is also mixed with anaesthetising gases during surgical operations. Mountaineers and deep-sea divers also use oxygen mixed with other gases to breathe when supplies of air are not available.

How does oxygen react with elements?

Some of the properties of oxygen are shown in Figure 1. One of its most important properties is the way it helps things to burn. If a substance burns in air, it will burn much more easily in oxygen.

The simple test for oxygen is that it will cause a glowing splint to relight.

Most elements will react with oxygen on heating. Some elements react slowly at room temperature. Iron slowly develops a layer of rust (iron oxide) on exposure to the air. Similarly, shiny aluminium surfaces become dull with a layer of white aluminium oxide. The iron and aluminium have reacted with oxygen in the air. Table 1 shows the results obtained when various elements are heated strongly in oxygen.

All the elements burn better in oxygen than in air. The substances produced are called **oxides**.

$$\text{sodium } + \text{ oxygen} \rightarrow \text{ sodium } \textbf{oxide}$$
$$\text{carbon } + \text{ oxygen} \rightarrow \text{ carbon di}\textbf{oxide}$$

Notice in Table 1 that:

- The metal oxides (e.g. sodium oxide, magnesium oxide, iron oxide and copper oxide) are all solids.

- The non-metal oxides (e.g. carbon dioxide and sulphur dioxide) are both gases.

How do oxides react with water?

Look at Table 1 again. Each of the oxides was shaken with water and the solution produced was then tested with universal indicator.

Sodium oxide and magnesium oxide both react with water to form alkaline solutions with a pH greater than 7.

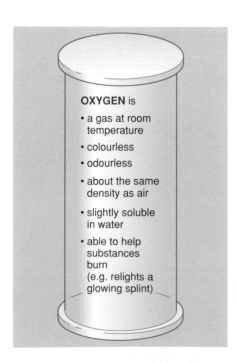

OXYGEN is
- a gas at room temperature
- colourless
- odourless
- about the same density as air
- slightly soluble in water
- able to help substances burn (e.g. relights a glowing splint)

Figure 1 *Properties of oxygen*

24

Table 1 *Comparing the reactions of some elements with oxygen*

Element	Reaction with oxygen	Product	Add water to product, then add universal indicator
Sodium	Bright yellow flame – white smoke and powder	White solid (sodium oxide)	Dissolves pH = 11 alkaline
Magnesium	Dazzling white flame – white clouds and powder	White solid (magnesium oxide)	Dissolves slightly pH = 8 alkaline
Iron	Glows red hot and burns with sparks	Black-brown solid (iron oxide)	Insoluble
Copper	Does not burn, but the surface turns black	Black solid (copper oxide)	Insoluble
Carbon	Glows red hot, reacts slowly	Colourless gas (carbon dioxide)	Dissolves pH = 5 acidic
Sulphur	Burns readily with a blue flame	Colourless gas (sulphur dioxide)	Dissolves pH = 3 acidic

sodium oxide + water → sodium hydroxide
magnesium oxide + water → magnesium hydroxide

Iron oxide and copper oxide do not react with water or dissolve in it. So, they do not change the colour of the indicator.

- The oxides of metals are called **basic oxides**. Most metal oxides are insoluble in water but a few, like sodium oxide and magnesium oxide, react with it to form alkaline solutions. These oxides are called **alkaline oxides**. Figure 2 shows the relationship between basic oxides and alkaline oxides in a Venn diagram.

- The non-metal oxides react with water to form acidic solutions with a pH less than 7. These oxides of non-metals which give acids in water are called **acidic oxides**.

carbon dioxide + water → carbonic acid
sulphur dioxide + water → sulphurous acid

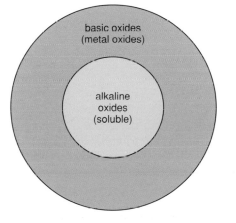

basic oxides (metal oxides)

alkaline oxides (soluble)

Figure 2 *A Venn diagram showing alkaline oxides as a sub-set of basic oxides*

Study Questions

1 a) What are the main uses of oxygen?
   b) Why do rockets carry liquid oxygen?
2 What is meant by the following: *basic oxide; acidic oxide; alkaline oxide?*

3 Barium burns in air to form a solid oxide. This oxide reacts with water to give an alkaline solution.
   a) Is barium a metal or a non-metal?
   b) Write word equations for the reactions described above.
   c) Which of the following elements would react like barium: *copper; sulphur; sodium; iron; nitrogen; calcium; carbon; potassium?*

3 Burning and Breathing

The Greeks believed that Prometheus took pity on humans and stole fire from the gods to give warmth to men and women

Some fuels produce sparks and flames when they burn

Lavoisier showed that part of the air is used up when things burn. He said this part of the air was oxygen

Why is burning so important?

Burning was the first chemical process used by humans. Our ancestors burnt fuels to keep warm, to cook food and to produce new materials, like metals and clay pots. Burning is just as important to us. We burn fuels to keep warm, cook food, drive motor cars and generate electricity.

> Any substance which burns in air to produce heat is a **fuel**.

The most important fuels are coal, oil and natural gas. These fuels are compounds containing mainly carbon and hydrogen. During burning, these elements combine with oxygen in the air to produce carbon dioxide and water. Heat is given out at the same time.

$$\text{fuel} \;+\; \text{oxygen} \;\rightarrow\; \text{carbon dioxide} \;+\; \text{water} \;+\; \text{heat}$$

> Reactions like this which give out heat are called **exothermic reactions**.

Sometimes, when a fuel burns, so much heat is produced that the products burst into flames. This happens in a Bunsen burner or a gas cooker when gases react with oxygen in the air to produce the flame. Reactions like these can be hazardous and must be carefully controlled.

Some fuels, like hydrogen, and explosives, like TNT and dynamite, react so fast that they cause explosions. Because of this, *great care is needed in handling and using fuels and explosives.*

Study Questions

1 a) What fuels are used for each of the following: *barbecueing; cooking in a tent; heating a school; getting a spaceship into orbit; lighting a housefire; running a car?*

   b) For each of the uses in part a) say why the particular fuel is chosen.

2 Look at the photo of the French scientist Lavoisier on page 26. In May 1794, during the French Revolution, Lavoisier was arrested on a trumped-up charge and guillotined. The judge pushed aside his defence with the words *'The Republic has no need of men of science'*. A friend of Lavoisier is reported to have said *'Only a moment to cut off his head and a hundred years may not give us another like it'.*

   a) What is meant by: (i) trumped-up charge, (ii) the Republic?

   b) Find out about Lavoisier's experiments.

   c) What important results did Lavoisier obtain?

   d) How did Lavoisier's results help scientists to understand burning?

   e) Pretend that you were Lavoisier's lawyer at his trial. How would you reply to the judge when he said 'The Republic has no need of men of science'?

3 Figure 1 shows the fire triangle.

   a) Why are heat, oxygen and fuel shown along the sides?

   b) What happens if one of these is missing?

   c) What must you do to stop a fire?

   d) Have you ever needed to stop a fire? If so, what did you do and why?

Breathing and respiration

When we breathe, air is taken into our lungs and then breathed out. But what happens to it in between? One way to find out is to compare the air breathed in (**inhaled**) with the air breathed out (**exhaled**). The temperature and the percentages of oxygen, carbon dioxide and water vapour in ordinary air and in exhaled air are shown in Table 1.

Table 1 *Look at these results. How does inhaled air compare with exhaled air?*

	Ordinary air (inhaled air)	Exhaled air
% oxygen	20	15
% carbon dioxide	0.03	5
% water vapour	2	5
temperature/°C	15 (variable)	25

Once the air is in our lungs, oxygen can get into our bloodstream. The oxygen then passes to the rest of our bodies where it reacts with substances in our food. This process is called **respiration**. The results in Table 1 show that during respiration:

● oxygen is used up,

● water is produced,

● carbon dioxide is produced,

● heat is produced.

So respiration can be summarised as:

$$\text{food} + \text{oxygen} \rightarrow \text{carbon dioxide} + \text{water} + \text{heat}$$

Notice the similarity between this word equation and that for fuels on page 26. Foods are special kinds of fuels which are used in our bodies. They contain carbon and hydrogen in compounds such as fats, carbohydrates and proteins. Respiration is a kind of very slow burning. The same amount of heat is produced whether a substance burns in the air with flames or whether it is used up slowly in our bodies as a food.

Some athletes chew glucose sweets before a marathon. Glucose is a carbohydrate. It is a very good supply of fuel during a long race.

Figure 1 *The fire triangle*

4   Rusting

Articles made of iron and steel rust much faster if they are left outside in wet weather. Steel parts on a bicycle rust more quickly when the bike is left out in the rain than when it is kept in a shed. This suggests that water plays a part in rusting.

When aluminium is exposed to air, it becomes coated with a layer of oxide. The metal has reacted with oxygen in the air. If rusting is similar to this, iron may also react with oxygen in the air.

The apparatus in Figure 1 can be used to investigate whether water and oxygen are involved in rusting. The test tubes are set up and left for several days. Tube 1 is the *control experiment*. It is the standard which we use to compare the results in the other tubes. It contains iron nails in moist air. Tube 2 contains iron nails and anhydrous calcium chloride which absorbs water vapour and keeps the air dry. Tube 3 contains nails covered with boiled distilled water. The water has been boiled to remove any dissolved air. The layer of olive oil prevents air dissolving in the water. Tube 4 contains iron nails in distilled water and pure oxygen.

Nails in tubes 1 and 4 rust, but those in tubes 2 and 3 do not.

1 Does iron rust if there is:
   (i) no water; (ii) no air; (iii) no oxygen?

2 What conditions are necessary for rusting?

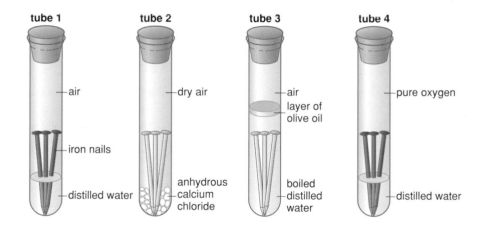

Figure 1 *Investigating whether water and oxygen are involved in rusting*

What happens when iron rusts?

Iron will only rust if both oxygen and water are present.

During rusting, iron reacts with oxygen to form brown iron oxide.

$$\text{iron} + \text{oxygen} \rightarrow \text{brown iron oxide}$$

As the iron oxide forms, it reacts with water to form hydrated brown iron oxide. This is rust.

$$\text{iron oxide} + \text{water} \rightarrow \text{hydrated iron oxide (rust)}$$

Substances, like rust, that have water as part of their structure are described as **hydrated** and we call them **hydrates**.

Blue copper sulphate crystals are also hydrated. They form when water is added to white anhydrous copper sulphate.

$$\text{anhydrous copper sulphate} \ + \ \text{water} \ \rightarrow \ \text{hydrated copper sulphate}$$
$$\text{(white)} \qquad\qquad\qquad\qquad\qquad \text{(blue)}$$

The water present in hydrates, such as blue copper sulphate and rust, is called **water of crystallisation**.

Although iron and steel rust more easily than several other metals, steel is used for ships, cars, bridges and other structures because it is cheaper and stronger than other building materials.

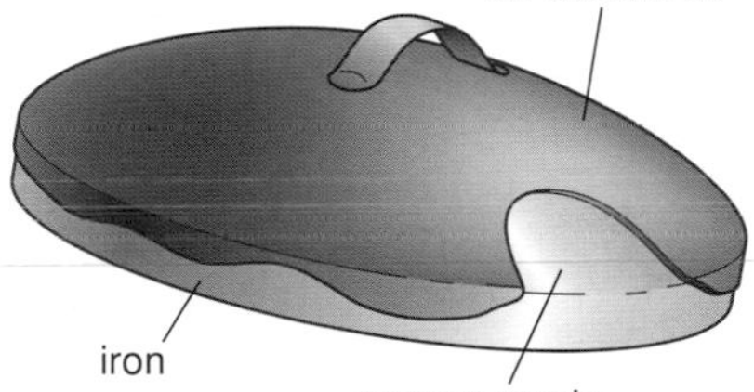

How is rusting prevented?

In order to stop iron and steel rusting, we must protect them from water and oxygen. There are a number of important ways of doing this.

- **Painting.** This is the usual method of preventing rusting in ships, vehicles and bridges. Paint covers the iron (steel), but if the paint is scratched, then rusting starts.

- **Oiling or greasing.** The moving parts of machines cannot be protected by paint which would get scratched off. Instead, they are oiled or greased. This also helps to lubricate the moving parts.

- **Alloying.** Iron and steel can be mixed with other metals to form alloys which do not rust. These *stainless* steels contain chromium or nickel. They are used for cutlery, tools and other expensive equipment which might easily rust.

- **Coating (plating) with a more reactive metal.** Zinc is often used to coat steel dustbins and gates. This process using zinc is described as **galvanizing**. Zinc is more reactive than iron, so oxygen in the air reacts with the zinc before it reacts with the iron. Zinc is 'sacrificed' to protect the iron and this is sometimes called **sacrificial protection** (Figure 2). Other articles, like taps and kettles, are plated with chromium. This is more expensive than galvanizing and the chromium is only slightly more reactive than iron. So, the sacrificial protection is poorer, but the chromium plating is more attractive.

zinc coating on dustbin lid

iron

oxygen reacts with zinc, but not with iron

Figure 2 *On a galvanized dust bin, zinc reacts before the iron, even when the zinc coating is scratched or broken*

Study Questions

1. a) What is rust?
   b) How does rust form?
2. What methods are used to stop rusing?
3. Explain the following terms: *control experiment; hydrates; anhydrous; water of crystallisation.*
4. Explain the following statements.
   a) Iron objects rust away completely in time.
   b) The bottom of iron railings rust more quickly than the top.
   c) Iron on shipwrecks in deep seawater rusts very slowly.
5. What experiments would you do to find out whether:
   a) iron rusts more quickly in seawater or in distilled water,
   b) steel rusts more quickly than iron?
   Draw a labelled diagram of the apparatus you would use in each case. What results would you expect?

Oxidation and Reduction

The burning of the match is a redox reaction. Match heads contain phosphorus or antimony compounds plus substances containing oxygen. The head of the match or the strip on the box also contains finely powdered glass. When the match is struck, friction caused by the powdered glass creates heat to start a reaction in which the phosphorus or antimony are oxidised to their oxides

Many reactions which occur in everyday life involve substances reacting with oxygen to form oxides. Burning, breathing and rusting are three important examples.

During burning, fuels containing carbon and hydrogen react with oxygen to form carbon dioxide and water (hydrogen oxide).

$$\text{fuel} \;+\; \text{oxygen} \;\rightarrow\; \text{carbon dioxide} \;+\; \text{water}$$

During respiration, foods containing carbon and hydrogen react with oxygen to form carbon dioxide and water.

$$\text{food} \;+\; \text{oxygen} \;\rightarrow\; \text{carbon dioxide} \;+\; \text{water}$$

During rusting, iron reacts with oxygen and water to form hydrated iron oxide.

$$\text{iron} \;+\; \text{oxygen} \;+\; \text{water} \;\rightarrow\; \text{hydrated iron oxide}$$

Chemists use a special word for a reaction in which a substance combines with oxygen. They call the reaction **oxidation** and the substance is said to be **oxidised**.

But if one substance combines with and gains oxygen, another substance (possibly oxygen itself) must lose oxygen.

Substances which lose oxygen in chemical reactions are **reduced** and we call the process **reduction**.

Oxidation and reduction always happen together. If one substance combines with oxygen and is oxidised, another substance must lose oxygen and be reduced. We call the combined process **redox** (**RED**uction + **OX**idation).

Notice that some redox reactions, like burning and respiration, are very useful, but other redox reactions like rusting and the spoiling of food, are a problem.

Redox in industrial processes

A redox reaction is sometimes used in welding steel. A mixture of powdered aluminium and iron oxide (known as 'thermit') is used. Aluminium is more reactive than iron, so it removes oxygen from iron oxide to form aluminium oxide and iron. (Figure 1).

When food goes bad, substances in the food combine with oxygen in the air. The process involves oxidation. Carbon dioxide and water are produced

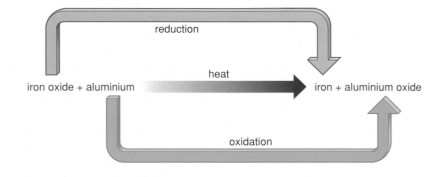

reduction

iron oxide + aluminium — heat → iron + aluminium oxide

oxidation

Figure 1

Study Questions

1. Look at the photo of food going bad on page 30.
   a) What chemical processes occur when food decays?
   b) What methods and precautions do we use at home to stop food going off?
   c) How do these methods work?

2. Which substance is oxidised and which is reduced in each of the redox reactions below?
   a) aluminium + water → aluminium oxide + hydrogen
   b) hydrogen + oxygen → water
   c) copper oxide + hydrogen → copper + water

3. a) Will copper oxide and magnesium react on heating? Explain your answer.
   b) Will magnesium oxide and copper react on heating? Explain your answer.
   c) Element **W** reacts with the oxide of element **X** but not with the oxide of element **Y**. Write **W**, **X**, and **Y** in order of reactivity (most reactive first).

4. A sample of dry rust was heated strongly in a test tube. Droplets of a liquid, **A**, formed on the cooler parts of the tube. **A** turned anhydrous copper sulphate blue. The residue left in the tube, **B**, was heated strongly in a stream of gas, **C**. A grey-black solid, **D**, was formed (which conducted electricity) and a colourless liquid, **E**, condensed on the cooler parts of the apparatus. **E** turned anhydrous copper sulphate blue.
   a) Identify the substances **A–E**.
   b) One of the reactions described above involves redox.
   (i) Which is it? (ii) Write a word equation for the raction involved. (iii) Explain which substance is oxidised and which is reduced.

Aluminium gains oxygen and is oxidised. Iron oxide loses oxygen and is reduced. The whole process involves both oxidation and reduction. It is an example of redox.

This reaction between aluminium and iron oxide is very exothermic. The iron is produced in a molten state. As the iron solidifies, it will weld together two pieces of steel. Welding together railway lines using this method has increased the average 'life' of the track from 23 to 30 years. The photo below shows the process in action.

The redox reaction between aluminium and iron oxide can be used to weld railway lines together. Molten iron from the reaction runs into a mould around the rails to be joined. When the iron has cooled, the mould is removed and excess metal is trimmed off. This workman is almost ready to release molten iron into a mould around the rails.

Redox reactions also occur in the manufacture of metals. In a blast furnace, iron is manufactured from iron ore (iron oxide) by reaction with carbon monoxide.

iron oxide + carbon monoxide → iron + carbon dioxide
(iron ore)

In this process, iron oxide is reduced to iron, whilst carbon monoxide gets oxidised to carbon dioxide.

Zinc is manufactured from zinc oxide by reaction with coke (carbon).

zinc oxide + carbon → zinc + carbon monoxide
(coke)

Which substance is oxidised and which substance is reduced in this process?

Redox is studied further in Unit F3.

6 How Pure is Our Air?

Motor vehicles and power stations are the source of most air pollution

People have worried about the purity of their air ever since our ancestors could make fires. Smoke from fires made their eyes water and the smells were unbearable. So, air pollution isn't new, but the concerns about air purity have increased. This is because there are now many more people on Earth and more people mean more homes, more industries, more vehicles and therefore more air pollution.

What substances cause air pollution?

Air pollution is caused by the release of poisonous and harmful gases into the air. These gases harm living things. Most air pollution is caused by burning fossil fuels in our homes, in our vehicles and in power stations. The substances responsible for most air pollution are shown in Table 1. The table also shows their harmful effects and the possible methods of control.

Table 1 *Substances causing most air pollution*

Air pollutant	Source	Effects	Methods of control
Soot and smoke	Burning fuels	Deposit soot on buildings, etc. Smoke harms our lungs	Use of smokeless fuels. Improve supply of air to burning fuels
Carbon dioxide	Burning fuels	Increased concentration of carbon dioxide leading to greenhouse effect and global warming	Burn less fossil fuels by: • improving insulation in our buildings • making vehicles more efficient
Carbon monoxide	Burning fuels – especially in vehicles	Poisonous to humans and animals. Prevents haemoglobin in the blood from carrying oxygen	Make vehicles burn fuel more efficiently. Fit catalytic converters
Sulphur dioxide	Burning coal and oil which contain small amounts of sulphur	Sulphur dioxide and nitrogen oxides react with rainwater to form sulphurous acid, nitrous acid and nitric acid – 'acid rain'.	Burn less coal and oil. Remove sulphur dioxide from waste gases
Nitrogen oxides	Vehicle exhaust gases contain nitrogen oxides	This • harms plants • gets into rivers and lakes, harming the fish • attacks stonework of buildings and metals	Adjust engines so that nitrogen oxides do not form. Fit catalytic converters
Chlorofluorocarbons (CFCs)	Refrigerators, aerosol sprays	Damage from ultra violet radiation from the Sun (see Unit E8)	Reduce use of CFSs by using other substances

There are two serious consequences from air pollution – **acid rain** and **global warming**.

Did you know?

The pH of acid rain is between 5 and 2. pH 2 is as acidic as vinegar

Acid rain

Some fuels, like coal and coke, contain small amounts of sulphur. When these fuels burn, sulphur dioxide is produced. This is a colourless, toxic and choking gas which irritates our eyes and lungs. The sulphur dioxide reacts with rainwater to form sulphurous acid. This is further oxidised to sulphuric acid, and this together with sulphurous acid causes acid rain.

sulphur dioxide + water → sulphurous acid

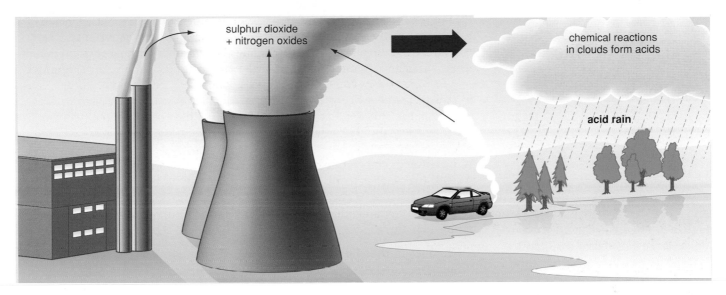

Figure 1 *The formation of acid rain*

Vehicle exhaust gases also contribute to acid rain. Engines need air to burn petrol. When the mixture is sparked, nitrogen and oxygen in the air combine to produce nitrogen oxides. These nitrogen oxides react with rainwater to form nitrous and nitric acids which also cause acid rain (Figure 1).

Acid rain harms all living things. It has been blamed for the poor growth of trees in Scandinavia and the death of fish in rivers and lakes. It is thought that the sulphur dioxide is produced in the industrial areas of Northern England and Scotland and then carried by the prevailing winds across the North Sea to Scandinavia. Acid rain also attacks metals and the stonework of buildings.

Global warming

Figure 2 *The Earth's atmosphere can act like a greenhouse by trapping some of the Sun's radiation*

The air and soil inside a greenhouse are warmer than those outside. This is because the greenhouse glass can trap some of the Sun's radiation.

The Earth's atmosphere can also act like a greenhouse by trapping some of the Sun's radiation. This is called the **greenhouse effect** (Figure 2).

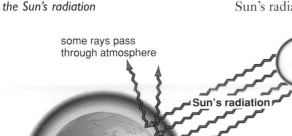

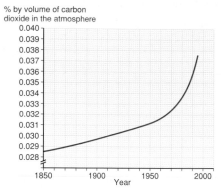

% by volume of carbon dioxide in the atmosphere

Figure 3 *Average percentages of carbon dioxide in the atmosphere since 1850*

Different gases trap the Sun's radiation to a different extent. Nitrogen and oxygen are very poor, but carbon dioxide and chlorofluorocarbons (CFCs), are very effective at trapping the sun's radiation. Unfortunately, the concentration of carbon dioxide in the atmosphere (though very small) is steadily rising (Figure 3).

This increased concentration of carbon dioxide causes an increased greenhouse effect and the Earth's temperature has risen by about 0.5°C in the last 20 years. The effect is called **global warming**.

An increase in temperature of only 0.5°C may seem very little, but it is beginning to cause big changes to the Earth. Scientists are still unsure about the causes and long-term effects of global warming. Although scientists differ in their views about global warming, the following changes support the view that it is taking place.

- **Changes in the climate are occurring.** Higher temperatures than ever are being recorded in some areas. There are also changes in the rainfall pattern with more violent storms and more frequent flooding. The higher average temperatures in Britain are causing birds to make nests and lay eggs earlier in the spring.

- **Patterns of food production are changing.** In certain parts of the world, particularly East Africa, rainfall has decreased and crops are failing more frequently than in the past.

- **Sea levels are rising.** The polar ice caps are slowly melting and coastal flooding is causing more damage.

Advances in modern technology bring advantages and disadvantages. We have the benefits of more fuels and better transport, but we also have the problems of more pollution, acid rain and global warming. Fortunately, many countries have strict laws to control air pollution. In Britain, this began in 1956 with the '*Clean Air Act*'. This made it an offence to pollute the air with soot and smoke from factories and homes.

In recent years, a number of countries including Britain have committed themselves to reducing the levels of carbon dioxide emitted into the atmosphere. They have set targets for reductions by specified dates.

Study Questions

1. a) What are the main substances that cause air pollution?
   b) How do they get into the air?
   c) Suggest three ways in which air pollution causes damage.
2. a) What is acid rain and how is it caused?
   b) How does acid rain affect: (i) lakes; (ii) forests?
3. a) What further steps could be taken to reduce air pollution in heavily industrialised areas?
   b) What problems are there with stricter controls over air pollution?
4. Design a poster to show the problems of global warming.
5. It is the year 2030. You have just been elected as the first British Prime Minister to belong to the Green Party. Write down what you would say in your first interview about your policy on the environment.

Bird watchers in Britain have studied nest building and egg laying trends. They have found that magpies are now starting to do these 17 days earlier than they did in the 1940s. Is this evidence for global warming?

Water is the most abundant substance on the surface of the Earth. We drink it, wash in it, swim in it and complain when it rains. In many ways, water controls our lives. It determines where we can live. It determines whether we can grow crops and produce enough food. It determines our weather. All living things need water – people, animals and plants.

Using water

Most of the time, we take water for granted. It is only during a very dry summer that we need to use it carefully. In the UK, each person uses about 180 litres of water every day. In some parts of Africa, each person must survive on less than 10 litres per day. Figure 1 shows the amounts of water that we might use for different purposes each day.

Water controls our lives. It affects our crops, our food, our health and the weather. 60% of the people in Asia and Africa cannot obtain clean water easily

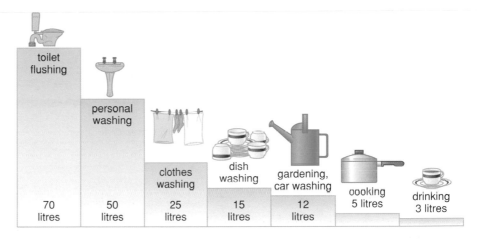

Figure 1 *The amounts of water used by one person each day in the UK*

Large amounts of water are used in industry. Most of the water is used for cooling. A large power station uses about 5 million litres of water per day. The other large industrial uses of water are for washing and as a solvent. When all these uses are added together, it takes:

> 10 litres of water to make 1 litre of lemonade or beer,
> 200 litres of water to make 1 newspaper,
> 50 000 litres of water to make 1 average sized car.

Where does water come from?

At the turn of a tap we expect to get as much clean water as we need. But where does this treated water (Unit A4) come from? If we trace the flow of water backwards, we find that it comes from rain.

When rain falls on the ground, some of it soaks deep into the Earth as groundwater in underground wells and saturated rocks. But, most rain runs off the land into rivers and lakes as surface water. This surface water covers 70% of the Earth. But where does the rain come from?

Did you know?

Everyday you need about 2 litres (3½ pints) of water. This water may be part of your food or drinks. It replaces the water that you lose when you breathe, urinate or perspire. Water is more important than food. Most people can survive for 7 to 8 weeks without food, but only 5 to 10 days without water.

Did you know?

A large power station uses 5 million litres of water every day for cooling. Because of this, power stations are often built near a large source of water, such as the sea, or a major river

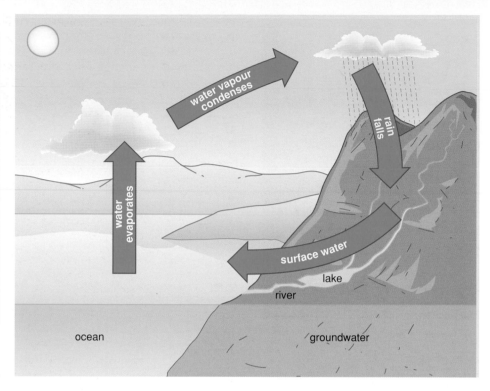

Figure 2 *The water cycle*

Heat from the Sun causes surface water to evaporate into the air from rivers, lakes and oceans. This water vapour rises into the atmosphere and forms clouds. As the clouds rise, they cool and the water vapour condenses to form drops of water. When these drops become large enough, they fall back to the Earth as rain. This rain either soaks into the soil or joins rivers and oceans and the whole cycle begins again. This continuous movement of water from the Earth's surface to clouds and then back to the Earth as rain is called the **water cycle** (Figure 2).

Water pollution

There are vast amounts of water in oceans, lakes and rivers, but it is easily polluted. The main sources of water pollution are listed in Table 1.

Sewage is the main cause of water pollution. At one time, all sewage was pumped into rivers and the sea. This caused health hazards and diseases such as cholera. Sewage also affects living things in the water. If the amount of sewage is small, then bacteria in the water can break it down to harmless materials like carbon dioxide, nitrates and water. But, if the amount of sewage is large, then the bacteria use up all the oxygen dissolved in the water as they feed on the sewage. Once the oxygen concentration gets too low, most of the living organisms in the water (including the bacteria) die. The decaying materials make the water cloudy and smelly.

In order to avoid this pollution, sewage plants treat the waste before it is returned to rivers and the sea. The sewage is pumped into large tanks and mixed with air (**aerated**) so that it can be decomposed more rapidly by bacteria. Nowadays, water companies have to work to strict levels of pollution control and this has led to cleaner rivers and beaches in Britain.

Table I *The main sources of water pollution*

Main sources of water pollution
Sewage
Fertilisers
Industrial chemicals
Pesticides
Oil
Detergents

Table 2 summarises the sources and effects of other substances which cause water pollution.

Table 2 *The sources and effects of various water pollutants*

Polluting substance	Source	Effect
Fertilisers	Rain washes fertilisers into rivers and lakes	Bacteria and algae grow faster, use up all the dissolved oxygen and die
Industrial chemicals	Oils, metal compounds, acids alkalis, dyes, etc. from factories	Toxic to animals, plants and bacteria in the water
Pesticides	Spraying of crops with chemicals	Toxic chemicals accumulate in the bodies of larger animals
Oil	Oil from refineries and ship-wrecked tankers	Covers sea birds with oil; pollutes beaches

Heat can also be a serious water pollutant. It is a particular problem near the cooling water outlets from large nuclear power stations where the water temperatures may be 10°C higher than normal. The higher water temperatures increase the corrosion of steel structures in the water and reduce the amount of oxygen dissolved in the water. The reduced oxygen content is harmful to some fish such as salmon and trout, although other species thrive in the warmer water.

This beach in Jamaica has been badly polluted by the run off from a bauxite mine

Getting the balance right

It is easy to adopt a simple view of pollution and say, 'Pollution is wrong'. But, if we did this and passed laws to protect our rivers and lakes, then industries would spend more money on avoiding pollution and removing waste. These additional costs would be passed on to the customers and goods from our factories would be more expensive. As a society, we must decide between more pollution control and higher prices or less pollution control and lower prices. Remember that *everyone* is responsible for pollution. We are all members of a society which consumes goods and materials and requires oil, fertilisers, pesticides and detergents.

Study Questions

1 Look at Figure 1.
   a) Which of the uses of water requires: (i) the purest water; (ii) the least pure water?
   b) Write down the uses, in order from those needing the purest water to those needing the least pure water.
   c) Which of the uses could be avoided in order to save water during a drought?
   d) Suppose you saved all the water from personal washing. How could this water be used by your family?

2 a) Why does sewage cause fresh water to become murky and smelly?
   b) Why are bacteria mixed with sewage at some treatment plants?
   c) Why is solid sewage sometimes heated to 30°C and aerated regularly at the sewage plant?

3 a) Suppose that each person in your family uses 150 litres of water every day. How much water is used by your family in one year?
   b) Suppose your family pays £200 in water rates for the supply and treatment of water each year.
      (i) What is the cost of water per litre for your family?
      (ii) Compare this with the cost of one litre of petrol or milk.

8 The Properties of Water

Living things, like this seal, can survive in water even in the Antarctic because ice floats on water

Table 1 *The solubility of some substances in water at 20°C*

Solute	Mass of solute which dissolves in 100 g of water at room temp. (20°C)
Sand	insoluble
Salt	36.0 g
Sugar	204 g
Alcohol	infinite
Oxygen	0.004 g
Carbon dioxide	0.014 g

Water covers about 70% of the Earth's surface in oceans, lakes and rivers. It freezes at 0°C and boils at 100°C so it is a liquid at most places on the Earth. This is unusual. Can you think of another substance which occurs naturally as a liquid?

Water is also a very good solvent. It will dissolve substances as different as salt, sugar, alcohol and oxygen. Look at Table 1. You will see that some substances are more soluble than others.

When the temperature falls below 0°C, water turns to ice. If the water is trapped in pipes as it freezes, then the pipes may split open and cause a burst. The pipes split because water *expands* when it freezes and the ice takes up more space than the water. This is another unusual property of water. Almost all other substances contract when they freeze. The expansion of water as it changes to ice means that ice is less dense than water. This expansion causes rocks to crack and potholes to appear in the roads.

When ice forms on the surface of a pond, it acts as an insulator and it prevents the water below from freezing. Because of this, living things can survive in water even in Arctic conditions.

Water as a solvent – solubility

When you stir a spoonful of instant coffee into a cup of *hot* water, it dissolves very quickly. If you tried to make a cup of coffee with *cold* water, the coffee would not dissolve. You may also have noticed that sugar dissolves better in hot coffee than in cold coffee. These everyday examples show that solids dissolve better in water as the temperature increases.

When sugar is stirred into coffee, it dissolves until a certain amount has been added. If more sugar is then added, this does not dissolve, provided the volume of the liquid and its temperature do not change. The coffee is **saturated** with sugar.

> A saturated solution is one in which no more solute will dissolve at that temperature.

The extent to which a solute, like sugar, can saturate a solvent like coffee is shown by its **solubility**.

> The solubility of a solute in a particular solvent is the mass of solute that saturates 100 g of solvent at a given temperature.

Table 1 shows the solubilities of various substances in water at 20°C. The solubility of most solids increases with temperature.

Figure 1 shows graphs of the solubilities of sodium chloride and potassium chlorate in water at different temperatures. These graphs which show the variation in solubility with temperature are called **solubility curves**. Look carefully at Figure 1 and make sure that you understand the following points.

● At 40°C, sodium chloride is more soluble in water than potassium chlorate.

● Sodium chloride and potassium chlorate have the same solubility at 78°C.

● The solubility of potassium chlorate at 80°C is 40 g per 100 g of water and at 20°C is 7 g per 100 g of water.

● If 100 g of water is saturated with potassium chlorate at 80°C, 33 g of the solid will crystallise if the temperature falls to 20°C.

Study Questions

1 What unusual properties does water have?

2 The solubilities of potassium nitrate and potassium chloride are given below at temperatures between 0°C and 60°C.

Temperature /°C	0	10	20	30	40	50	60
Solubility of potassium nitrate/g per 100 g water	13	21	31	47	63	83	106
Solubility of potassium chloride/g per 100 g water	28	31	33	36	39	42	45

a) Draw the solubility curves of the two solids by plotting solubility on the vertical axis and temperature on the horizontal axis.

b) Which is the more soluble solid at 28°C?

c) At what temperature are they equally soluble?

d) How much potassium nitrate will crystallize from 100 g of water saturated with this substance at 50°C, if the temperature falls to 23°C?

3 Discuss the following questions in groups of three or four.

a) Why is it necessary to give the temperature at which a solubility is measured?

b) How could you make sure that a solution is saturated at a particular temperature?

c) Why do you think that solids get more soluble in water as the temperature rises, but gases get less soluble?

d) Why does the water in fish tanks need aeration (air bubbled in)?

4 Design an experiment to show that water expands when it freezes.

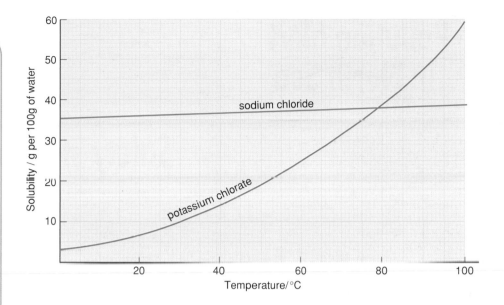

Figure 1 *The solubility curves of sodium chloride and potassium chlorate*

Although most solids become *more soluble* in water as the temperature rises, gases become *less soluble* as the temperature rises. Natural water in lakes and rivers contains dissolved gases from the air such as oxygen and carbon dioxide. More gas dissolves if the water is colder or if the water flows over waterfalls where it mixes more freely with air.

Many animals and plants depend on oxygen dissolved in the water. Fish die if there is less than 0.0004 g of dissolved oxygen per 100 g of water. This explains why fish caught in rivers cannot survive in fish tanks indoors where the water is warmer with a lower concentration of dissolved oxygen.

Some fish species require more dissolved oxygen in the water than others. Because of this they cannot survive at higher temperatures. Salmon require higher concentrations than most fish. They cannot survive if the water temperature is above 15°C

Pollution alert in North Sea

By Pearce Wright

Ships which monitor North Sea pollution and radioactivity levels for the Ministry of Agriculture and Fisheries have been alerted to track a flood of mercury due to be discharged from the Rhine later this week.

Their measurement of how this lethal plume is dispersing will be relayed to experts on the protection of coastal and offshore North Sea fisheries.

Aquatic life in the Rhine was destroyed as an estimated 30 tons of mercury and other chemicals

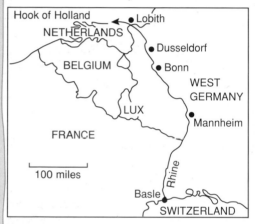

used in the manufacture of pesticides drifted down the river from Basle in Switzerland, through Germany, and to the Netherlands at the weekend.

The mercury, the key ingredient of a powerful fungicide, was washed into the river when firemen fought a blaze at the Sandoz chemical plant, near Basle

It undid efforts of 10 years to clean up the Rhine, which had been criticized as "becoming Europe's sewer" because of the effluent from rapid industrial growth in Germany, Switzerland and France.

Mercury is one of the heavy metals that are mined for various industrial purposes. Others include lead, arsenic and cadmium. They are also called the toxic metals because very small concentrations are required to poison animals and plants.

A similar incident with mercury 25 years ago, though spread over a longer period, gave the first hints of the extreme toxicity of the heavy metals.

It happened in the small Japanese coastal town of Minamata, where mercury poisoning originating in wastes from a chemical factory spread from fish to fishermen and their families.

The disaster occurred because the mercury was transformed into a highly biologically active form of organic mercury compound after it was discharged. That anxiety will exist over the mercury pouring into the North Sea.

1 Pollution of the River Rhine and the North Sea

A few years ago, *The Times* newspaper published reports concerning pollution of the River Rhine. One report is reproduced on the left. Read the report and the article below.

Safety standards questioned

The Sandoz chemical plant in Basle has been accused of insufficient safety standards after a fire which led to serious pollution of the Rhine.

A report suggests that the storage building where the fire broke out had no trays to catch leaking chemicals, no automatic sprinklers and no smoke-warning or heat warning system.

The building stored a powerful fungicide containing mercury. Only 10 metres from this building , there was another store containing sodium. If water, which was used to fight the fire, had reacted with the sodium a serious explosion might have resulted.

An investigation into the cause of the fire will probably take weeks to prepare. Meanwhile, many German towns along the Rhine face a water shortage because their wells have been closed.

In Basle, demonstrators marched through the city to the Sandoz Chemical Company. They carried banners saying, 'We don't want to be tomorrow's fish.'

The demonstrators were angry about the reports that at least 200 gallons of a poisonous liquid containing mercury had leaked into the River Rhine. The West German government may demand damages for the accident and press for more co-ordination between countries over inland waterway disasters.

The Rhine Fishing Federation claimed that plants and animals would be killed in 155 miles of the Rhine between Basle and Manheim. Salvage workers had recently removed several hundred kilograms of dead eels from the river.

The enquiry

Imagine that an enquiry has been set up to look into the accident. Some people have been asked to prepare statements for the enquiry team. These people include:

(i)   a scientist who is particularly interested in the toxic (poisonous) properties of mercury and its compounds,

(ii)   a safety officer required to enforce safety standards in industrial plants,

(iii)   the Mayor of Basle.

The statements

Make a group with two other students. Decide who will act as the scientist, who will act as the safety officer and who will act as the Mayor of Basle. Discuss the issues in your group. Then, write down the statements you will each make to the enquiry team (about 300 words). Practise your talks to each other. (Your teacher may ask you to read your statements to the rest of the class.)

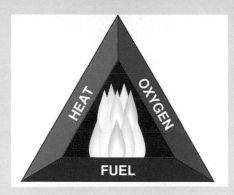

The fire triangle

2 Fire fighting

The fire triangle can be used to explain how fires start and how they can be put out.

1 Why does the fire triangle have labels for fuel, oxygen and heat?

2 When the fire services are called to a fire, they try to remove either the fuel, the oxygen, the heat or more than one of these three. Why is this?

3 Which one of fuel, oxygen or heat is being removed from the fires described below?

    a) When the fat in the chip pan suddenly caught fire, Nicola grabbed a damp cloth and covered the chip pan.

    b) When the forest fire started, the foresters cleared the fire breaks (i.e. the wide tracks in the forest) just ahead of the fire.

    c) The fireman sprayed water on the burning beams of the warehouse.

    d) Julian was sitting close to the fire. Suddenly, his coat was in flames. Shakila acted quickly and rolled Julian in the rug on which he was sitting.

3 Searching the web for a water purifier

The Sanders family recently decided to install a water purifier in their home. They heard of two companies who advertise on the web. One was called '*Lifeguard Systems*' and the other was '*Water Wise*'.

1 Find these two sites and compare their claims.

2 Which purifier would you recommend?

3 Explain the science behind your recommendation to the Sanders.

4 Using *Excel* to plot and interpret solubility curves

The table below lists the solubilities of four compounds at different temperatures. The solubilities are expressed as the number of grams of each compound which dissolve in 100 g of water at the stated temperatures.

Temperature (°C)	10	20	30	40	50
Potassium chloride	31.0	34.5	37.5	40.0	43.0
Sodium nitrate	80.5	88.0	96.0	105.0	114.0
Potassium nitrate	21.0	31.5	45.5	62.5	84.5
Copper(II) sulphate	17.5	20.5	25.0	28.5	33.5

Temperature (°C)	60	70	80	90
Potassium chloride	45.5	48.5	51.0	54.0
Sodium nitrate	124.0	135.0	148.0	161.0
Potassium nitrate	108.0	137.0	168.0	203.0
Copper(II) sulphate	40.0	45.5	55.0	67.5

- Enter the values into a spreadsheet and then plot scatter graphs of each set of data by selecting all the data.
- Label the x-axis **temperature/°C** and the y-axis **g/100 g**. Click on **Chart, Source Data** to name each line. Now use your graphs to answer the following questions.

1 What is the number of grams of each compound which can be dissolved in 100 g of water at:

    a) 25°C, **b)** 55°C, **c)** 75°C?

2 What is the lowest temperature at which 35 g of the following chemicals will dissolve in 100 g of water?

    a) potassium nitrate, **b)** copper(II) sulphate

3 At what temperature do **a)** potassium nitrate and sodium nitrate, **b)** potassium chloride and copper(II) sulphate, have the same solubility?

4 Predict the solubility of potassium nitrate at **a)** 100°C, **b)** 0°C.

    (In order to do this you need to click the line for potassium nitrate on your graph, then click **Chart, Add Trend Line**. Click the 'Type' tab and choose polynomial, then click the 'Options' tab and change 'Forward' and 'Backward' dialogue boxes to 10 units each. You can make more accurate readings by right-clicking the line, then clicking **Format Gridlines**. Then click the 'Scale' tab and change the minimum to 20, maximum to 60 and the minor unit to 1.)

Section B   Summary

1 Air

- Air, and specifically oxygen, is essential for all life.
- Clean, dry air contains approximately $\frac{4}{5}$ nitrogen and $\frac{1}{5}$ oxygen.
- The gases in air can be separated by liquefying air followed by fractional distillation.

2 Oxygen

- Oxygen helps substances to burn.
- A test for oxygen is to show that it will relight a glowing splint.
- Oxygen reacts with elements to form oxides.

The oxides of metals are called **basic oxides**.
Soluble basic oxides react with water to form alkaline solutions and are known as **alkaline oxides**.
The oxides of non-metals react with water to form acids and are known as **acidic oxides**.

3 Redox

- Burning, breathing and rusting are examples of redox (**red**uction/**ox**idation) reactions.
- These reactions are also **exothermic reactions** which give out heat.
- Oxidation involves gain of oxygen and reduction involves loss of oxygen.

4 Air pollution

- Air pollution is caused by the release of poisonous and harmful gases into the air. Most air pollution is caused by burning fossil fuels in our homes, in our vehicles and in power stations.
- The two serious consequences of air pollution are **acid rain** and **global warming**.

5 Water

- Water is essential for life on Earth.
- Water is also an important raw material for industry. It is used as a coolant, as a solvent and for washing.
- Water is a very good solvent for many solutes. A saturated solution is one in which no more solute will dissolve at a particular temperature.
- The solubility of a solute in a particular solvent is the mass of solute that saturates 100 g of solvent at a given temperature.

Section B Exam Questions

1 Air is passed over excess heated copper using the apparatus shown in the diagram below. This experiment is used to determine the percentage of oxygen in air.

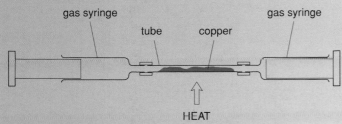

(a) (i) What percentage of the air is oxygen?
(ii) Write a word equation for the reaction which occurs in the tube.
(b) Redraw and complete the table below to:
(i)   name TWO gases present in the apparatus after all the oxygen has been removed;
(ii) give the percentage, by volume, of each of these gases present in a sample of unpolluted, dry air;
(iii) state an industrial use for each of these gases.

Name of gas	Percentage	Industrial use for gas

Edexcel 1998

2 The fire triangle shows the factors necessary to start and maintain a fire.

(a) Give the name of the gas present in the air which is necessary for combustion.
(b) State **two** methods by which air can be removed during fire-fighting.
(c) Give a fire-**fighting** method, choosing a **different method in each case**, for the following situations. Use the fire triangle to explain your method in each case.
(i) House fire.
State the method and then give an explanation

(ii) Forest fire.
State the method and then give an explanation
WJEC (specimen question, 2003)

3 (a) The exhaust gases from older cars are tested each year. These exhaust gases contain carbon monoxide, unburned hydrocarbons and smoke.
If the amount of one of these is too high, the car will fail its test. Look at these results from an exhaust test. Use these results to answer the questions.

item	test result	maximum limit
carbon monoxide	4.0%	3.5%
unburned hydrocarbons	197 ppm	1200 ppm
idle speed	pass	
smoke level	pass	

(i) What is the maximum limit of carbon monoxide allowed?
(ii) This car failed its test. Why? Choose one of the following answers.
● There is too much carbon monoxide.
● There is too much unburned hydrocarbon.
● There is too much smoke.
(b) Why is carbon monoxide dangerous?
(c) As well as carbon monoxide, unburned hydrocarbons, smoke and water, car exhausts contain other gases.
One of these gases may cause a change in the Earth's weather.
Explain this.

AQA 2000

4 Sam looks up the solubilities of three different substances at different temperatures in a database.
The results of her search are shown in the table.
In each case the solubility is given as grams of the substance dissolved in 100 g of water to form a saturated solution.

substance dissolved	temperature in °C				
	10	20	40	60	80
potassium nitrate	21	32	62	106	167
sodium chloride	36	36	36	37	37
potassium chloride	33	35	40	46	54

(a) What mass of potassium nitrate would be needed to produce a saturated solution of potassium nitrate in **50 g of water** at 40°C?
You **must** show your working.
(b) Sam makes a saturated solution of potassium chloride in water at 80°C.
She leaves the solution to cool to room temperature.
What would she see as the solution cools? Explain your answer.

(c) (i) Plot the data for the solubility of sodium chloride and potassium chloride in water. Temperature (°C) on x-axis and solubility (g per 100 g of water) on y-axis. Draw two solubility curves.

(ii) At which temperature is the solubility of the two substances the same?
Show on the grid how you obtained tour answer.

OCR 2001

5 (a) Explain what is meant by:
(i) a **saturated** solution,
(ii) a **saturated** hydrocarbon.
(b) The table shows data for the solubility of ammonium chloride in water at different temperatures.

Temperature (°C)	0	20	40	60	80	100
Solubility (g per 100 g water)	29.4	37.2	40.5	55.2	65.6	77.3

Select a suitable scale for each axis and plot the data on graph paper. Plot Solubility (g per 100 g water) on the vertical axis and Temperature (°C) on the horizontal axis.
Draw a smooth curve to show how the solubility of ammonium chloride in water changes with temperature, allowing for any anomalous point.
(c) Use your graph to answer the following questions.
(i) What is the solubility of ammonium chloride in g per 100 g of water at 90°C?
(ii) What is the lowest temperature at which 50 g of ammonium chloride dissolves completely in 100 g of water?
(iii) What mass of ammonium chloride crystals would be obtained if a saturated solution of ammonium chloride, prepared using 50 g of water, was cooled from 100°C to 30°C?

AQA 2000

6 This question is about the rusting of iron and steel.

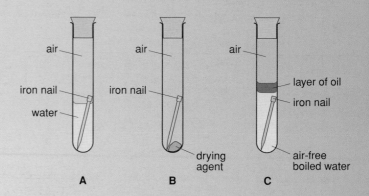

A   B   C

Identical shiny iron nails are put into test tubes as in the diagrams.
Each test tube is then firmly corked.
The nail in **A** rusts. The nails in **B** and **C** do **not** rust.
Explain all these observations.

OCR 2000

7 (a) Iron corrodes in air forming rust.
(i) Give the chemical name for rust.
(ii) Name the chemical process for rusting.
(b) The rusting of five identical nails was investigated by treating each nail as shown in the table below. All five nails were left exposed to the atmosphere for a few months.
One of the results in the table is incorrect.

Using only the information in the table below give the treatment:
(i) which gives the best protection
(ii) which is usually used to protect steel bridges from rusting
(iii) which is usually used to protect steel garden tools from rusting
(iv) which has the incorrect result.
(c) Explain why, although aluminium is more reactive than iron, it appears to be corrosion resistant.

WJEC 2000

Nail	Treatment used	Cost of treatment	Mass of nail and coating *before* exposure to the atmosphere (grams)	Mass of nail and coating *after* exposure to the atmosphere (grams)
A	oiled	cheap	2.0	2.3
B	chromium plated	expensive	2.0	2.0
C	painted	cheap	2.0	2.2
D	galvanised	fairly expensive	2.0	1.2
E	untreated	nil	1.9	2.7

Particles, Reactions and Equations

A painting of John Dalton collecting marsh gas which is mainly methane. John Dalton was the first scientists to use the word 'atom'

By the end of this section you should be able to:
- Understand that all matter is composed of tiny, invisible moving particles.
- Explain changes of state, diffusion and Brownian motion in terms of moving particles.
- Understand the difference between atoms and molecules.
- Understand how elements and compounds react in terms of atoms and molecules.
- Represent chemical reactions by balanced equations using symbols and formulas.
- Appreciate the relevance of relative atomic masses in determining reacting quantities.
- Determine the formulas of simple compounds from reacting masses.
- Calculate reacting quantities from balanced chemical equations.

Evidence for Particles

When sugar is added to tea or coffee, it dissolves quickly. The sugar seems to disappear. What happens to the sugar when it dissolves? Where does the sugar go?

How does the liquid get through the filter paper when filter coffee is made? The coffee grains don't get through the paper. Why is this?

Look at the photos above and try to answer the questions in the captions.
In order to answer these questions, you will need to use the idea that:

> All materials are made up of particles.

If possible, get some sugar and stir it into a cup of warm water (Figure 1). Watch the sugar disappear as you stir the water. We can explain how the sugar dissolves and disappears using the idea of particles. Both sugar and water are made up of very small particles. These particles are much too small to see, even under a microscope. When sugar dissolves, tiny particles break off each solid granule. These tiny invisible sugar particles mix with the water particles in the liquid. So, the solution tastes sweet even though you cannot see the sugar.

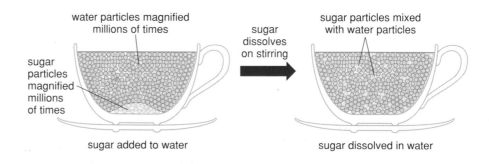

Figure 1 *Explaining what happens when sugar dissolves in water*

How large are the particles of materials?

Anyone who cooks knows that a small amount of pepper, ginger or curry powder will give food a really strong taste. Too much spice can spoil the whole meal. This suggests that tiny particles in the spice can spread throughout the whole meal.

Figure 2 shows an experiment which will help you to get some idea about the size of particles.

Dissolve 1 g of dark purple potassium manganate(VII) crystals in 1000 cm³ of water. Take 100 cm³ of this solution and dilute it to 1000 cm³ with water. Now take 100 cm³ of the once-diluted solution and dilute this to 1000 cm³ with water. Carry out further dilutions until you get a solution in which you can only *just* see the pink colour. It is possible to make 6 dilutions before the pink colour is so faint that it is only just noticeable. When the potassium manganate(VII) dissolves, its particles spread throughout the water making a dark purple solution. When this solution is diluted, the particles spread further apart.

This experiment shows that the tiny particles in only 1 g of potassium manganate(VII) can colour 1 000 000 000 cm³ of water. This suggests that there must be millions and millions of tiny particles in only 1 g of potassium manganate(VII).

Similar experiments show that the particles in all substances are extremely small. For example, there are more air particles in a thimble, than grains of sand on a large beach.

Figure 2 *Estimating the size of particles in potassium manganate(VII). (If you try this experiment, **wear eye protection**)*

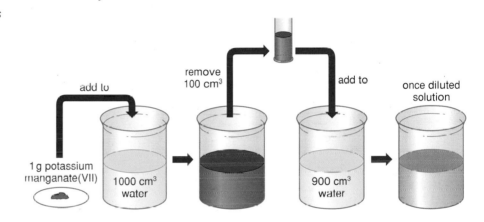

Study Questions

1 Krisnan and Christine were talking about dissolving sugar in tea. Krisnan thought that the sugar would weigh less when it was dissolved because it would be floating in the tea.
   a) What do you think happens to the mass of a substance when it dissolves?
   b) Plan an experiment to test your suggestions in part a).
   c) If possible, carry out your suggested experiment. Explain your results.
2 Get into groups of two or three. Use the idea of particles to discuss and explain what happens when:
   a) water in a kettle boils to produce steam,
   b) you add water to a clay flower pot and the outside of the pot becomes wet,
   c) puddles disappear on a fine day,
   d) tightly tied balloons go down after some time.
3 Look back at Figure 2 and the experiment involved. Suppose that 1 g of potassium manganate(VII) has a volume of 1 cm³ and that there is one particle of potassium manganate(VII) in every drop of the final 1 000 000 000 cm³ of faint pink solution.
   a) Estimate the number of drops in 1 cm³ of the faint pink solution.
   b) How many particles of potassium manganate(VII) are there in 1 000 000 000 cm³ of the faint pink solution?
   c) Calculate the volume of one particle of potassium manganate(VII) in the crystal.
4 A goldsmith used 1.93 g of gold (density 19.3 g/cm³) to make an extremely thin sheet of gold, 100 cm² in area.
   a) What is the volume of the gold foil? (Use the equation, density = mass/volume, to obtain this.)
   b) What is the thickness of the gold foil?
   c) What is the largest possible size of gold particles?

The best evidence that particles of matter are constantly moving comes from studies of **diffusion** and **Brownian motion**.

Diffusion

Fish and chips have a delicious smell. How does the smell get from the fish and chips to your nose? Particles of gas are released from the fish and chips. These particles mix with air particles and move away from the chips.

> This movement and mixing of particles is called **diffusion**.

Gases consist of tiny particles moving at high speeds. The particles collide with each other and with the walls of their container. Sooner or later, gases like those from the fish and chips, will diffuse into all the space they can find.

Diffusion also occurs in liquids, but it takes place much more slowly than in gases (Figure 1). This means that liquid particles move around more slowly than gas particles. Diffusion does not happen in solids.

Diffusion is very important in living things. It explains how the food you eat gets into your bloodstream where it is carried by your blood to different parts of your body. After a meal, food passes into your stomach. Here, large particles are broken down into smaller particles. These smaller particles can *diffuse* through the walls of the intestines into the bloodstream.

Why is it possible to smell the perfume that someone is wearing from several metres away?

Figure 1 *Add 2 drops of blackcurrant juice very carefully to a glass of water. The juice colours a small part of the water purple. Leave the glass in a safe place where it cannot be disturbed. The purple juice moves away from the top of the water. After a week, **all** the water is a pale lilac colour. Particles in the purple juice have moved about and mixed with the water particles*

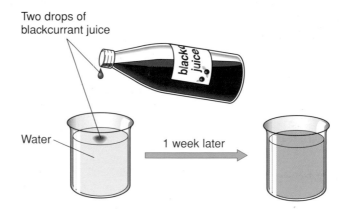

Brownian motion

In 1827, a biologist called Robert Brown was using a microscope to look at pollen grains in water. To his surprise, the pollen grains kept moving and jittering about randomly. Similar random movements can be seen when you look at smoke particles through a microscope (Figure 2).

> This movement of tiny particles in a gas or liquid is called **Brownian motion**.

Smoke from a smouldering piece of string is injected into the smoke cell using a teat-pipette. Through the microscope, the smoke particles look like tiny points of light which jitter about.

The movement of the smoke particles is caused by the random motion of oxygen and nitrogen particles in the air around them. The particles of smoke are small, but they are much larger than air particles. Through the microscope, you can see smoke particles, but air particles are much too small to be seen. These air particles move very fast, hitting the smoke particles at random. The smoke particles are therefore knocked first this way and then that way, so they appear to jitter about (Figure 3).

Figure 2 *Observing the Brownian motion of smoke particles*

As the temperature rises, particles have more energy and they move about faster. This means that gases and liquids diffuse faster when the temperature rises. Particles showing Brownian motion also jitter about faster as the temperature rises because they are being bumped more often by the small particles in the gas or the liquid.

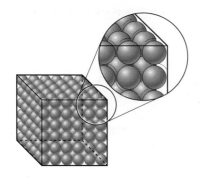

Figure 4 *Particles in a solid*

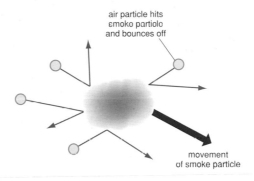

air particle hits smoke particle and bounces off

movement of smoke particle

Figure 3

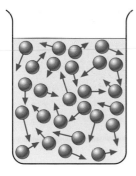

Figure 5 *Particles in a liquid*

The kinetic theory of matter

The idea that all substances contain incredibly small moving particles is called the **kinetic theory of matter**.

The word 'kinetic' comes from a Greek word meaning moving. The main points of the kinetic theory are:

- All matter is made up of tiny, invisible, moving particles. These particles are actually atoms, molecules and ions (Unit C3).

- Particles of different substances have different sizes. Particles of elements, like iron, copper and sulphur, are very small. Particles of compounds, like petrol and sugar, are larger.

- Small particles move faster than larger particles at the same temperature.

- As the temperature rises, the particles have more energy and move around faster.

- In a solid, the particles are very close and they can only vibrate about fixed positions (Figure 4)

- In a liquid, the particles are further apart. They have more energy and they can roll around each other (Figure 5).

- In a gas, the particles are far apart. They move very fast and randomly in all the space they can find (Figure 6).

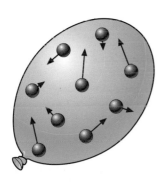

Figure 6 *Particles in a gas*

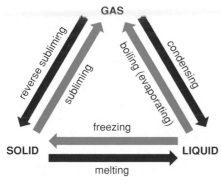

Figure 7 *Changes of state*

Changes of state

The kinetic theory can be used to explain how a substance changes from one state to another. A summary of the different changes of state is shown in Figure 7. These changes are usually caused by heating or cooling a substance.

Gases fill their container completely

Melting and freezing

When a solid is heated, its particles gain energy. The particles vibrate faster and faster until they break away from their fixed positions. The particles begin to move around each other and the solid has melted to form a liquid.

The temperature at which the solid melts is called the **melting point**.

The temperature at which a solid melts tells us how strongly its particles are held together. Substances with high melting points have strong forces between their particles. Substances with low melting points have weak forces between their particles. Metals and alloys, like iron and steel, have high melting points. This suggests that there are strong forces between their particles. This is why metals can be used as girders and supports.

Evaporating and boiling

The particles in a liquid can move around each other. Some particles near the surface of the liquid may have enough energy to escape from the liquid into the air. When this happens, the liquid evaporates to form a gas.

If the liquid is heated, its particles move faster. This gives more of them sufficient energy to escape from the surface. So, evaporation increases as the temperature of the liquid rises.

On further heating, the liquid particles are moving so rapidly that bubbles of gas form inside the liquid.

The temperature at which evaporation occurs in the bulk of the liquid is the **boiling point**.

Boiling points tell us how strongly the particles are held together in liquids. Volatile liquids, like petrol, evaporate easily and boil at low temperatures. They have weak forces between their particles.

Study Questions

1 What do you understand by the following terms:
   diffusion; kinetic theory; states of matter; melting point; boiling point?
2 What happens to the particles of a liquid: (i) as it cools down, (ii) as it freezes?
3 Use the kinetic theory to explain why: (i) gases exert a pressure on the walls of their container; (ii) you can smell hot, sizzling bacon several metres away, but you have to be near cold bacon to smell it; (iii) liquids have a fixed size but not a fixed shape; (iv) solid blocks of air freshener disappear without leaving any solid; (v) you can smell some cheeses even when they are wrapped in clingfilm.

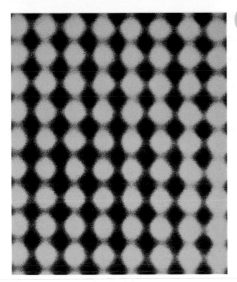

Figure 1 *This photo of a gold crystal was taken through an electron microscope. The yellow blobs are individual gold atoms*

What is an atom?

> An **atom** is the smallest particle of an element.

The word 'atom' comes from a Greek word meaning 'indivisible' or 'unsplittable'. At one time, scientists thought that atoms could not be split. We now know that atoms can be split. But, if an atom of one element is split, it becomes a different element.

> Elements contain only one kind of atom.

So, copper contains only copper atoms and carbon contains only carbon atoms.

So far we have learnt that all substances and all materials are made of particles. There are only three different particles in all substances – **atoms, molecules** and **ions**.

Electron microscopes can magnify objects more than a million times. In 1958, scientists in the USSR observed individual atoms of barium and oxygen using an electron microscope. Figure 1 shows an electron microscope photo of a gold crystal. The magnification is 40 000 000 times. Each yellow blob is an individual gold atom.

Representing atoms with symbols

The word 'atom' was first used by John Dalton in 1807 when he put forward his 'Atomic Theory of Matter'. Dalton suggested the name atom for the smallest particle of an element and he also suggested a method of representing atoms with **symbols**. Figure 2 shows some of Dalton's symbols.

Did you know?

*John Dalton called the smallest particle of an element an **atom**. He was born in 1766 in the village of Eaglesfield in Cumbria. His father was a weaver. For most of his life, Dalton taught at the Presbyterian College in Manchester*

Figure 2 *Dalton's symbols for some common elements*

The modern symbols which we use for different elements are based on Dalton's suggestions.

Table 1 gives a list of the symbols for some of the common elements. (A longer list of symbols appears on page 301). Notice that most elements have two letters in their symbol. The first letter is *always* a capital, the second letter is *always* small. These symbols come from either the English name (O for oxygen, C for carbon) or from the Latin name (Au for gold – Latin: aurum; Cu for copper – Latin: cuprum).

Table 1 The symbols for some elements

Element	Symbol	Element	Symbol	Element	Symbol
Aluminium	Al	Hydrogen	H	Oxygen	O
Argon	Ar	Iodine	I	Phosphorus	P
Bromine	Br	Iron	Fe	Potassium	K
Calcium	Ca	Krypton	Kr	Silicon	Si
Carbon	C	Lead	Pb	Silver	Ag
Chlorine	Cl	Magnesium	Mg	Sodium	Na
Chromium	Cr	Mercury	Hg	Sulphur	S
Copper	Cu	Neon	Ne	Tin	Sn
Gold	Au	Nickel	Ni	Uranium	U
Helium	He	Nitrogen	N	Zinc	Zn

Compounds and atoms

Elements contain only one kind of atom.

> Compounds contain more than one kind of element combined together chemically, so they *must* contain more than one kind of atom.

Water contains both hydrogen and oxygen atoms combined together chemically and carbon dioxide contains both carbon and oxygen.

What is a molecule?

> A molecule is a particle containing two or more atoms joined together chemically.

Atoms of different elements can join together to form molecules. These molecules joined by chemical bonds are compounds.

For example, a molecule of water contains two atoms of hydrogen combined with one atom of oxygen. A molecule of carbon dioxide contains one atom of carbon combined with two atoms of oxygen (Figure 3).

Figure 3 *Atoms of hydrogen, oxygen and carbon above molecules of water and carbon dioxide*

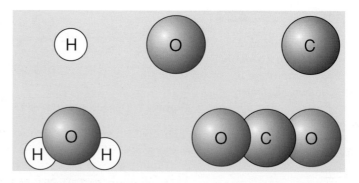

The symbols for elements can also be used to represent molecules and compounds. So, water is represented as H_2O – two hydrogen atoms (H) and one oxygen atom (O). Carbon dioxide is written as CO_2 – one carbon atom (C) and two oxygen atoms (O).

'H₂O' and 'CO₂' are called **molecular formulas** or just formulas, for short.

A **molecular formula** shows the numbers of atoms of the different elements in a molecule.

Numbers are written after symbols as subscripts if there are two or more atoms of the same element in a molecule. Some other pictures (structures) of molecules and their chemical formulas are shown in Figure 4.

Some molecules are very simple, like hydrogen chloride (HCl) and water (H_2O). Others are more complex like sulphuric acid (H_2SO_4) and alcohol (C_2H_6O). Others, such as chlorophyll, are very complex ($C_{51}H_{72}O_4N_4Mg$).

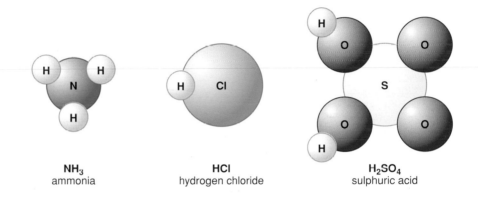

NH₃
ammonia

HCl
hydrogen chloride

H₂SO₄
sulphuric acid

Figure 4 *Pictures (structures) of three molecules and their formulas*

Atoms and molecules of elements

Almost all elements, like iron (Fe), aluminium (Al) and copper (Cu), can be represented by their symbols because they contain single atoms. But, this is not the case with oxygen, hydrogen, nitrogen or chlorine. These elements exist as molecules containing two atoms combined together.

So, oxygen is best represented as O_2 and not O, hydrogen as H_2 not H, nitrogen as N_2 and chlorine as Cl_2 (Figure 5).

These molecules of elements containing two atoms are described as **diatomic molecules**.

What is an ion?

Compounds containing non-metals, like water (H_2O), ammonia (NH_3) and carbon dioxide (CO_2) consist of molecules. But, compounds containing metals and non-metals, like sodium chloride (NaCl) and copper oxide (CuO) consist of ions, not molecules.

In these metal/non-metal compounds, the metal is positively charged and the non-metal is negative (e.g. Na^+Cl^-). The Na^+ and Cl^- particles are called **ions**.

An **ion** is a charged particle formed from an atom by the loss or gain of one or more electrons.

There is more about the formation and properties of ions in Units D3, D4, F3 and H6.

Study Questions

1 Look at the electron microscope photo of a gold crystal on page 51.
   a) Estimate the diameter of one gold atom in the photo.
   b) Calculate the actual diameter of a gold atom. (Assume the magnification is 40 000 000.)
2 Find out about the life and work of John Dalton. Prepare a short talk about Dalton for the rest of your class.
3 How many atoms of the different elements are there in one molecule of: (i) methane (natural gas), CH_4; (ii) sulphuric acid, H_2SO_4; (iii) sugar, $C_{12}H_{22}O_{11}$; (iv) chloroform, $CHCl_3$?
4 Look at Dalton's symbols for the elements in Figure 2.
   a) What do we call 'Azote' and 'Platina' today?
   b) Six of the substances in Dalton's list are compounds and *not* elements. Pick out two of these compounds and write their correct chemical names.
   c) Which one of Dalton's symbols do you think is the most appropriate? Why do you think it is appropriate?
5 The formula for nitrogen is N_2. What does this mean?

symbol **O**

an oxygen atom

formula **O₂**

an oxygen molecule

Figure 5 *An atom and a molecule of oxygen*

Measuring Atoms

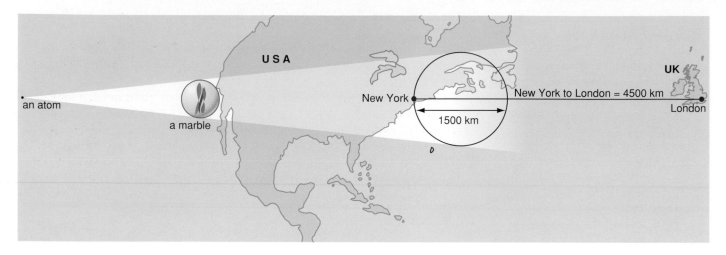

Figure 1 *If atoms are magnified to the size of marbles, on the same scale, a marble would have a diameter of 1500 km*

How large are atoms?

Experiments with a thin film of oil on water show that olive oil particles are about 1/10 000 000 cm thick. But olive oil particles are large molecules containing more than 50 atoms. If we estimate that one molecule of olive oil is about 10 atoms thick, how big is a single atom?

Electron microscope photos and X-ray diffraction studies suggest that atoms are about one hundred millionth (1/100 000 000) of a centimetre in diameter. So, if you put 100 million of them in a straight line, they would still only measure one centimetre in length. It is very difficult to imagine anything as small as this, but Figure 1 should give you some idea of the size of atoms. If atoms were magnified to the size of marbles then, on the same scale, marbles would have a diameter of 1500 km. That's one third of the distance between New York and London.

Figure 2 will also help you to realize just how small atoms are. It shows a step-by-step decrease in size from 1 cm to 1/100 000 000 cm. Each object is one hundred times smaller than the one before it. The dice on the left is about 1 cm wide. In the next picture, the grain of sand is about 1/100 cm across. The bacterium in the middle is 100 times smaller again – about 1/10 000 (10^{-4}) cm from end to end. In the next picture, the molecule of haemoglobin is 100 times smaller than this – about 1/1 000 000 (10^{-6}) cm in diameter. Finally, in the right-hand picture, the atom is one hundredth of the size of the haemoglobin molecule – about 1/100 000 000 (10^{-8}) cm in diameter.

Figure 2 *Step-by-step to the size of atoms*

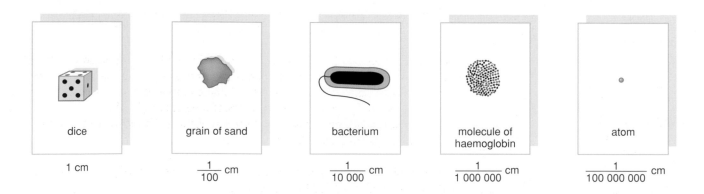

dice	grain of sand	bacterium	molecule of haemoglobin	atom
1 cm	$\dfrac{1}{100}$ cm	$\dfrac{1}{10\,000}$ cm	$\dfrac{1}{1\,000\,000}$ cm	$\dfrac{1}{100\,000\,000}$ cm

How heavy are atoms?

A single atom is so small that it cannot be weighed on a balance. But, the mass of one atom can be *compared* with that of another atom using an instrument called a **mass spectrometer** (Figure 3).

In a mass spectrometer, atoms are passed along a tube and focused into a thin beam. This beam of particles passes through an electric field (which speeds them up) and then through a magnetic field where they are deflected. The extent to which an atom is deflected depends on its mass – the greater the mass, the smaller the deflection. From the extent of deflection, it is possible to compare the masses of different atoms and make a list of their relative masses.

Study Questions

1 The radius of a potassium atom is 2/100 000 000 cm. How many potassium atoms can be arranged next to each other to make a line 1 cm long?

2 Use the relative atomic masses on page 301 to answer the following questions.
 a) Which element has the lightest atoms?
 b) Which element has the next lightest atoms?
 c) How many times heavier are carbon atoms than hydrogen atoms?
 d) Which element has atoms four times as heavy as oxygen?

3 Put the following in order of size from the largest to the smallest: *a bacterium; the thickness of a human hair; a molecule of sugar (which contains about 50 atoms); a smoke particle; a copper atom; a fine dust particle.*

4 Write the following elements in order of decreasing deflection in a mass spectrometer (put the element which is deflected the most first): *copper; calcium; carbon; cobalt; chlorine.*

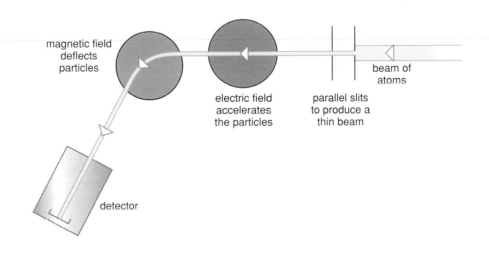

Figure 3 *A simple diagram of a mass spectrometer*

Relative atomic masses

Table 1 *The relative atomic masses of a few elements*

Element	Symbol	Relative atomic mass
Carbon	C	12.0
Hydrogen	H	1.0
Magnesium	Mg	24.0
Oxygen	O	16.0
Iron	Fe	55.8
Copper	Cu	63.5
Gold	Au	197.0

The relative masses which scientists use for different atoms are called **relative atomic masses**.

> The element carbon is the standard for relative atomic masses. Carbon atoms are given a relative mass of exactly 12.

The relative masses of other atoms are then obtained by comparison with carbon. For example, carbon atoms are 12 times as heavy as hydrogen atoms. So, the relative atomic mass of hydrogen is 1.0. Magnesium atoms are twice as heavy as carbon atoms, so the relative atomic mass of magnesium is 24.0.

A few relative atomic masses are listed in Table 1. Other relative atomic masses are given on page 301.

The symbol for relative atomic mass is A_r. So, we write A_r (C) = 12.0, A_r (Mg) = 24.0, or simply C = 12.0, Mg = 24.0, etc.

5 Using Relative Atomic Masses

The photo shows an aluminium colander (mass 108 g), a copper bracelet (mass 16 g), some iron nails (mass 5.58 g) and some barbecue charcoal (mass 150 g). How many moles of each element do the objects contain?
(Relative atomic masses: Al = 27, Cu = 64, Fe = 55.8, C = 12)

The relative atomic mass of an element in grams is sometimes called one **mole**.

So, 12 g of carbon   = 1 mole
      1 g of hydrogen   = 1 mole
    24 g of carbon   = 2 moles.

Notice that: numbFer of moles = $\dfrac{\text{mass}}{\text{relative atomic mass}}$

Relative atomic masses show that one atom of carbon is 12 times as heavy as one atom of hydrogen. So, 12 g of carbon will contain the same number of atoms as 1 g of hydrogen. An atom of oxygen is 16 times as heavy as an atom of hydrogen, so 16 g of oxygen will also contain the same number of atoms as 1 g of hydrogen.

The relative atomic mass in grams (i.e. one mole) of every element (1 g of hydrogen, 12 g carbon, 16 g oxygen, etc.) will contain the same number of atoms. This number is called **Avogadro's constant**.

The term, Avogadro's constant, was chosen in honour of the Italian scientist Amedeo Avogadro.

Experiments show that Avogadro's constant is 6×10^{23}. Written out in full this is 600 000 000 000 000 000 000 000. Thus, *1 mole of an element always contains 6×10^{23} atoms.*

We can use the mole idea to count (calculate) the number of atoms in a sample of an element. For example:

12 g (1 mole) of carbon contains 6×10^{23} atoms
so 1 g ($\frac{1}{12}$ mole) of carbon contains $\frac{1}{12} \times 6 \times 10^{23}$ atoms
$\Rightarrow$ 10 g ($\frac{10}{12}$ mole) of carbon contains $\frac{10}{12} \times 6 \times 10^{23} = 5 \times 10^{23}$ atoms

Chemists often need to count atoms. In industry, nitrogen is reacted with hydrogen to form ammonia, NH_3, which is then used to make fertilisers. In a molecule of ammonia, there is one nitrogen atom and three hydrogen atoms. In order to make ammonia, chemists must therefore react:

1 mole of nitrogen + 3 moles of hydrogen
(14 g of nitrogen)   (3×1 g = 3 g of hydrogen)

not 1 g of nitrogen and 3 g of hydrogen.

To get the right quantities, chemists must measure in moles, *not* in grams. Thus the mole is the chemist's counting unit.

Chemists are not the only people who 'count' by weighing. Bank clerks use the same idea when they count coins and even notes by weighing them. For example, one hundred 1p coins weigh 356 g. So, it is quicker to take one hundred 1p coins by weighing 356 g of them than by counting

Finding formulas

We have used some formulas already, but how are they obtained? How do we know that the formula of water is H_2O?

All formulas are obtained by doing experiments to find the masses of elements which react. When water is decomposed into hydrogen and oxygen, results show that:

Study Questions

1 How many moles are there in
(i) 52 g chromium ($Cr = 52$);
(ii) 2.8 g nitrogen ($N = 14$);
(iii) 0.36 g carbon ($C = 12$);
(iv) 20 g bromine ($Br = 80$)?

2 What is the mass of (i) 3 moles of bromine ($Br = 80$); (ii) $\frac{1}{4}$ mole of calcium ($Ca = 40$); (iii) 0.1 mole of sodium ($Na = 23$)?

3 Methane in natural gas is found to contain 75% carbon and 25% hydrogen. Calculate the formula of methane using a method like that in Table 1

4 What are the formulas of the following compounds?
a) A compound in which 10.4 g chromium ($Cr = 52$) combines with 48 g bromine ($Br = 80$).
b) A nitride of chromium in which 0.26 g chromium forms 0.33 g of chromium nitride ($N = 14$).

5 a) What masses of calcium, carbon and oxygen react to form one mole of calcium carbonate ($CaCO_3$)? ($Ca = 40, C = 12, O = 16$)
b) What are the percentages of calcium, carbon and oxygen in calcium carbonate?

18 g of water give 2 g of hydrogen + 16 g of oxygen
= 2 moles of hydrogen + 1 mole of oxygen
= $\frac{2 \times 6 \times 10^{23} \text{ atoms}}{\text{of hydrogen}}$ + $\frac{6 \times 10^{23} \text{ atoms}}{\text{of oxygen}}$

12×10^{23} hydrogen atoms combine with 6×10^{23} atoms of oxygen, so 2 hydrogen atoms combine with 1 oxygen atom. Therefore, the formula of water is H_2O.

These results are set out in Table 1. By finding the masses of reacting elements, we can use relative atomic masses to calculate the number of moles of atoms that are present and this gives us the formula of a compound.

Table 1 *Finding the formula of water*

	H	O
Masses reacting	2 g	16 g
Mass of 1 mole	1 g	16 g
∴ moles reacting	2	1
Ratio of atoms	2	1
⇒ Formula	H_2O	

Finding the formula of magnesium oxide

When magnesium ribbon is heated, it burns with a very bright flame to form white, powdery magnesium oxide.

$$\text{magnesium} + \text{oxygen} \rightarrow \text{magnesium oxide}$$

If you try this experiment, **wear eye protection**.

Weigh accurately 0.24 g of clean magnesium ribbon. Heat this strongly in a crucible until all of it forms magnesium oxide (Figure 1). Have a lid on the crucible to stop magnesium oxide escaping, but keep a small gap so that air can enter. When the magnesium has finished reacting, reweigh the crucible + lid + magnesium oxide.
Calculate the mass of oxygen reacting from the mass of magnesium oxide minus the mass of magnesium.

Table 2 shows how to obtain the formula of magnesium oxide from the results.

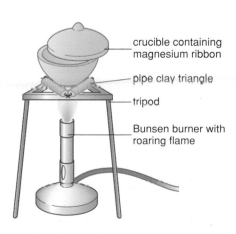

crucible containing magnesium ribbon

pipe clay triangle

tripod

Bunsen burner with roaring flame

Figure 1

Table 2 *Finding the formula of magnesium oxide*

Mass of magnesium reacting		= 0.24 g
Mass of magnesium oxide produced		= 0.40 g

	Mg	O
Masses reacting	0.24 g	0.16 g
Mass of 1 mole	24 g	16 g
∴ moles reacting	0.01	0.01
Ratio of moles	1	1
∴ ratio of atoms	1	1
⇒ Formula	MgO	

Particles in Reactions – Equations

The photo on the left shows sparks from a sparkler. These sparks are bits of burning magnesium. What is the equation for this reaction?

When magnesium burns in air, it reacts with oxygen to form magnesium oxide. The word equation for this is:

$$\text{magnesium} + \text{oxygen} \rightarrow \text{magnesium oxide}$$

Chemists usually write symbols and formulas rather than names in equations. So, in this word equation, we should write Mg for the element magnesium, O_2 for oxygen and MgO for magnesium oxide.

$$Mg + O_2 \rightarrow MgO$$

But, notice that this doesn't balance. There are two oxygen atoms in O_2 on the left and only one oxygen atom in MgO on the right. So, MgO must be doubled to give:

$$Mg + O_2 \rightarrow 2MgO$$

Unfortunately, the equation still doesn't balance. There are now two Mg atoms on the right in 2MgO, but only one on the left in Mg. This is easily corrected by writing 2Mg on the left to give:

$$2Mg + O_2 \rightarrow 2MgO$$

The numbers of different atoms are now the same on both sides of the arrow. This is a **balanced chemical equation**.

> A chemical equation is a summary of the starting substances (reactants) and the products in a chemical reaction.

The example above shows the three stages in writing an equation.

Step 1 Write a word equation for the reaction:

$$\text{e.g. hydrogen} + \text{oxygen} \rightarrow \text{water}$$

Step 2 Write symbols and formulas for the reactants and products:

$$\text{e.g. } H_2 + O_2 \rightarrow H_2O$$

Remember that oxygen, nitrogen, hydrogen and chlorine are diatomic and written as O_2, N_2, H_2 and Cl_2. All other elements are shown as single atoms i.e. Zn for zinc, C for carbon, etc.

Step 3 Balance the equation by making the number of atoms of each element the same on both sides:

$$\text{e.g. } 2H_2 + O_2 \rightarrow 2H_2O$$

Remember that *you must never change a formula* to make an equation balance. The formula for water is always H_2O and never HO or HO_2. Similarly, the formula of magnesium oxide is always MgO.

You can only balance an equation by putting numbers in front of symbols or in front of formulas, i.e. 2Mg and $2H_2O$.

> Balanced chemical equations are more useful than word equations because they show:
>
> ● the symbols and formulas of the reactants and products,
>
> ● the relative numbers of atoms and molecules of the reactants and products.

When natural gas burns, methane (CH_4) reacts with oxygen in the air to form carbon dioxide and water. Write a word equation and then a balanced chemical equation for this reaction

Balanced equations also help us to understand how the atoms are rearranged in a reaction. You can see this even better using models as in Figure 1.

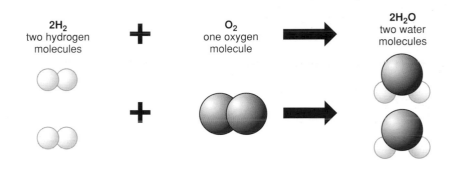

Figure 1 *Using models to represent the reaction between hydrogen and oxygen to form water*

Diagrams like that in Figure 1 explain the 'Law of Conservation of Mass', (Unit A2) because the products in a chemical reaction are made up from exactly the same atoms as the reactants.

Study Questions

1 Write balanced chemical equations for the following word equations.
   a) sodium + oxygen → sodium oxide (Na_2O)
   b) sodium oxide + water → sodium hydroxide (NaOH)
   c) hydrogen + chlorine → hydrogen chloride
   d) zinc + hydrochloric acid (HCl) → zinc chloride ($ZnCl_2$) + hydrogen

2 Look at the photos on this page and answer the questions in the captions.

3 Write word equations and then balanced chemical equations for the following reactions:
   (i) aluminium with oxygen to give aluminium oxide (Al_2O_3);
   (ii) copper oxide with sulphuric acid to give copper sulphate ($CuSO_4$) and water; (iii) nitrogen with hydrogen to give ammonia (NH_3); (iv) charcoal (carbon) burning in oxygen to give carbon dioxide; (v) iron with chlorine to give iron chloride ($FeCl_3$).

The copper dome on Brighton Pavilion is green because the copper has reacted with oxygen in the air to form copper oxide (CuO). This has then reacted very slowly with water to form green copper hydroxide ($Cu(OH)_2$). Write word equations and then balanced chemical equations for these two reactions

State symbols

State symbols are used in equations to show the state of a substance. (s) after a formula indicates the substance is a solid. (l) is used for liquid; (g) for gas and (aq) for an aqueous solution (i.e. a substance dissolved in water). For example,

$$\text{zinc} + \text{sulphuric acid} \rightarrow \text{zinc sulphate} + \text{hydrogen}$$
$$Zn(s) + H_2SO_4(aq) \rightarrow ZnSO_4(aq) + H_2(g)$$

7 Formulas and Equations

The yellow substance in 'no parking' double lines is lead chromate, $PbCrO_4$. What does this formula tell us about the elements in lead chromate? What is the relative formula mass of lead chromate? ($Cr = 52$, $Pb = 207$, $O = 16$)

Relative formula masses

In Unit C4, we learnt that relative atomic masses can be used to compare the masses of different atoms. Relative atomic masses can also be used to compare the masses of molecules in different compounds. The relative masses of compounds are called **relative formula masses** (symbol M_r). The relative formula mass of a compound is obtained by adding up the relative atomic masses of all the atoms in its formula. For example:

the relative formula mass of water, H_2O is:

$$M_r(H_2O) = 2 \times \text{relative atomic mass of hydrogen} + \text{relative atomic mass of oxygen}$$

$$= (2 \times 1.0) + 16.0 = 18.0$$

The relative formula mass of sulphuric acid, H_2SO_4,

$$M_r(H_2SO_4) = 2 \times A_r(H) + A_r(S) + 4 \times A_r(O)$$
$$= 2 \times 1.0 + 32.1 + 4 \times 16.0 = 98.1$$

The relative formula mass of aluminium oxide, Al_2O_3,
$$M_r(Al_2O_3) = 2 \times A_r(Al) + 3 \times A_r(O)$$
$$= 2 \times 26.9 + 3 \times 16.0 = 53.8 + 48 = 101.8$$

> The relative formula mass of a compound in grams is sometimes called one **mole**.

So, 1 mole of water is 18.0 g
0.1 mole of water is $0.1 \times 18.0 = 1.8$ g
1 mole of aluminium oxide is 101.8 g and
3 moles of aluminium oxide is $3 \times 101.8 = 305.4$ g
Relative atomic masses can also be used to calculate the percentage of different elements in a compound. For example:

carbon dioxide (CO_2) contains 12.0 g of carbon and 2×16 g of oxygen in 44.0 g of carbon dioxide.

So, it contains $\frac{12}{44}$ parts carbon and $\frac{32}{44}$ parts oxygen
$= \frac{12}{44} \times 100 = 27\%$ carbon and $\frac{32}{44} \times 100 = 73\%$ oxygen

This photo shows 58.5 g (one mole) of common salt, sodium chloride, (NaCl).
$$M_r(NaCl) = A_r(Na) + A_r(Cl)$$
$$= 23.0 + 35.5 = 58.5$$

Using equations

In industry, it is important to know the amounts of reactants that are needed for a chemical process and the amount of product that can be obtained. Very often, industrial chemists need to know how much product they can obtain from a given amount of staring material. In order to do this, they use relative formula masses and equations.

As an example, let's calculate how much lime (calcium oxide) we could obtain by heating 1 kg of pure limestone (calcium carbonate).

Study Questions

1 **60 g of a metal M** ($M = 60$) combine with 24 g of oxygen ($O = 16$).
   a) How many moles of O react with one mole of **M**?
   b) What is the formula of the oxide of **M**?

2 The fertiliser 'Nitram' (ammonium nitrate) has the formula NH_4NO_3.
   a) What are the masses of nitrogen, hydrogen and oxygen in 1 mole of Nitram? ($N = 14, H = 1, O = 16$)
   b) What are the percentages of nitrogen, hydrogen and oxygen in Nitram?

3 Iron is manufactured by reducing iron ore (Fe_2O_3) with carbon monoxide (CO).
   $$Fe_2O_3 + 3CO \rightarrow 2Fe + 3CO_2$$
   a) What does this equation tell you?
   b) What mass of iron is obtained from 1 mole of Fe_2O_3? ($Fe = 56, O = 16$)
   c) What mass of iron is obtained from one tonne of Fe_2O_3?
   d) What volume of CO at standard temperature and pressure reacts with 1 mole of Fe_2O_3?

This sulphur is being stored after mining. 32.1 g of sulphur can be reacted with oxygen and water to manufacture 98.1 g of sulphuric acid

The equation for the reaction is:

$$\text{calcium carbonate} \rightarrow \text{calcium oxide} + \text{carbon dioxide}$$
$$CaCO_3 \rightarrow CaO + CO_2$$
$$\therefore 1 \text{ mole } CaCO_3 \rightarrow 1 \text{ mole } CaO$$
$$(40 + 12 + (3 \times 16)) \text{ g } CaCO_3 \rightarrow (40 + 16) \text{ g } CaO$$
$$100 \text{ g } CaCO_3 \rightarrow 56 \text{ g } CaO$$
$$\therefore 1000 \text{ g } CaCO_3 \rightarrow 560 \text{ g } CaO$$

So, 1 kg of pure limestone produces 560 g of lime.

Using equations, it is also possible to calculate the volumes of gases which react.

Chemists have found that 1 mole of any gas occupies 24 dm^3 at room temperature (20°C) and atmospheric pressure. At standard temperature and pressure, or s.t.p., (0°C and 1 atmosphere), 1 mole of a gas occupies 22.4 dm^3. This is sometimes called the **molar volume**.

We can illustrate these ideas using the manufacture of ammonia (NH_3) from nitrogen (N_2) and hydrogen (H_2) in the Haber process.

$$\begin{array}{ccccc}
\text{nitrogen} & + & \text{hydrogen} & \rightarrow & \text{ammonia} \\
N_2 & + & 3H_2 & \rightarrow & 2NH_3 \\
\therefore 1 \text{ mole } N_2 & + & 3 \text{ moles } H_2 & \rightarrow & 2 \text{ moles } NH_3 \\
\text{i.e. } 24 \text{ dm}^3 \text{ nitrogen} & + & 3 \times 24 \text{ dm}^3 \text{ hydrogen} & \rightarrow & 2 \times 24 \text{ dm}^3 \text{ ammonia} \\
\text{So, } 1 \text{ dm}^3 \text{ nitrogen} & + & 3 \text{ dm}^3 \text{ hydrogen} & \rightarrow & 2 \text{ dm}^3 \text{ of ammonia}
\end{array}$$

Ammonia is important in producing fertilisers such as ammonium nitrate. What mass of ammonia is needed to react with nitric acid to make 1 tonne of ammonium nitrate?

$$\begin{array}{ccc}
\text{ammonia} + \text{nitric acid} & \rightarrow & \text{ammonium nitrate} \\
NH_3 + HNO_3 & \rightarrow & NH_4NO_3 \\
\therefore 1 \text{ mole of } NH_3 & \rightarrow & 1 \text{ mole of } NH_4NO_3 \\
14 + (3 \times 1) \text{ g } NH_3 & \rightarrow & 14 + (4 \times 1) + 14 \times (3 \times 16) \text{ g } NH_4NO_3 \\
17 \text{ g } NH_3 & \rightarrow & 80 \text{ g } NH_4NO_3
\end{array}$$
$$\Rightarrow 80 \text{ g of } NH_4NO_3 \text{ is obtained from } 17 \text{ g of } NH_3$$
$$\therefore 1 \text{ g of } NH_4NO_3 \text{ is obtained from } \tfrac{17}{80} \text{ g } (= 0.21 \text{ g}) \text{ of } NH_3$$

So, 1 tonne of ammonium nitrate is obtained from 0.21 tonne of ammonia

Section C   Activities

1 Soluble aspirin

When a soluble aspirin tablet is added to water, bubbles start to form. The mass of the solution after the tablet has dissolved is less than the mass of the tablet plus the mass of the water before mixing.

1 Why is there a loss in mass when the soluble aspirin is added to water?

2 Describe an experiment which you could carry out to test your ideas for the loss in mass. (Draw diagrams if it will help.) You should try to use materials and apparatus which are readily available in the lab.

3 What happens to particles in the soluble aspirin when it is added to water?

4 Soluble aspirins dissolve faster in warm water than in cold water. Why is this?

Why do people take soluble aspirin? Why do the tablets fizz when added to water?

2 Extracting tin from tinstone

The production manager at a tin smelter has to meet certain production targets. The smelter must produce 595 tonnes of tin each month. In order to do this, the manager must calculate how much purified tinstone (tin oxide) he must buy to produce 595 tonnes of tin. The basis for his calculation is the equation:

$$\text{tin oxide} + \text{coke (carbon)} \rightarrow \text{tin} + \text{carbon monoxide}$$
$$SnO_2 + 2C \rightarrow Sn + 2CO$$

SnO_2 means that tin oxide contains 2 atoms of oxygen for every 1 atom of tin. CO means that carbon monoxide contains 1 atom of carbon for every 1 atom of oxygen.

Using relative atomic masses, the manager can now calculate how much tin can be obtained from a certain amount of tin oxide (SnO_2). The relative formula masses of SnO_2 and CO can be calculated by adding together the correct number of relative atomic masses for the atoms of the elements in each compound.

Relative atomic mass of tin	$= 119$
Relative atomic mass of oxygen	$= 16$
Relative atomic mass of carbon	$= 12$
$\therefore$ the relative formula mass of SnO_2	$= 119 + (2 \times 16) = 151$

1 What is the relative formula mass of CO?

When we put relative masses below the formulas in the equation, we get:

$$SnO_2 + 2C \rightarrow Sn + 2CO$$
Relative masses: 151 + ?   → 119 +   ?

This means that 151 tonnes of tin oxide (tinstone) can produce 119 tonnes of tin. If the production manager has a monthly production target of 119 tonnes of tin, then 151 tonnes of tinstone are required.

2 What mass of tinstone is needed to meet the production target of 595 tonnes of tin per month?

3 What mass of coke (carbon) is needed each month?

4 The smelter normally operates all night and day. It produces about 1 tonne of tin per hour. Is the production target possible? Explain your answer.

5 In 2000, tin from the smelter was sold at £3500 per tonne. Suppose the smelter produces 600 tonnes of tin in December. What is the value of this tin?

6 What concerns will the production manager have regarding the tin smelter and environmental issues?

The disused tin mine at Wheal Coates, near St Agnes in Cornwall. Why did the mines have tall chimneys? Why is tinstone no longer mined in Cornwall?

3 Using *Excel* to find the formula of red copper oxide

Jason and Meera had just completed their experiment with black copper oxide. Their results showed that its formula was CuO. After the experiment, Jason read about a second oxide of copper called red copper oxide. So he and Meera decided to investigate its formula.

They took a weighed amount of red copper oxide and reduced it to copper. In order to get a more reliable result, they carried out the experiment five times, starting with different amounts of red copper oxide. Their results are shown in Table 1.

Table 1 *The results of experiments to investigate the formula of red copper oxide*

Expt No.	Mass of red copper oxide taken/g	Mass of copper in the oxide/g
1	1.43	1.27
2	2.10	1.87
3	2.86	2.54
4	3.55	3.15
5	4.29	3.81

Recording the results

1 Start a spreadsheet program (e.g. Excel) on a computer and open up a new spreadsheet for your results.

2 Enter the experiment numbers and the masses of copper oxide and copper as in Table 1 in the first 3 columns of your spreadsheet.

3 Enter a formula in column 4 to work out the mass of oxygen in the red copper oxide taken. (If you cannot do this, ask your teacher to help you type it in.)

4 Enter a formula in column 5 to find the number of moles of copper in the oxide (Cu = 63.5).

5 Enter a formula in column 6 to find the number of moles of oxygen in the oxide (O = 16).

6 From the spreadsheet, plot a line graph of moles of copper (y-axis) against moles of oxygen (x-axis). (If you cannot pick graphs directly from the spreadsheet, draw the graph by hand.)

7 Look at your graph.
   a) What is the average value for $\dfrac{\text{moles of copper}}{\text{moles of oxygen}}$ in red copper oxide?
   b) How many moles of copper combine with one mole of oxygen in red copper oxide?
   c) What is the formula for red copper oxide?

8 Print a copy of your spreadsheet and your graph if possible.

Section C   Summary

1 The kinetic theory **says that:**

- All materials and substances are made up of tiny, invisible, moving particles.

- Small particles move faster than larger particles at the same temperature.

- As the temperature rises, the particles have more energy and move faster.

- In a solid, the particles are very close with strong forces between them, so the particles can only vibrate about fixed points.

- In a liquid, the particles are a little further apart, the forces between them are not so strong as solids and the particles can roll around each other.

- In a gas, the particles are far apart with no forces between them and the particles move very fast in all the space available.

- The moving and mixing of particles in gases and liquids is called **diffusion**.

an atom of chlorine

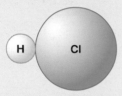

a molecule of hydrogen chloride

a chloride ion

2 Atoms, ions and molecules

- Atoms, ions and molecules can be represented using the **symbols** for different elements (e.g. C for carbon, Fe for iron).

- An **atom** is the smallest particle of an element.

- A **molecule** contains two or more atoms chemically joined together.

- An **ion** is formed from an atom by the loss or gain of one or more electrons.

3 Elements and compounds

- Symbols can be used to represent one atom of an element (e.g. Fe for one atom of iron).

- Formulas can be used to represent one molecule of a compound (e.g. H_2O for one molecule of water). Molecular formulas, like H_2O, show the number of atoms of each element in one molecule of the compound.

4 Relative atomic masses

- Atoms of carbon are given a relative mass of exactly 12. The masses of other atoms are then obtained by comparison with carbon. e.g. the relative atomic mass of copper is 63.5; that is $A_r(Cu) = 63.5$ or $Cu = 63.5$.

- The relative atomic mass in grams of every element contains 6×10^{23} atoms. This is called **Avogadro's constant**.

- The relative atomic mass of an element in grams is sometimes called one **mole**. So, 12 g of carbon is one mole.

- The mole is the chemist's counting unit for the amounts of substances because it indicates the number of particles.

- Number of moles = $\dfrac{\text{mass}}{\text{relative atomic mass}}$

- Using relative atomic masses, it is possible to calculate the **relative formula mass** (M_r) of a compound.
  Relative formula mass of alcohol (C_2H_6O) = $M_r(C_2H_6O)$
  $= 2 \times A_r(C) + 6 \times A_r(H) + A_r(O) = 2 \times 12 + 6 \times 1 + 16 = 46$

5 Equations

- A word equation is a summary in words of the reactants and products in a reaction. e.g. hydrogen + chlorine → hydrogen chloride

- Balanced chemical equations can be developed from word equations by:
  – writing symbols and formulas,
    e.g. $H_2 + Cl_2 \rightarrow HCl$
  – and then balancing the number of atoms of each element on both sides,
    e.g. $H_2 + Cl_2 \rightarrow 2HCl$

- Using equations with relative atomic masses it is possible to calculate the masses of reactants and products.

  $$\text{e.g.} \quad H_2 \quad + \quad Cl_2 \quad \rightarrow \quad 2HCl \qquad [A_r(H) = 1, A_r(Cl) = 35.5]$$
  $$\phantom{\text{e.g.}} \quad \text{1 mole } H_2 \quad \text{1 mole } Cl_2 \quad \text{2 moles HCl}$$
  $$= \quad 2 \text{ g} \quad = 71 \text{ g} \quad = 73 \text{ g}$$

- Using equations and the molar volume, it is possible to calculate the volumes of gases in reactions.

  $$\text{e.g. } H_2 \quad + \quad Cl_2 \quad \rightarrow \quad 2HCl \quad [\text{molar volume at s.t.p.} = 22.4 \text{ dm}^3]$$
  $$\text{1 mole } H_2 + \text{ 1 mole } Cl_2 \rightarrow \text{ 2 moles HCl}$$
  $$= 22.4 \text{ dm}^3 \quad = 22.4 \text{ dm}^3 \quad = 44.8 \text{ dm}^3$$

1 This question is about the changes of state which take place when a pure substance is heated.
Some of the pure substance is placed in a test-tube and is heated steadily.
The temperature of the substance is measured at regular intervals.
The results of this experiment are shown on the graph.

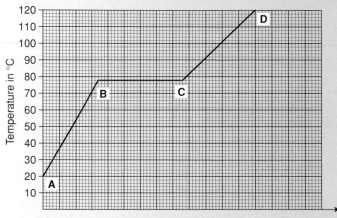

Time in minutes

(a) What is the melting point of the substance?
(b) On which part of the graph is the substance completely liquid?
(c) Explain the shape of the graph.
Use your knowledge of energy and forces between particles in your answer.

OCR 1999

2 John Dalton was a famous chemist who lived 200 years ago.
He made a list of substances he thought were elements. He gave symbols to these elements. Here is a copy of his table.

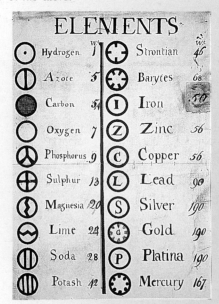

(a) We now know that some substances (such as hydrogen, carbon, oxygen and zinc) are elements. Write down the **names** of two other substances in his list that we now know are elements.
(b) Here are three compounds shown using Dalton's symbols.
Write down the names of the compounds. One has been done for you.

zinc oxide

(c) Dalton stated that
   1. All elements are made up of atoms.
   2. Atoms cannot be split up into simpler particles.
We now know that atoms contain smaller particles.
Describe the structure of an atom such as carbon.

OCR 1999

3 (a) The diagrams show the particles present in four samples of gas.
Each circle represents an atom.
Circles of the same size and shading represent atoms of the same element.

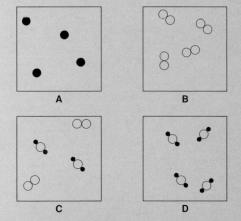

Which diagram represents:
(i) oxygen, O_2; (ii) steam, $H_2O(g)$; (iii) a mixture of gases; (iv) a monatomic gas?
(b) Copy the diagram below and draw circles in the box to represent the arrangement of particles in a solid element. One particle has been drawn for you.

(c) Describe how the arrangement and movement of particles in a solid change when it is heated until it is liquid.

Edexcel 1999

4   Bottled water is sold throughout the world.
(a) Which of the arrangements of particles, A, B or C, relate to each of the three labelled parts in the diagram below.

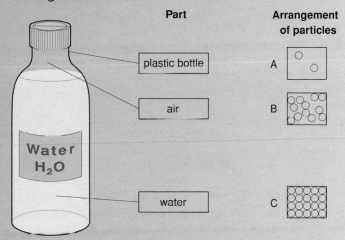

Part | Arrangement of particles

plastic bottle — A

air — B

water — C

(b) Use **one** of the words in the box to complete and write out the sentence below.

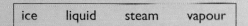

| ice | liquid | steam | vapour |

The bottle of water was put into a freezer to cool it down. It was left too long, so the water changed to ....

(c) Write **two** things that the chemical formula H_2O tells you about water.

5   Sea water contains magnesium ions. Magnesium oxide can be obtained from sea water using the following process.

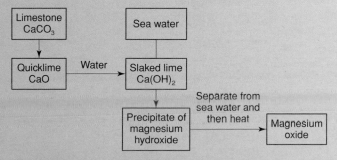

(a) State the chemical name for limestone.
(b) Write a word equation for the action of heat on limestone.
(c) State the chemical name for slaked lime.
(d) Write a balanced chemical equation for the addition of water to quicklime.
(e) How can magnesium hydroxide be separated from sea water?

(f) Suggest and explain how magnesium could be obtained from magnesium oxide.

AQA 2000

6   This item appeared in the *Wolverhampton Express and Star* on 31 October 1997.
Read the passage and answer the questions that follow.

Fumes scare at factory

Workers were forced to flee a factory after a chemical alert. The building was evacuated when a toxic gas filled the factory.
    It happened when nitric acid spilled on to the floor and mixed with magnesium metal powder.

(a) What does toxic mean?
(b) The reaction of nitric acid with magnesium metal powder is more dangerous than if the acid had fallen on to the same mass of magnesium bars. Explain why.
(c) Water was sprayed on to the magnesium and nitric acid to slow down the reaction. Explain, in terms of particles, why the reaction would slow down.
(d) (i) Copy and balance the equation for the reaction between magnesium and nitric acid.

$$Mg + ... HNO_3 \rightarrow Mg(NO_3)_2 + ... H_2O + 2NO_2$$

    (ii) The toxic gas was nitrogen dioxide NO_2. Calculate the mass of nitrogen dioxide produced when 96 g of magnesium reacts completely with nitric acid.
(Relative atomic masses: N = 14, O = 16, Mg = 24).

AQA 1999

7   Copper oxide reacts with hydrogen.
The hydrogen combines with the oxygen and copper is left.
In an experiment, some copper oxide is put into a porcelain boat inside a tube.
Hydrogen gas is passed over the heated copper oxide until all the copper oxide has changed into copper.
The apparatus used is shown in the diagram.

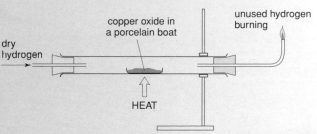

67

(a) What type of change occurs to the copper oxide when it changes into copper?
Choose the correct answer.
The copper oxide is

neutralised   oxidised   reduced.

(b) (i)   Here are the results of the experiment.
Calculate the **two** missing values.

Mass of empty porcelain boat   =   10.0 g
Mass of boat and copper oxide before
heating   =   17.2 g
Mass of boat and copper after heating   =   16.4 g
Mass of copper oxide before heating   =   7.2 g
Mass of copper after heating   =   ___ g
Mass of oxygen removed   =   ___ g

(ii)   Work out the mass of oxygen needed to combine with 64 g of copper.
You **must** show how you work out your answer.

(iii) What is the formula of this oxide of copper?
You **must** show how you work out your answer.

OCR 2000

8   As the world population increases there is a greater demand for fertilisers.

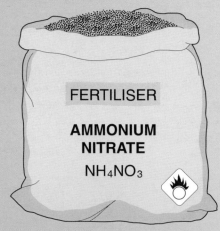

(a) Explain what fertilisers are used for.
(b) The amount of nitrogen in a fertiliser is important.
(i)   How many nitrogen atoms are there in the formula, NH_4NO_3?
(ii) Work out the relative formula mass of ammonium nitrate, NH_4NO_3.
Relative atomic masses: H 1; N 14; O 16.
(c) Ammonium mitrate (NH_4NO_3) is manufactured by neutralising mitric acid (HNO_3) with ammonia (NH_3) solution.

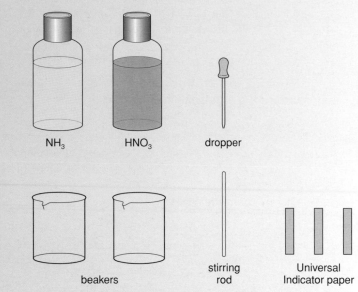

(i)   Using these materials describe how you would make a neutral solution of ammonium nitrate (NH_4NO_3).
(ii) Write a balanced chemical equation for the reaction of nitric acid with ammonia to produce ammonium nitrate.

AQA 2000

9   A waste solution from a factory contains copper(II) sulphate.
Copper is recovered from this solution.
After further treatment the water goes into a local river.
(a) Suggest **one** reason why copper is recovered from the solution.
(b) To recover the copper, excess iron fillings are added to the solution containing copper(II) sulphate. The reaction taking place is shown in the equation.

$$Fe(s) + CuSO_4(aq) \rightarrow Cu(s) + FeSO_4(aq)$$

(i)   How is solid copper removed from the solution?
(ii)   Suggest why iron fillings react faster than lumps of iron.
(iii) Calculate the maximum mass of copper that could be recovered using 1 tonne of iron.
(Relative atomic masses: Fe = 56, Cu = 64)
You **must** show how you worked out your answer.

OCR 2000

Electricity and Electrolysis

Electricity is transmitted across the country from power stations to our homes, schools and factories. Sometimes the pylons and cables spoil the countryside. Why are the cables not buried below ground?

By the end of this section you should:

- Understand that an electric current is a flow of electrons.
- Know that metals and graphite are the only common solids which conduct.
- Understand how electrolysis results in the decomposition of molten and aqueous substances containing ions.
- Be able to predict and explain the electrolysis of simple compounds in terms of freely-moving ions.
- Know how metals, like copper, can be purified or recycled by electrolysis.
- Know how reactive metals, like aluminium, can be extracted by electrolysis.
- Appreciate that the charge on an ion relates to the quantity of electricity required to produce one mole of the element.
- Understand the processes of electroplating and anodising as applications of electrolysis.

A city at night. How could we survive without electricity?

It is hard to imagine life without electricity. Every day we depend on electricity for cooking, for lighting and for heating. At the flick of a switch, we use electric fires, electric kettles and dozens of other electrical gadgets. All these electrical appliances use mains electricity. The electricity is generated in power stations from coal, oil, natural gas or nuclear fuel. Heat from the fuel is used to boil water. The steam produced drives turbines and generates electricity. In this way, chemical energy in the fuel is converted into electrical energy.

In addition to the many appliances which use mains electricity, there are others, like torches, mobile phones and calculators, that use electrical energy from cells and batteries.

Electricity can also be used to manufacture some important chemicals. For example, salt (sodium chloride) cannot be decomposed using heat, but it can be decomposed using electricity. Sodium hydroxide, chlorine and hydrogen are manufactured by passing electricity through concentrated sodium chloride solution (brine).

$$\text{sodium chloride solution} \xrightarrow{\text{electricity}} \text{sodium hydroxide + chlorine + hydrogen}$$

These uses of electricity show why it is so useful to our society.

- It can be used to transfer energy easily from one place to another.

- It can be converted into other forms of energy and used to warm a room, light a torch or cook a meal.

Electric currents

Plastic and glass insulators are used to hold the cables to pylons in the National Grid

Some materials, like wood, rubber and plastics, will not allow electricity to pass through them. These materials are called **insulators**. Plastics like polythene and PVC are used to insulate electrical wires and cables (Table 1).

The cut-away end of an electrical cable carrying copper wires used in the mains and lighting circuits in UK homes. Copper is used because it is such a good conductor. Plastic covering around the copper provides insulation and protection

Materials, like metals, that do allow electricity to pass through them are called **conductors**.

Table 1 *Some conductors and insulators*

Conductors			Insulators
Good	**Moderate**	**Poor**	
Metals, e.g. copper aluminium iron	Carbon (graphite) Silicon	Water	Plastics, e.g. polythene PVC rubber wood

Copper, iron and aluminium, which are easily made into wire, are used for fuses, wires and cables in electrical machinery. Copper is used more than any other metal in electrical wires and cables because electricity moves through it easily. It is a very good conductor.

An electric current is simply a flow of electrons.

When copper wires are attached to a battery (Figure 1), negative electrons in the outer parts of the copper atoms are attracted towards the positive terminal of the battery. At the same time, extra electrons are repelled into the copper wire from the negative terminal of the battery.

Electrons flow through the metal rather like water flows through a pipe or traffic moves along a road.

Study Questions

1 Electricity is used more widely than gas for our energy supplies. Why is this?

2 a) List four important uses of electricity in your home.
   b) How might the jobs in a) be done without electricity?

3 What is: (i) an electric current; (ii) a conductor; (iii) an insulator?

4 a) Name four elements which conduct electricity when solid.
   b) Name four elements which conduct electricity when liquid.
   c) Name four elements which do *not* conduct electricity when solid.

5 Design an experiment to compare the conduction of electricity by thin copper wire and thick copper wire.
   a) Draw a diagram of the apparatus you would use.
   b) Say what you would do.
   c) Say what measurements you would make.
   d) Say how you would compare the two wires.

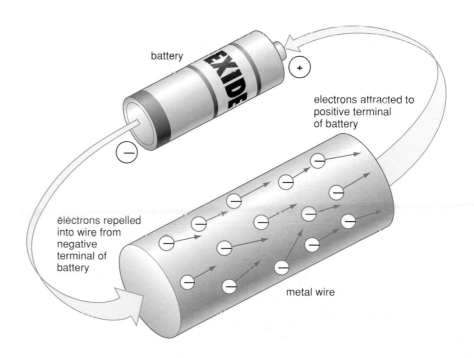

battery

electrons attracted to positive terminal of battery

electrons repelled into wire from negative terminal of battery

metal wire

Figure 1

Which Substances Conduct Electricity?

Which solids conduct?

The apparatus in Figure 1 can be used to test whether a solid conducts electricity. If the solid conducts, what happens when the switch is closed? Experiments show that:

> The only common solids which conduct electricity are metals and graphite.

When metals and graphite conduct electricity, electrons flow through the material, but there is *no chemical reaction*. No solid *compounds* conduct electricity.

Which liquids conduct?

Pure water does not conduct electricity. But, water containing a little sulphuric acid will conduct electricity. Unlike metals, the water changes when it conducts electricity. It is decomposed into hydrogen and oxygen. Electricity is a form of energy like heat. We can use it to boil water, to cook food and to cause chemical reactions.

> The decomposition of a substance, such as water, by electricity is called **electrolysis**.
> The compound which is decomposed is called an **electrolyte** and we say that it has been **electrolysed**.

Figure 2 shows how we can test the conductivity of liquids. The terminals through which the current enters and leaves the electrolyte are called **electrodes**. The electrode connected to the positive terminal of the battery is positive itself and is called the **anode**. The electrode connected to the negative terminal of the battery is negative itself and is called the **cathode**.

Table 1 shows the results of tests on various liquids and aqueous solutions.

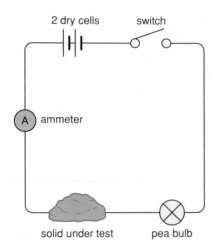

Figure 1 *Which solids conduct?*

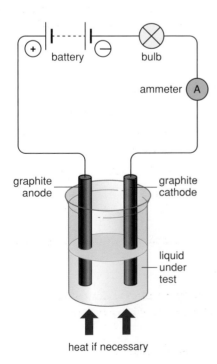

Figure 2 *Which liquids conduct?*

Table 1 *Testing to see which liquids and aqueous solutions conduct*

Pure liquids	Does the liquid conduct?	Aqueous solutions	Does the solution conduct?
Bromine	No	Ethanol (C_2H_6O)	No
Mercury	Yes	Sugar ($C_{12}H_{22}O_{11}$)	No
Molten sulphur	No	Sulphuric acid (H_2SO_4)	Yes
Molten zinc	Yes	Acetic acid ($C_2H_4O_2$)	Yes
Water (H_2O)	No	Copper sulphate ($CuSO_4$)	Yes
Ethanol (C_2H_6O)	No	Potassium iodide (KI)	Yes
Molten sodium chloride (NaCl)	Yes	Sodium chloride (NaCl)	Yes
Molten zinc chloride ($ZnCl_2$)	Yes		

Study Questions

1 Explain the following words: *electrolysis; electrolyte; electrode; anode; cathode.*

2 From the following list name: (i) two metals; (ii) two non-metals; (iii) two electrolytes; (iv) two pure liquids at 20°C; (v) two elements which conduct; (vi) two compounds that are gases at 110°C; (vii) three compounds that are non-electrolytes.
calcium; carbon disulphide; copper sulphate solution; lead; carbon; water; methane (natural gas); phosphorus; dilute sulphuric acid

3 Prepare a short talk about the life and work of Michael Faraday for the rest of your class.

Aluminium is manufactured by electrolysis from aluminium oxide. At this factory, molten aluminium is removed from the electrolysis tanks using the suspended and moveable vat shown in the photo

Did you know?

Michael Faraday – one of the first scientists to investigate electrolysis

Michael Faraday was the son of a blacksmith. Although he came from a poor family, he taught himself science whilst working for a bookbinder. Faraday found ways to liquefy gases and he discovered benzene. He made discoveries in electrolysis and invented the first electric generator.

Look at the results in Table 1.

1 Do the liquid metals conduct electricity?

2 Do the liquid non-metals conduct electricity?

3 Do the compounds containing only non-metals (non-metal compounds) conduct: (i) when liquid; (ii) in aqueous solution?

4 Do the compounds containing both metals and non-metals (metal/non-metal compounds) conduct electricity: (i) when liquid; (ii) in aqueous solution?

The answers to these questions and the results of the experiment are summarised in Table 2.

Table 2 *The conduction of electricity by elements and compounds*

	Elements		Compounds	
Substance	**Metals and graphite**	**Non-metals except graphite**	**Metal/ non-metal**	**Non-metal**
Examples	Fe, Zn	Br$_2$, S	NaCl, CuSO$_4$	C$_2$H$_6$O, CCl$_4$
Solid	Yes	No	No	No
Liquid	Yes	No	Yes	No
Aqueous solution	–	–	Yes (and acids)	No (except acids)

Notice the following points from these results.

Metal/non-metal compounds conduct electricity when they are molten (liquid) and when they are dissolved in water (aqueous). These compounds are decomposed during electrolysis.

Non-metal compounds do not conduct in the liquid state or in aqueous solution (except aqueous solutions of acids).

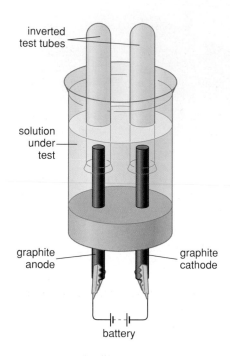

Figure 1 *Investigating the products when solutions are electrolysed*

What are the products of electrolysis?

When compounds are electrolysed, new substances are produced at the electrodes. For example, when electricity is passed through molten sodium chloride, pale green chlorine gas comes off at the anode and sodium forms at the cathode (Table 1).

The products at the electrodes when aqueous solutions are electrolysed can be investigated using the apparatus in Figure 1. When copper sulphate solution is electrolysed using this apparatus, a pink deposit of copper appears on the cathode (Table 1). Bubbles of a colourless gas stream off the anode and collect in the inverted test tube. This gas relights a glowing splint, showing that it is oxygen.

Table 1 also lists the products formed at the electrodes when various other liquids and aqueous solutions are electrolysed. Remember that water in the aqueous solutions may be electrolysed.

Table 1 *The products formed at the electrodes when some liquids and aqueous solutions are electrolysed*

Substance electrolysed	Product at anode	Product at cathode
Molten sodium chloride	Pale green chlorine gas	Sodium
Molten zinc chloride	Pale green chlorine gas	Zinc
Aqueous potassium iodide	Iodine which colours the solution brown	Hydrogen
Aqueous copper sulphate	Oxygen	Copper (deposited on the cathode)
Dilute hydrochloric acid	Chlorine	Hydrogen
Dilute sulphuric acid	Oxygen	Hydrogen
Aqueous zinc bromide	Bromine which colours the solution brown	Zinc (deposited on the cathode)
Conc. aqueous sodium chloride	Chlorine	Hydrogen

1 Which elements are produced at the anode?
2 Which elements are produced at the cathode?

When acids and metal/non-metal compounds conduct electricity:

● a metal or hydrogen is formed at the cathode,

● a non-metal (except hydrogen) is formed at the anode.

These compounds are decomposed by electrical energy and an element is produced at each electrode. This is very different from the conduction of electricity by metals which are not decomposed during conduction. The first two electrolyses in Table 1 can be summarised in word equations as:

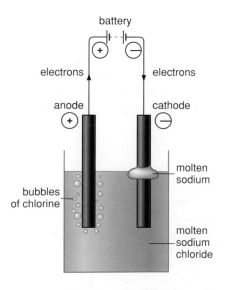

Figure 2 *Explaining the electrolysis of molten sodium chloride*

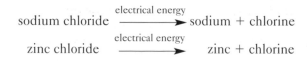

Explaining electrolysis

Sodium and chlorine are manufactured by the electrolysis of molten sodium chloride. When an electric current passes through molten sodium chloride, a shiny bead of sodium is produced at the cathode and chlorine gas forms at the anode (Figure 2). This decomposition is caused by electrical energy in the current, but how does this happen? Sodium particles in the electrolyte must be positive as they are attracted to the negative cathode. At the same time, chlorine is produced at the anode, so chloride particles in the electrolyte are probably negative.

The formula of sodium chloride is NaCl so we can think of this as positive Na^+ particles and negative Cl^- particles. As NaCl is neutral, the positive charge on one Na^+ must balance the negative charge on one Cl^-.

> These charged particles, like Na^+ and Cl^-, which move to the electrodes during electrolysis are called **ions**.

During electrolysis, Na^+ ions near the cathode combine with negative electrons on the cathode forming neutral sodium atoms (Figure 3a).

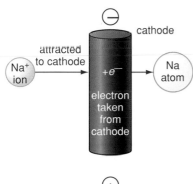

$$Na^+ \qquad + \qquad e^- \qquad \longrightarrow \qquad Na$$

sodium ion in	electron on	sodium atom
sodium chloride	cathode from	in metal
electrolyte	battery	

Cl^- ions are attracted to the positive anode where they lose an electron to the anode leaving neutral chlorine atoms (Figure 3b).

$$Cl^- \qquad \longrightarrow \qquad e^- \qquad + \qquad Cl$$

| chloride ion | electron given | chlorine atom |
| in electrolyte | to anode | |

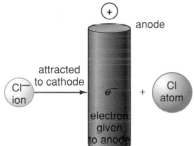

Figure 3a) and Figure 3b)

The Cl atoms then join up in pairs to form molecules of chlorine gas, Cl_2.

$$Cl \qquad + \qquad Cl \qquad \longrightarrow \qquad Cl_2$$

| chlorine atom | chlorine atom | chlorine molecule |

These equations show that Na^+ ions remove electrons from the cathode, and Cl^- ions give up electrons to the anode during electrolysis. The electric current is being carried through the molten sodium chloride by ions. The electrolysis of other molten and aqueous substances can also be explained in terms of ions.

Study Questions

Write *true* or *false* to each answer in questions 1 and 2.

1 When pure zinc chloride is electrolysed:
   A it must be molten
   B zinc forms at the anode
   C decomposition occurs
   D a brown gas forms at the anode
   E the process is exothermic.

2 The following substances are electrolytes:
   A copper sulphate solution
   B sugar solution
   C dilute sulphuric acid
   D copper
   E molten wax
   F liquid sulphur

3 Plan an experiment to coat a steel paper clip with copper.

4 Complete and balance the following half-equations for reactions at electrodes.
   a) $Br^- \rightarrow e^- + Br_2$
   b) $O^{2-} \rightarrow e^- + O_2$
   c) $Al^{3+} + e^- \rightarrow Al$

4 Charges on Ions

Measuring electric charge (electricity)

If one coulomb of charge passes along a wire in one second, then the rate of charge flow (i.e. the electric current) is 1 coulomb per second or 1 **ampere** (A). If 3 coulombs pass along the wire in 2 seconds, then the current is $\frac{3}{2}$ coulombs per second or $\frac{3}{2}$ A. If Q coulombs flow along a wire in t seconds, the electric current (I) is given by:

$$I = \frac{Q}{t}$$

This equation can be rearranged to give:

$$
\begin{array}{ccccc}
Q & = & I & \times & t \\
\text{charge} & & \text{current} & & \text{time} \\
\text{(in coulombs)} & & \text{(in amps)} & & \text{(in seconds)}
\end{array}
$$

$$
\begin{aligned}
\therefore \ 1 \text{ A for 1 sec} &= 1 \times 1 = 1 \text{ C} \\
2 \text{ A for 1 sec} &= 2 \times 1 = 2 \text{ C} \\
2 \text{ A for 5 sec} &= 2 \times 5 = 10 \text{ C}
\end{aligned}
$$

The equation: *charge = current × time*, can be compared to the flow of water along a pipe since:

amount of water passed = rate of flow of water × time
                                    (i.e. current)

So far, we know that during electrolysis:

- a metal or hydrogen forms at the negative cathode,

- a non-metal (except hydrogen) forms at the positive anode.

The negative cathode attracts positive ions and the positive anode attracts negative ions. So, we can deduce that:

- metals and hydrogen have positive ions. These ions are called **cations** because they are attracted to the cathode,

- non-metals (except hydrogen) have negative ions. These ions are called **anions** because they are attracted to the anode.

How much electric charge (electricity) is needed to deposit 1 mole (63.5 g) of copper?

Using the apparatus in Figure 1, we can find the amount of charge required to deposit 1 mole of copper (63.5 g) on the cathode during electrolysis. From this result, we can decide how much charge the copper ion has (i.e. whether the copper ion should be written as Cu^+, Cu^{2+}, Cu^{3+}, etc.). The rheostat (variable resistor) is used to keep the current constant and quite low. If the current is too large, the copper deposits too fast and drops off the cathode.

Make sure the copper cathode is clean and dry and then weigh it. Connect up the circuit and pass about 0.15 A for at least 45 minutes. Now, remove the cathode, wash it in distilled water and then acetone. When it is completely dry, reweigh it.

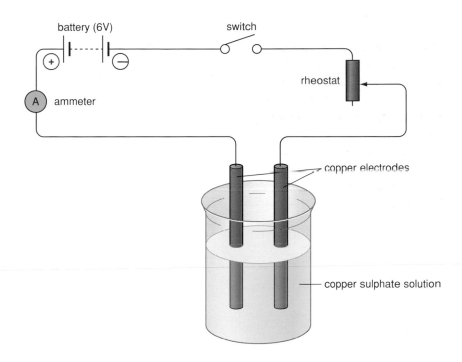

Figure 1

1 Why must the cathode be clean and dry when it is weighed before electrolysis?

2 Why is the cathode washed in distilled water and then acetone after electrolysis?

Here are the results of one experiment.

Mass of copper cathode before electrolysis   =   43.53 g
Mass of copper cathode after electrolysis   =   43.66 g
∴ Mass of copper deposited   =   0.13 g

Time of electrolysis = 45 min   =   2700 seconds
Current   =   0.15 A
Quantity of electric charge used   = $I \times t$
   = 0.15×2700
   =   405 coulombs (C)

0.13 g copper is produced by 405 C

∴ 1 g copper is produced by $\frac{405}{0.13}$ C

so, 1 mole of copper (63.5 g) is produced by $\frac{405}{0.13} \times 63.5$

     =   198 000 C

Accurate experiments show that 1 mole of copper is deposited by 193 000 coulombs. This amount of electricity would operate a 2–bar electric fire for about 6 hours.

Table 1 shows the amount of charge required to produce 1 mole of atoms for five different elements. Notice that twice as much charge is required to produce one mole of copper as is required to produce one mole of sodium. And, three times as much charge is required to produce 1 mole of aluminium.

Table 1 *The amount of charge needed to produce 1 mole of atoms, for 5 elements*

Element	Number of coulombs required to produce 1 mole of atoms
Copper	193 000
Sodium	96 500
Silver	96 500
Aluminium	289 500
Lead	193 000

When molten liquids and aqueous solutions are electrolysed, the quantity of electricity needed to produce one mole of an element is always a multiple of 96 500 coulombs (i.e. 96 500 or 193 000 ($2 \times 96\ 500$) or 289 500 ($3 \times 96\ 500$)). Because of this, 96 500 coulombs is called the **Faraday constant** (F), in honour of Michael Faraday. Faraday was the first scientist to measure the masses of elements produced during electrolysis.

Copper-plated sheets being removed from an electroplating bath

Charges on ions

During electrolysis, the positive charge on 1 mole of sodium ions requires 96 500 C of negative charge from electrons on the cathode to form 1 mole of sodium atoms.

Since one electron has a charge of 1.6×10^{-19} C, the number of electrons carrying 96 500 C

$$= \frac{96\ 500}{1.6 \times 10^{-19}} \quad = \quad 6 \times 10^{23} \quad = \quad 1\ \text{mole}$$

So, 1 mole of sodium ions requires 1 mole of electrons and 1 sodium ion requires 1 electron.

We can write this as:

$$\text{Na}^+ \quad + \quad e^- \quad \rightarrow \quad \text{Na}$$
sodium ion   electron   sodium atom

Twice as much charge (193 000 C) is required to produce 1 mole of copper as is required to produce 1 mole of sodium (96 500 C). Thus, the charge on one copper ion is twice as great as that on a sodium ion, and the copper ion is written as Cu^{2+}.

Look at Table 1.

1 How much charge is required to produce 1 mole of silver?

2 What is the charge on one silver ion?

3 What is the formula for a silver ion?

In this way we can build up a list of ions with their charges, like those in Table 2. Notice that copper can form two ions, Cu^+ and Cu^{2+}. We show this in the names of the compounds by using the names copper(I) and copper(II). Thus, copper forms two oxides, two chlorides, two sulphates, etc. The correct names for its two oxides are copper(I) oxide which is red, and copper(II) oxide which is black. Most of the common copper compounds are copper(II) compounds. These include copper(II) oxide and blue copper(II) sulphate. Iron can also form two different ions, Fe^{2+} and Fe^{3+}, and we use the names iron(II) and iron(III) for their respective compounds.

Common metal ions have a charge of 2+ except:

- Ag^+, Na^+ and K^+ with a charge of 1+ (To remember this, say 'AgNaK').

- Cr^{3+}, Al^{3+} and Fe^{3+} with a charge of 3+ (To remember this, say 'CrAlFe').

Notice in Table 2 that some negative ions are made from a group of atoms. For example, nitrate, (NO_3^-) contains one nitrogen atom and three oxygen atoms. Ions and ionic compounds are studied further in Units H6 and K6.

Copper has two oxides and two chorides

Table 2 *Common ions and their charges*

Positive ions (cations)		Negative ions (anions)	
Hydrogen	H^+	Chloride	Cl^-
Sodium	Na^+	Bromide	Br^-
Potassium	K^+	Iodide	I^-
Silver	Ag^+	Nitrate	NO_3^-
Copper(I)	Cu^+	Hydroxide	OH^-
Copper(II)	Cu^{2+}	Oxide	O^{2-}
Magnesium	Mg^{2+}	Carbonate	CO_3^{2-}
Calcium	Ca^{2+}	Sulphide	S^{2-}
Zinc	Zn^{2+}	Sulphate	SO_4^{2-}
Iron(II)	Fe^{2+}	Sulphite	SO_3^{2}
Iron(III)	Fe^{3+}		
Aluminium	Al^{3+}		
Chromium	Cr^{3+}		

Study Questions

1 Explain the following:
cation; anion; the Faraday constant.

2 The current in a small torch bulb is 0.25 A. How much electricity flows if the torch is used for 15 minutes?

3 When nickel electrodes were used in a solution of nickel nitrate, 0.11 g of nickel was deposited in 60 minutes using a current of 0.10 A.
  a) What quantity of electric charge passes when a current of 0.10 A flows for 60 minutes?
  b) How many coulombs will deposit 1 g of nickel?
  c) How many coulombs will deposit 1 mole (59 g) of nickel?

4 Draw a clearly labelled diagram of the apparatus you would use to coat a graphite rod with copper.

5 Suppose your best friend has been absent from school. Write down what you would say to him or her to explain why an aluminium ion is written as Al^{3+}, but a silver ion is written as Ag^+.

Liming the soil. Lime is calcium oxide. It contains calcium ions and oxide ions. What are the formulas of these ions?

Aluminium has a relatively low density. It can also be made harder, stronger and stiffer by alloying with other metals, like titanium. These aluminium alloys are used for the bodywork of aircraft

Obtaining metals by electrolysis

Reactive metals like sodium and aluminium cannot be obtained by reducing their oxides to the metal with carbon (coke). These metals can only be obtained by electrolysis of their molten (fused) compounds. We cannot use electrolysis of their aqueous compounds because hydrogen (from the water), and *not* the metal, is produced at the cathode (see Unit D3).

Metals low in the reactivity series, such as copper and silver, can be obtained by reduction of their compounds or by electrolysis of their aqueous compounds. When their aqueous compounds are electrolysed, the metal is produced at the cathode rather than hydrogen (from the water).

Manufacturing aluminium by electrolysis

Aluminium is manufactured by the electrolysis of *molten* aluminium oxide. This is obtained from bauxite. Bauxite is aluminium ore (impure aluminium oxide).

Aluminium oxide is not used by itself as the electrolyte because it does not melt until 2045°C. The energy needed to produce such a high temperature would make the process uneconomic. The aluminium oxide is therefore dissolved in molten cryolite (Na_3AlF_6) which melts below 1000°C. Figure 1 shows a diagram of the electrolytic process. During electrolysis, aluminium ions in the electrolyte are attracted to the negative carbon cathode lining the cell. Here they gain electrons to form neutral aluminium atoms.

Cathode $(-)$ $\quad Al^{3+} + 3e^- \rightarrow Al$

Figure 1 *The electrolytic cell for aluminium manufacture*

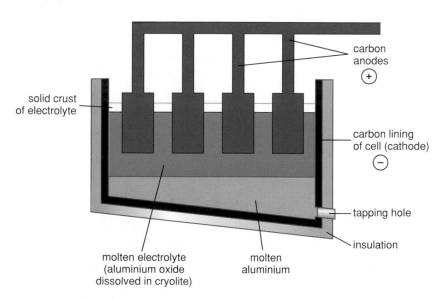

carbon anodes $\oplus$

solid crust of electrolyte

carbon lining of cell (cathode) $\ominus$

tapping hole

insulation

molten electrolyte (aluminium oxide dissolved in cryolite)

molten aluminium

Aluminium is obtained from bauxite, impure aluminium oxide. This picture shows bauxite being mined

Molten aluminium collects at the bottom of the cell and is tapped off at intervals. It takes about 16 kilowatt-hours of electricity to produce 1 kg of aluminium. (One kilowatt-hour is the amount of electricity required by a one-bar electric fire for one hour.) The cost of this electricity is a major factor. So, extraction plants are usually sited near sources of cheap electricity, such as hydroelectric power stations.

Oxide ions (O^{2-}) in the electrolyte are attracted to the carbon anodes. Here they give up their electrons forming neutral oxygen atoms.

Anode $(+)$ $\quad O^{2-} \rightarrow O + 2e^-$

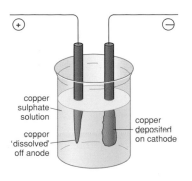

Figure 2 *Purifying copper by electrolysis*

The oxygen atoms then combine in pairs to form oxygen gas (O_2). This oxygen reacts with the carbon of the anodes at the high temperatures in the cell. The product is carbon dioxide. So, the anodes slowly wear away and need to be replaced from time to time.

Purifying and recycling copper by electrolysis

When copper sulphate solution is electrolysed with copper electrodes, copper is deposited on the cathode and the copper anode loses weight (Figure 2).

The copper sulphate solution contains copper ions (Cu^{2+}) and sulphate ions (SO_4^{2+}). During electrolysis, Cu^{2+} ions are attracted to the negative cathode. Here they gain electrons and form neutral copper atoms. This copper is deposited on the cathode.

Cathode ($-$) $Cu^{2+} + 2e^- \rightarrow Cu$

SO_4^{2-} ions are attracted to the anode, but they are not discharged. Instead, copper atoms, which make up the anode, each give up two electrons and go into solution as Cu^{2+} ions.

Anode ($+$) $Cu \rightarrow Cu^{2+} + 2e^-$

The overall result of this electrolysis is that the anode loses weight and the cathode gains weight. Copper metal goes into solution as Cu^{2+} ions at the anode. At the same time, copper metal is deposited on the cathode from Cu^{2+} ions in the solution.

This method is used industrially to purify crude copper or recycle used copper. The impure or used copper is the anode of the cell. The cathode is a thin sheet of pure copper. The electrolyte is copper sulphate solution. The impure or used copper anode 'dissolves' away and pure copper deposits on the cathode.

Impure copper anodes being transferred to an electrolysis tank for purification

Study Questions

1 Suggest reasons for each of the following.
   a) Aluminium extraction plants are usually sited near hydroelectric power stations.
   b) Clay is the most abundant source of aluminium, but the metal is never extracted from clay.
2 *The costs of manufacturing aluminium*. It takes about 16 units (kilowatt-hours) of electricity to produce 1 kg of aluminium.
   a) Suppose aluminium manufacturers pay 6p a unit for electricity. How much is the cost of electricity in producing 1 kg of aluminium?
   b) What other costs are involved in manufacturing aluminium besides the cost of electricity?
3 Magnesium is manufactured by electrolysis of molten magnesium chloride.
   a) Give the symbols and charges on the ions in the electrolyte.
   b) Draw a circuit diagram to show the directions in which the ions and electrons move during electrolysis.
   c) Write equations for the processes which occur at the anode and the cathode.
   d) The anode in this process is made of carbon and *not* steel which would be cheaper. Why is this?

This picture shows the bodywork of a car rising out of an electroplating bath. Notice the wire carrying the current from the bodywork

The method for purifying impure copper described in the last unit can be used industrially to coat (plate) articles with copper. The process is called **electroplating**. Several metals can be used for electroplating articles. The most commonly used metals, apart from copper, are chromium, nickel, silver and gold. During electroplating, a metal coating is deposited on the cathode from ions in the electrolyte. So,

● the article to be plated is made the cathode,

● the electrolyte is a solution containing ions of the plating metal,

● the anode is a piece of the plating metal.

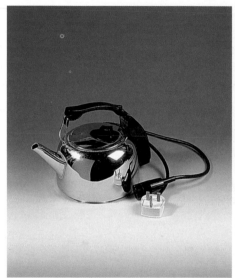

These two photos show a steel electric kettle electroplated with chromium and a Norwegian girl in traditional costume with a large brooch electroplated with silver

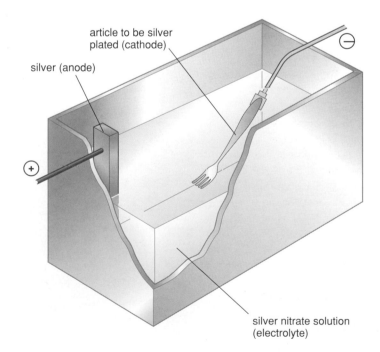

Figure 1 *A fork being electroplated with silver*

This Maglite torch has a coloured and anodised aluminium case. This makes it attractive and resistant to corrosion.

Figure 1 shows a steel fork being electroplated with silver.

The fork is the cathode of the cell.
The electrolyte is silver nitrate solution.
The anode is silver.

During electrolysis, silver ions (Ag^+) in the electrolyte are attracted to the cathode (the fork). Here they gain electrons and form a deposit of silver:

Cathode (−) $Ag^+ + e^- \rightarrow Ag$

The anode is a piece of silver. Nitrate ions (NO_3^-) in the electrolyte are attracted to the anode, but they are not discharged. Instead, silver atoms in the anode give up electrons to the anode and go into solution as Ag^+ ions.

Anode (+) $Ag \rightarrow Ag^+ + e^-$

Reactions at the anode and cathode during electrolysis and electroplating are examples of **redox** (Unit F3). The reactions at anodes always involve a loss of electrons. Usually, negatively charged ions lose electrons and this is **oxidation**. At negative cathodes, positively charged ions gain electrons which is **reduction**.

Anodising

Anodising aluminium also involves an electrolytic process. Aluminium is a fairly reactive metal, but it is resistant to corrosion. This is because it reacts with oxygen in the air to form a thin layer of aluminium oxide which protects the aluminium from further reaction.

$$4Al(s) + 3O_2(g) \rightarrow 2Al_2O_3(s)$$

In order to protect the aluminium even further, the thickness of the oxide layer can be increased by anodising. This involves using aluminium as the anode during the electrolysis of dilute sulphuric acid.

H^+ ions from the acid are attracted to the negative cathode during electrolysis. Here, they gain electrons and form hydrogen gas (H_2).

Cathode (−) $2H^+(aq) + 2e^- \rightarrow H_2(g)$

Sulphate ions (SO_4^{2-}) are attracted to the positive anode, but they are not discharged. Instead, OH^- ions in the water give up their electrons to the anode forming water and oxygen.

Anode (+) $4OH^- \rightarrow 4e^- + O_2(g) + 2H_2O(l)$

The oxygen which forms on the surface of the aluminium anode reacts with it to form a thicker oxide layer.

Study Questions

1   Suggest two precautions that you would take to obtain a good coating of metal during electroplating.

2   a)   The object to be electroplated is made the cathode in an electrolytic cell. Why is this?
    b)   Suppose you want to nickel plate an article. What substance would you choose for: (i) the anode; (ii) the electrolyte?

3   Some cutlery is stamped 'EPNS'. This stands for electroplated nickel silver. How is this plating done?

4   a)   Articles of jewellery (e.g. bracelets) are often electroplated with gold, silver or copper. Why?
    b)   Give two reasons for electroplating steel.

Section D Activities

1 Recycling aluminium

Aluminium is obtained from bauxite which is impure aluminium oxide. If we continue to use aluminium at our present rate, the reserves of bauxite that we have will only last another 30 years. This means that we must look for ways of recycling aluminium.

We waste aluminium when we throw away milk bottle tops, aluminium foil and cans.

In this activity you will try to estimate:

● how much aluminium we use each year,

● how much we could save by recycling aluminium.

How much aluminium do we use each year?

1 Estimate the number of milk bottle tops your family uses (on average) each week.

2 Estimate the area of aluminium foil (in square centimetres) that your family uses each week for cooking, wrapping food, etc.

3 Use your answer to question 1 to work out the mass of aluminium which your family uses each week in milk bottle tops. (Assume that one milk bottle top weighs 0.25 g.)

4 Use your answer to question 2 to work out the mass of aluminium your family uses each week in foil. (Assume 100 cm² of foil weighs 0.4 g.)

5 From your answers in questions 3 and 4, calculate the total mass of aluminium (milk bottle tops plus foil) which your family uses in one week.

6 How much aluminium does your family use in one year?

7 Estimate the total mass of aluminium which we use in the UK in one year. (Assume that the population of the UK is 60 million.)

How much could we save by recycling aluminium?

8 From your answer to question 7, calculate the *total cost* of the aluminium which we use for milk bottle tops and foil each year in the UK. (Aluminium costs £1000 per tonne from the factory. 1 tonne = 1000 kg.)

9 If possible, collect answers to question 8 from others in the class and calculate an average value.

10 Would we save the amount of money estimated in questions 8 and 9 if we recycled aluminium milk bottle tops and foil? Explain your answer.

11 About 35% of the aluminium used in the UK is recycled. What do you think are the difficulties in recycling more aluminium?

12 Which forms of aluminium are easiest to recycle? (Remember that aluminium has many other uses besides milk bottle tops and foil.)

13 Why is it important to recycle resources, like aluminium?

14 What properties of aluminium make it particularly useful for: (i) aircraft construction; (ii) greenhouse frames; (iii) cooking foil?

Bales of crushed aluminium cans being checked before recycling

2 Anodising aluminium

When aluminium is exposed to the air, it becomes coated very quickly with a thin layer of oxide about 10^{-6} cm thick. This layer does not flake off, nor does it increase in thickness on standing. In order to protect the aluminium even more than its natural oxide layer does, it is possible to thicken the layer to 10^{-3} cm by a process called anodising.

The aluminium is first degreased and then anodised by making it the anode during the electrolysis of sulphuric acid. The oxygen released at the anode combines with the aluminium and increases the thickness of the oxide layer.

1 Why is anodising useful?

2 Why does aluminium not corrode away like iron, even though aluminium is coated very quickly with a layer of oxide?

3 Write a word equation for the reaction which takes place when aluminium is exposed to the air.

4 Tetrachloromethane (carbon tetrachloride) can be used to degrease aluminium before anodising. Name one other liquid which would be a suitable degreasing agent.

5 Why is water not used to degrease aluminium?

6 Why is it necessary to degrease aluminium?

7 Write out and balance the following equation for the process at the anode during anodising.

$$OH^- \rightarrow e^- + O_2 + H_2O$$

8 How many times thicker is the oxide coating after anodising?

9 Why is anodised aluminium especially useful as a building material?

3 Using *Excel* to find the number of coulombs to deposit one mole of copper during electrolysis

Seven groups of students measured the gain in mass of a copper cathode in the electrolysis of copper(II) chloride solution. The gain in mass, the current used and the time the current was passed for each group are recorded in the table below.

Group	Mass gain (g)	Current (A)	Time (seconds)
1	0.94	2.00	1475
2	1.17	1.25	2950
3	0.75	0.75	3145
4	0.37	1.00	1165
5	1.37	1.25	3435
6	1.23	2.00	1925
7	0.15	0.50	940

1 Open a new spreadsheet and input the data shown in the table above into columns A to D.

2 In cell E1 type 'COULOMBS' and in cell E2 input the formula 'C2*D2.' Copy E2 to E3—E8.

3 In cell F1 type 'MOLES Cu' and in cell F2 input the formula 'B2/63.5.' Click **Format**, **Cells**, **Number** and specify five decimal places. Copy F2 to F3—F8.

4 In cell G1 type 'COULOMBS/MOLE' and in cell G2 input the formula 'E2/F2.'

5 Repeat the **Format** instruction above, specifying 0 decimal places. Copy G2 to G3—G8.

6 In cell G9 click *fx*, **Statistical** and then **Average** to work out the average of G2—G8.

1 An electric current is a flow of electrons.

2 Metals and graphite are the only common solids which conduct electricity. They are called **conductors**. When metals and graphite conduct electricity, there is no chemical reaction.

3 When molten or aqueous compounds conduct electricity, decomposition of the substance occurs. The process is called **electrolysis** and the compound which is decomposed is called an **electrolyte**.

4 During electrolysis:

   • a metal or hydrogen is formed at the negative cathode,

   • a non-metal (except hydrogen) is formed at the positive anode.

   This leads to the conclusion that:

   • metals and hydrogen have positive ions called **cations**,

   • non-metals (except hydrogen) have negative ions called **anions**.

5 Common metal ions have a charge of 2+ except:

   • Ag^+, Na^+ and K^+ ('AgNaK') and

   • Cr^{3+}, Al^{3+} and Fe^{3+} ('CrAlFe').

   Common anions with a charge of 1− are Cl^-, NO_3^- and OH^-.

   Common anions with a charge of 2− are O^{2-}, S^{2-}, CO_3^{2-} and SO_4^{2-}.

6 Electrolysis can be used to:

   • extract reactive metals, like sodium and aluminium from their molten compounds,

   • purify or recycle poor metals, like copper, using impure or used copper as the anode and an aqueous solution of a copper compound,

   • electroplate articles with metals like copper, silver and gold,

   • anodise aluminium.

Section D   Exam Questions

1 Chlorine, hydrogen and sodium hydroxide are produced by the electrolysis of sodium chloride solution.
A student passed electricity through sodium chloride solution using the apparatus shown in the diagram.

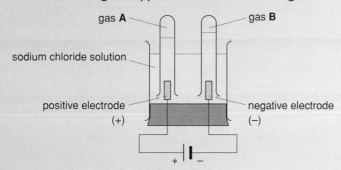

(a) Name (i) Gas A; (ii) Gas B
(b) (i) Describe a test you could do in a school laboratory to find out which gas is chlorine.
    (ii) Give the result of the test.
(c) Chlorine is used for treating water for drinking and in swimming pools. Why?
(d) (i) Write out and balance the half-equation for the production of hydrogen at the electrode.

$$.......... H^+ \; + \; .... \, e^- \; \rightarrow \; H_2$$

    (ii) Which word, from the list below, best describes the reaction in part (d)(i)?

decomposition   cracking   neutralisation
oxidation   reduction

(e) In an experiment the student collected 24 cm³ of chlorine gas, Cl_2, at room temperature and pressure. Calculate the mass of this volume of gas.
(Relative atomic mass of $Cl = 35.5$.)
The volume of the relative formula mass (M_r) of any gas at room temperature and pressure is 24 litres).
AQA 1999

2 (a) Magnesium is a reactive metal.
    (i) State **two** metals which can be displaced from solutions of their salts by magnesium.
    (ii) State **one** metal which **cannot** be displaced from solutions of its salts by magnesium.
(b) Magnesium is obtained industrially by electrolysing molten magnesium chloride.
Magnesium is formed at the cathode and chlorine at the anode.
    (i) The half-equation for the formation of chlorine at the anode is

$$2Cl^- \rightarrow Cl_2 + 2e^-$$

    Explain why this reaction is classified as oxidation.

    (ii) Write the half-equation for the formation of magnesium at the cathode.
Edexcel 2000

3 This question is about the purification and uses of copper.
(a) The diagram shows the method of purifying a lump of impure copper by electrolysis.

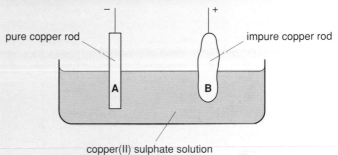

copper(II) sulphate solution

    (i) What would you see happening to the electrodes during the electrolysis?
    (ii) What is the job of the copper(II) sulphate solution?
    (iii) Write an ionic equation for the reaction at each electrode.
(b) Copper is used for making electricity cables and water pipes in your home. What are the physical and chemical properties of copper which make it suitable for (i) electricity cables, (ii) water pipes?

4 (a) The apparatus used to extract aluminium from aluminium oxide is shown.

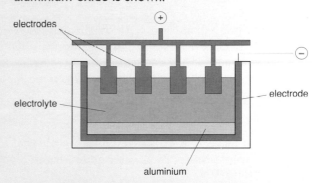

    (i) Name the process used to extract aluminium.
    (ii) What is the state of the aluminium oxide in this apparatus?
(b) Aluminium is often used in the form of an alloy.
    (i) What is an **alloy**?
    (ii) Why is an aluminium alloy more useful than pure aluminium?
    (iii) Aluminium alloys can be used to make stepladders and parts of aeroplanes. Give **two** reasons why aluminium alloys are better than steel for these uses.
OCR 1999

5 (a) The diagram shows a method for obtaining pure copper from impure copper.

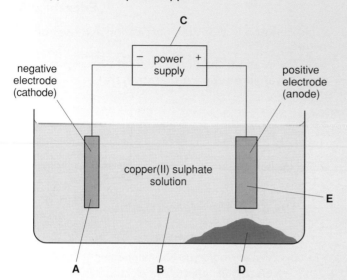

State the place, **A, B, C, D** or **E**, where:
  (i) the impure copper is placed
  (ii) the solid impurities collect
  (iii) the pure copper forms
(b) The solid impurities from this process contain silver.
Why does silver not react with the copper(II) sulphate solution?
(c) One of the reactions which takes place in this process is represented by the equation.

$$Cu(s) - 2e^- \rightarrow Cu^{2+}(aq)$$

Why is this reaction described as oxidation?
(d) Copper and silver conduct electricity.
Explain, in terms of particles, why they are good conductors of electricity.
(e) Silver is changed into silver chloride in two stages.
  (i) In Stage I silver is reacted with nitric acid to make silver nitrate, water and nitrogen oxide (NO).
  Write out and balance the symbol equation for this reaction.
  $$3Ag + 4HNO_3 \rightarrow ..... AgNO_3 + ... H_2O + NO$$
  (ii) Write out and complete the word equation for Stage 2.
  silver nitrate + ... → silver chloride + sodium nitrate
(f) Photographic film can be made by coating paper with silver chloride.
Explain what happens to the silver chloride when the film is exposed to light.

Edexcel 2001

6 Anna carries out an experiment to find the mass of zinc deposited at the cathode (negative electrode) during the electrolysis of zinc chloride.
The diagram shows the apparatus she uses.

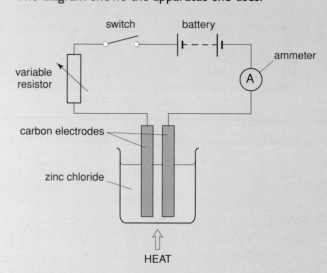

(a) Anna melts the zince chloride.
Describe and explain how the reading on the ammeter changes.
Use your knowledge of particles in zinc chloride in your answer.
(b) Chlorine gas is formed at the anode and zinc metal at the cathode.
  (i) Write out and finish the ionic equations
  $$Cl^- \quad \rightarrow \quad Cl_2$$
  $$Zn^{2+} \quad \rightarrow \quad Zn$$
  (ii) Explain why the electrolysis of zinc chloride is a redox reaction.
  Use ideas of electron transfer in your answer.
(c) (i) A current of 2A passes through the molten zinc chloride for 8 minutes.
  Calculate the number of Faradays of electricity Anna uses.
  (1 Faraday = 96 000 coulombs)
  You **must** show your working.
  (ii) How many Faradays of electricity are required to produce one mole of zinc atoms from Zn^{2+} ions?
  (iii) Calculate the mass of zinc deposited during her experiment.
  (Relative atomic mass Zn = 65)
(d) After Anna has continued this electrolysis for a long time, she notices that the current passing **suddenly rises**.
Even when the apparatus has cooled back to room temperature, current is **still passing**.
Suggest an explanation for these observations.

AQA 2000

Patterns and Properties

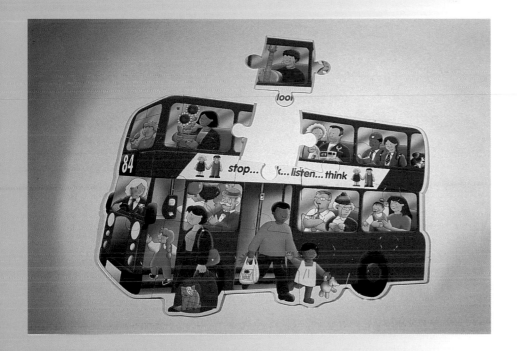

The periodic table is like a jigsaw. The pieces must be arranged correctly to give a pattern or a picture. In the periodic table, elements are arranged in order of atomic number to give a pattern in properties

By the end of this section you should be able to:

- Appreciate that the periodic table shows all the elements, arranged in order of atomic number.
- Understand that elements in the same group of the periodic table have similar properties.
- Understand how the properties of elements change gradually from the top to the bottom of a group.
- Describe the properties and reactions of the alkali metals.
- Recall the characteristic properties of the transition metals and their compounds.
- Recall some uses of transition metals.
- Describe the properties, reactions and uses of the halogens.
- Recall the properties and uses of the noble gases.

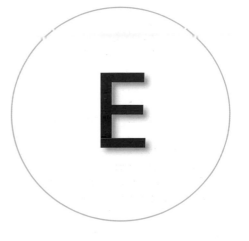

Looking for Patterns

How are the books arranged in a library?

Metals, non-metals and metalloids

Books in a library can be divided into two sections – fiction and non-fiction. These two sections are then divided into smaller sections. There are history books, poetry books, science books and so on. The books are classified like this so that you will know what the books on a particular shelf are like. Chemists also work in a similar way to librarians. They have tried to classify elements by grouping those with similar properties. One of the most useful ways of classifying elements is as metals and non-metals.

Unfortunately, it is not easy to classify some elements in this way. Take, for example, graphite and silicon. These two elements have high melting points and high boiling points (like metals), but they have low densities and they are brittle (like non-metals). They conduct electricity better than non-metals but not as well as metals. Elements with some properties like metals and other properties like non-metals are called **metalloids**.

Chemists realised that it would be impossible to classify all elements neatly as metals and non-metals. So they began to look for patterns in the properties and reactions of smaller groups of elements.

Families of elements

Graphite is a metalloid. Why are graphite strips used around the nose cone of rockets such as the Space Shuttle Atlantis in this photograph?

Early in the 19th century, a German chemist called Johann Wolfgang Döbereiner noticed that several elements could be arranged in groups of three. The three elements in each group had similar properties. These families of three elements became known as **Döbereiner's Triads**.

Two of these triads are shown in Figure 1. One of these triads contains the three metals lithium, sodium and potassium. Nowadays we call them **alkali metals**. Another of Döbereiner's triads was chlorine, bromine and iodine.

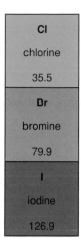

Figure 1 *Two of Döbereiner's triads*

Some of the similarities of lithium, sodium and potassium are shown in Table 1.

Table 1 *Similarities of lithium, sodium and potassium*

Property	Character
Appearance	Shiny but quickly form a dull layer of white oxide
Strength	Soft metals – easily cut with a knife
M.pt. and b.pt.	Low compared with other metals
Density	Less than 1.0 g/cm³, float on water
Reaction with air	Burn vigorously forming white oxides, e.g. sodium + oxygen → sodium oxide $4Na + O_2 \rightarrow 2Na_2O$
Reaction with water	React with water producing hydrogen and an alkaline solution of their hydroxide, e.g. sodium + water → sodium hydroxide + hydrogen $2Na + 2H_2O \rightarrow 2NaOH + H_2$

Döbereiner also noticed that when the three elements in a triad were arranged in order of relative atomic mass, the properties of the middle element were midway between those of the other two elements. For example, he found that the relative atomic mass of the middle element was very close to the average of the other two elements.

Thus, the relative atomic mass of sodium (23.0) is the average of the relative atomic masses of lithium and potassium (Figure 1):

$$\text{i.e.} \quad \frac{6.9 + 39.1}{2} = \frac{46.0}{2} = 23.0$$

The discovery of these triads and the link between the properties of elements and their relative atomic mass encouraged other chemists to search for patterns.

Study Questions

1 a) Write down three differences in the properties of metals and non-metals.
   b) How would you check whether an element is a metal or a non-metal?
2 What is: (i) a metalloid, (ii) a triad?
3 a) Write down two properties in which chlorine, bromine and iodine resemble one another.
   b) Calculate the average of the relative atomic masses of chlorine (35.5) and iodine (126.9). How close is this average to the relative atomic mass of bromine (79.9)?
4 Write word equations and balanced chemical equations for the following reactions:
   a) sodium burning in oxygen;
   b) potassium reacting with chlorine;
   c) lithium reacting with water.

Patterns of Elements

Newlands' octaves

In 1864, John Newlands, an English chemist, arranged all the known elements in order of their relative atomic masses. He found that one element often had properties like those of the element eight places in front of it in his list. Newlands called this the '**Law of octaves**'. He said that 'the eighth element is a kind of repetition of the first, like the eighth note of an octave in music'.

Figure 1 shows the first three of Newlands' octaves. Notice that similar elements sometimes occur eight places on and in the same column. For example, the second column contains lithium, sodium and potassium.

H	Li	Be	B	C	N	O
F	Na	Mg	Al	Si	P	S
Cl	K	Ca	Cr	Ti	Mn	Fe

Figure I *Newlands' octaves*

> The regular, or periodic, repetition of elements with similar properties led to the name **periodic table**.

Unfortunately, Newlands' classification grouped together some elements which were very different. For example, iron (Fe) was placed in the same family as oxygen (O) and sulphur (S). Because of this, Newlands was ridiculed. His ideas were criticised and rejected.

Mendeléev's periodic table

In spite of the criticism of Newlands' ideas, chemists carried on searching for a pattern linking the properties and relative atomic masses of the elements.

In 1869, the Russian chemist, Dmitri Mendeléev, produced new ideas to support the theory which Newlands had suggested five years earlier.

Figure 2 shows part of Mendeléev's periodic table. Notice that elements with similar properties, such as lithium, sodium and potassium, fall in the same vertical column. Which other pairs or trios of similar elements appear in the same vertical column of Mendeléev's table?

In the periodic table,

- The vertical columns of similar elements (i.e. the chemical families) are called **groups**.
- The horizontal rows are called **periods**.

Mendeléev was more successful than Newlands because of three brilliant steps he took with his periodic table.

- He left gaps in his table so that similar elements were in the same vertical group. Four of these gaps are shown as asterisks in Figure 2.
- He suggested that elements would be discovered to fill the gaps.

Dmitri Mendeléev was the first chemist to successfully arrange the elements into a pattern linking their properties and relative atomic masses

Figure 2 *Part of Mendeléev's periodic table*

	GROUP							
	I	II	III	IV	V	VI	VII	VIII
Period 1	H							
Period 2	Li	Be	B	C	N	O	F	
Period 3	Na	Mg	Al	Si	P	S	Cl	
Period 4	K	Ca	*	Ti	V	Cr	Mn	Fe Co Ni
	Cu	Zn	*	*	As	Se	Br	
Period 5	Rb	Sr	Y	Zr	Nb	Mo	*	Ru Rh Pd
	Ag	Cd	In	Sn	Sb	Te	I	

Did you know?

Mendeléev had a disastrous start in life. His family lived in Siberia. His father was a teacher and his mother managed a glassworks. Soon after Dmitri was born in 1834, his father died and then the glassworks burnt down. His mother had to care for Dmitri and his sixteen brothers and sisters.

● He predicted the properties of the missing elements from the properties of elements above and below them in his table.

Initially, Mendeléev's periodic table was nothing more than a *curiosity*. But it encouraged chemists to search for further patterns and look for more elements. Because of this, it became a *useful tool* for chemists. Within 15 years of Mendeléev's predictions, three of the missing elements in his table had been discovered. They were named scandium, gallium and germanium and their properties were very similar to Mendeléev's predictions.

The success of Mendeléev's predictions showed that his ideas were probably correct and this sparked off even more research. His periodic table was quickly accepted as an *important summary* of the properties of elements.

Study Questions

1. Explain the following terms in relation to the periodic table: periodic properties; group; period.
2. Look at Table 1. This shows the predictions which Mendeléev made in 1871 for the element in period 4 below silicon. This element was discovered in 1886.
   a) What is the name for this element?
   b) Use a data book to find the properties of the element and check Mendeléev's predictions.
   c) How accurate were Mendeléev's predictions?

Table 1

Mendeléev's predictions for the element below silicon

1 Grey metal

2 Density 5.5 g cm^{-3}

3 Relative atomic mass
   = average of relative atomic mass of Si and Sn
   $$= \frac{28.1 + 118.7}{2} = 73.4$$

4 Melting point higher than that of tin – perhaps about 800°C

5 Formula of oxide will be XO_2. Density of XO_2 = 4.7 g cm^{-3}

6 The oxide XO may also exist

3. Look at Figure 1.
   a) Why did Newlands use the word 'octaves'?
   b) Name one triad from one column of Newlands' octaves.
   c) How does the order of elements in Newlands' first three octaves compare with the order of elements in Mendeléev's table?
   d) Suggest the name of an element discovered between 1864 and 1869.
4. Why was Mendeléev more successful than Newlands?

3 Modern Periodic Tables

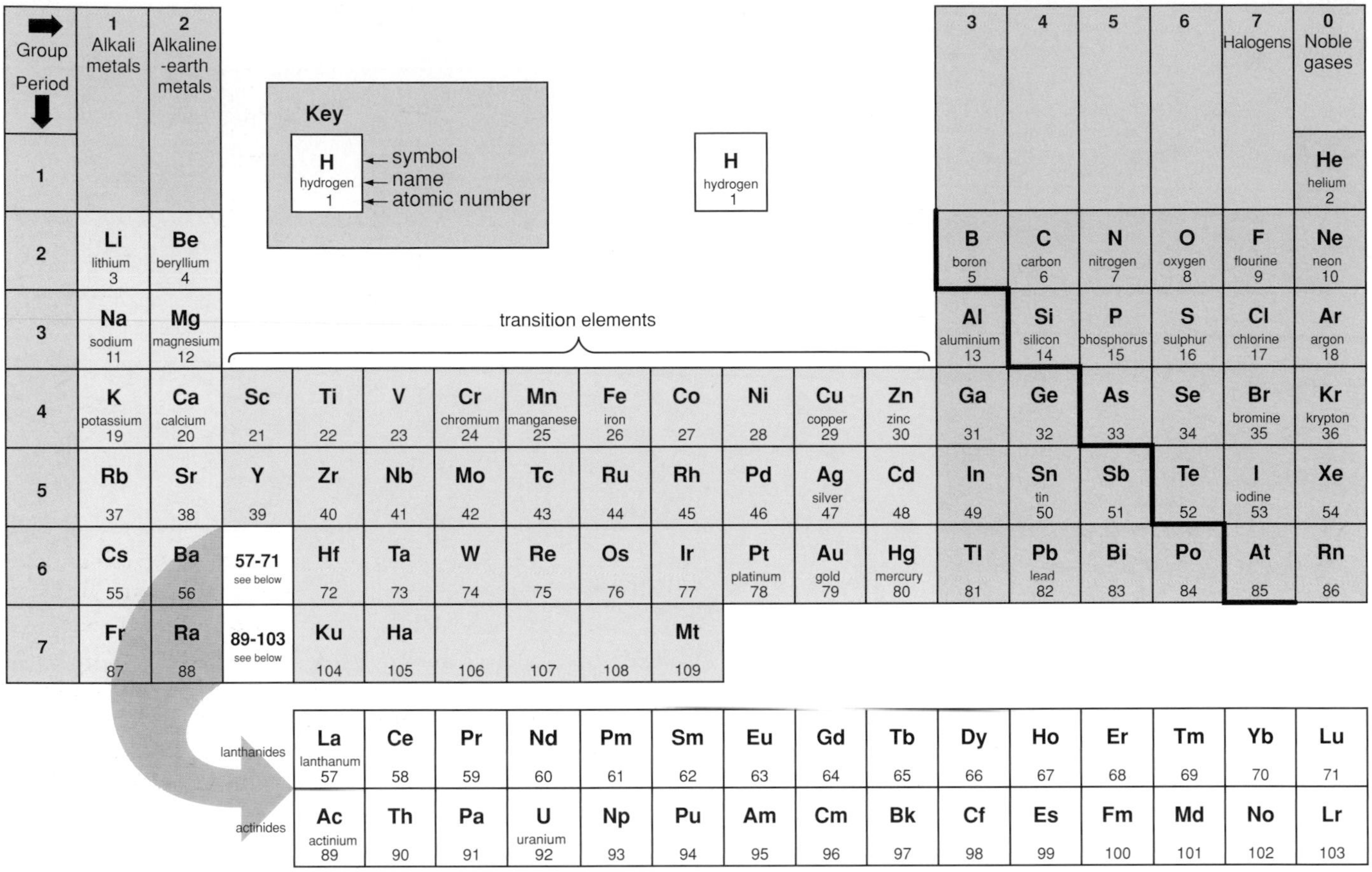

Figure 1 *The modern periodic table*

All modern periodic tables are based on the one proposed by Mendeléev in 1869. A modern periodic table is shown in Figure 1. The elements are numbered along each period, starting with period 1, then period 2, etc. The number given to each element is called its **atomic number**. Thus, hydrogen has an atomic number of 1, helium 2, lithium 3, etc. You will learn more about atomic numbers in section K.

There are several points to note about the modern periodic table.

1 The most obvious difference between modern periodic tables and Mendeléev's is the position of the **transition elements**. These have been taken out of the numbered groups and placed between group 2 and group 3. Period 4 is the first to contain a series of transition elements. These include chromium, iron, nickel, copper and zinc.

2 Some groups have names as well as numbers. These are summarised in Table 1.

3 Metals are clearly separated from non-metals. The 20 or so non-metals are packed into the top right-hand corner above the thick stepped line in Figure 1. Some elements close to the steps are metalloids. These elements have some properties like metals and some properties like non-metals.

Did you know?

More than three-quarters of the elements are metals.

Fewer than a quarter are non-metals.

Table 1 *The names of groups in the periodic table*

Group number	Group name
1	alkali metals
2	alkaline-earth metals
7	halogens
0	noble (inert) gases

group	1	2											3	4	5	6	7	0
period 1					H													He
period 2	Li	Be											B	C	N	O	F	Ne
period 3	Na	Mg											Al	Si	P	S	Cl	Ar
period 4	K	Ca	Sc	Ti	V	Cr	Mn	Fe	Co	Ni	Cu	Zn	Ga	Ge	As	Se	Br	Kr
period 5	Rb	Sr	Y	Zr	Nb	Mo	Tc	Ru	Rh	Pd	Ag	Cd	In	Sn	Sb	Te	I	Xe
period 6	Cs	Ba	La	Hf	Ta	W	Re	Os	Ir	Pt	Au	Hg	Tl	Pb	Bi	Po	At	Rn
period 7	Fr	Ra	Ac	Ku	Ha													

Figure 2 *Blocks of similar elements in the periodic table*

4 Apart from the noble gases, the most reactive elements are near the left and right-hand edges of the periodic table. The least reactive elements are in the centre. Sodium and potassium, two very reactive metals are on the left-hand edge. The next most reactive metals, like calcium and magnesium, are in group 2, whereas less reactive metals (like iron and copper) are in the centre of the table. Carbon and silicon, unreactive non-metals, are also near the centre of the periodic table. Sulphur and oxygen, which are nearer the right-hand edge, are more reactive. Fluorine and chlorine, the most reactive non-metals, are very close to the right-hand edge.

Study Questions

1 In modern periodic tables, you can pick out five blocks of elements with similar properties. These blocks are shown in different colours in Figure 2.
a) The five blocks of similar elements are called non-metals, noble gases, poor metals, reactive metals and transition metals. Which name belongs to which coloured block in Figure 2?
b) Which groups make up the reactive metals?
c) In the transition metals, the elements resemble each other across the series as well as down the groups. Pick out two sets of three elements to illustrate these similarities.
d) Some non-metals have properties like poor metals. Give two examples of this.

e) The noble gases are very unreactive. The first noble gas compound was not made until 1962. Today, several compounds of them are known.
   (i)   The noble gases were once called 'inert gases'. Why was this?
   (ii) Why do you think their name was changed to 'noble gases'?
   (iii) Why are there no noble gases in Mendeléev's periodic table?

2 Draw an outline of the periodic table similar to Figure 2. On your outline, indicate where you would find: (i) metals, (ii) non-metals, (iii) metalloids, (iv) elements with atomic numbers 11 to 18 inclusive, (v) the alkaline-earth metals, (vi) the most reactive metal,

(vii) the most reactive non-metal, (viii) elements that might be used as disinfectants, (ix) gases, (x) magnetic elements, (xi) elements used in jewellery, (xii) elements with the highest densities.

3 Suppose you are Mendeléev. The year is 1869. You are just about to announce the discovery of your periodic table by writing a letter to the President of the Russian Academy of Sciences. Write down what you would say.

4 A metal M is in group 3 of the periodic table. Its chloride has a formula mass of 176.5.
a) Write the formula for the chloride of M.
b) Calculate the relative atomic mass of M. (Chlorine has relative atomic mass = 35.5.)
c) Which element is M?

4 The Alkali Metals

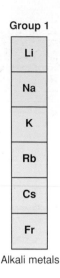

Alkali metals

Figure 1

The elements in group 1 are called **alkali metals** because they react with water to form alkaline solutions. Lithium, sodium and potassium are the best known alkali metals. The other elements in group 1 are rubidium, caesium and francium (Figure 1). Some properties of lithium, sodium and potassium are summarised in Table 1.

Table 1 *Some properties of lithium, sodium and potassium*

Property	Character
Appearance	Shiny grey but quickly form a dull layer of oxide
Hardness	Not as hard as other metals. Easily cut with a knife and becoming softer from lithium to potassium
M.pt. and b.pt.	Low compared with other metals
Density	Less than 1.0 g cm^{-3} – float on water
Reaction with air	Burn vigorously forming white oxides, e.g. sodium + oxygen → sodium oxide $$4Na + O_2 \rightarrow 2Na_2O$$
Reaction with cold water	Lithium reacts steadily, sodium vigorously, potassium violently. The metal floats, gets hot as it reacts, melts and moves around the surface of the water. The products are hydrogen and an alkaline solution of the metal hydroxide, e.g. sodium + water → sodium hydroxide + hydrogen $$2Na + 2H_2O \rightarrow 2NaOH + H_2$$
Colour of compounds	Compounds are white solids which dissolve in water to form colourless solutions (unless the anion is coloured)
Type of compound and ions	Compounds are ionic. Ions have a charge of 1+, so their compounds have similar formulas e.g. oxides are Li_2O, Na_2O, K_2O

Did you know?

The alkali metals are so reactive they must be stored under oil. This prevents reaction with oxygen and water vapour in the air.

Notice in Table 1 that alkali metals have some unusual properties for metals.

● They are soft enough to cut with a knife.

● Their melting points and boiling points are unusually low.

● Their densities are so low that they float on water.

Notice also how the elements react more vigorously with water moving down the group from lithium to potassium.

The alkali metals become more reactive as their relative atomic mass increases. This trend in reactivity is largely due to the increasing size of their atoms. As their atoms get larger, the outer electrons are further from the nucleus and are not attracted so strongly. This allows the outer electrons to be lost easier forming compounds containing ions with a charge of 1+.

Look at the physical properties of lithium, sodium and potassium in Table 2. These properties and the reactions of alkali metals illustrate another important feature of the periodic table.

Although the elements in a group have similar properties, there is a steady change in property from one element to the next.

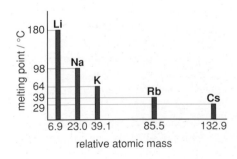

Figure 2 *The melting points of the alkali metals*

Table 2 *The physical properties of lithium, sodium and potassium*

Element	Relative atomic mass	Melting point/°C	Boiling point/°C	Density /g cm^{-3}
Lithium	6.9	180	1330	0.53
Sodium	23.0	98	892	0.97
Potassium	39.1	64	760	0.86

The graph in Figure 2 shows the steady change in the melting points of the alkali metals very neatly.

Once we know the general properties of the elements in a group, and how these properties vary from one element to the next, we can predict the properties of other elements in the group.

The uses of sodium compounds

Most sodium compounds are made from sodium chloride. In hot countries, impure sodium chloride is left when seawater is allowed to evaporate. Sodium chloride also occurs in salt beds beneath the Earth's surface. The sodium chloride can be obtained from these salt beds by **solution mining**. This involves piping hot water down to the salt bed to dissolve the salt. Concentrated salt solution is then pumped to the surface. Impure salt is used for de-icing roads. Pure salt is used in cooking. Sodium chloride is an important raw material from which sodium hydroxide and chlorine are manufactured (Unit H7).

Impure salt (rock salt) is used to de-ice roads

Study Questions

1 Write word equations and then balanced equations with symbols for the reaction of potassium with: (i) oxygen, (ii) water, (iii) chlorine.

2 Rubidium (Rb) is in group 1 below potassium. Use the information in Tables 1 and 2 to predict: (i) its melting point, (ii) its boiling point, (iii) its density relative to that of water, (iv) its relative atomic mass, (v) the symbol of its ion, (vi) the formula of its oxide and chloride, (vii) its reaction with water, (viii) how it burns in air.

3 The metals in group 2 are similar to those in group 1, but not so reactive. Magnesium and calcium are the commonest metals in group 2.
   a) What products will form when: (i) magnesium reacts with oxygen, (ii) calcium reacts with water?
   b) Which is the more reactive, magnesium or calcium?

4 a) Use a data book to find the boiling points and relative atomic masses of rubidium and caesium.
   b) Use your values from part a) and those in Table 2 to plot a graph of boiling point (vertically) against relative atomic mass for the elements in group 1.
   c) How do the boiling points of the alkali metals change as their relative atomic masses increase?

5 The Transition Metals

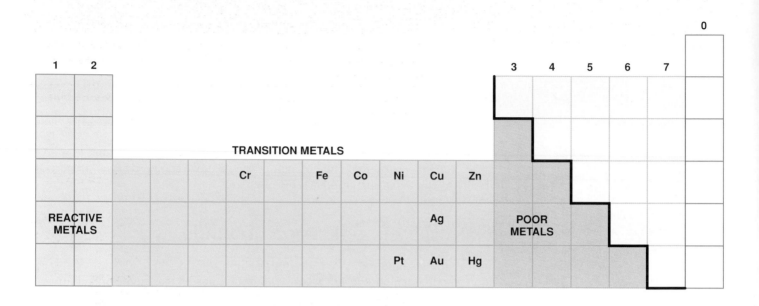

	1	2											3	4	5	6	7	0

TRANSITION METALS

Cr Fe Co Ni Cu Zn

REACTIVE METALS

Ag

POOR METALS

Pt Au Hg

Figure 1

This statue has been made from copper. Copper is used because it is easy to shape and it has an attractive green finish as it 'weathers'. The green colour is caused by a thin layer of copper hydroxide and copper carbonate on the surface of the copper

Figure 1 shows the position of the **transition metals** in the centre of the periodic table. They lie between the reactive metals in groups 1 and 2 and the poor metals in the triangle below the steps separating metals and non-metals. Symbols of the more common transition metals are also shown in Figure 1.

The transition metals have very similar properties. Unlike other parts of the periodic table, there are similarities throughout the whole block of transition metals across the periods as well as down the groups.

The most important transition metals are iron and copper. Iron is the most widely used metal. More than 700 million tonnes of it are manufactured every year throughout the world. Almost all of this is converted to steel which is hard, strong and relatively cheap. Steel is used in girders and supports for bridges and buildings, in vehicles, in engines and in tools.

After iron and aluminium, copper is the third most widely used metal. About 10 million tonnes are manufactured each year. Copper is a good conductor of heat and electricity. It is also malleable and can be made into different shapes and drawn into wires. Because of these properties, copper is used in electrical wires and cables and in hot water pipes and radiators.

The uses of copper are increased by *alloying* it with other metals. Alloying copper with zinc produces brass which is harder and stronger than pure copper. Alloys of copper and tin produce bronze. This is stronger than copper and easier to cast into moulds. There is more about alloys in Unit F2.

Properties of transition metals

Some properties of iron and copper are shown in Table 1. Compare these with the properties of alkali metals in Tables 1 and 2 in the previous unit.

Table 1 *Properties of iron and copper*

Element	Melting point/°C	Boiling point/°C	Density /g cm^{-3}	Reaction with water	Formulas of oxides	Symbols of ions	Colour of salts
Iron	1540	3000	7.9	Does not react with pure water; reacts slowly with steam	FeO Fe$_2$O$_3$	Fe^{2+} Fe^{3+}	Fe^{2+} salts are green Fe^{3+} salts are yellow or brown
Copper	1080	2600	8.9	No reaction with water or steam	Cu$_2$O CuO	Cu$^+$ Cu^{2+}	Cu^{2+} salts are blue or green

The information in Table 1 illustrates the typical properties of transition metals.

1 High melting points and boiling points – much higher than alkali metals.

2 High densities – much higher than alkali metals.

3 Hard strong metals (high tensile strength), unlike the soft alkali metals. This property makes transition metals very useful as structural materials (e.g. steel for bridges).

Iron is so strong that it can be used as steel in girders and supports like those in this building

4 Much less reactive than alkali metals and do not react so quickly with oxygen or water. None of the transition metals react with cold water, but a few of them, like iron, react slowly with steam.

5 More than one ion. Most of the transition metals form more than one stable ion, each with its own series of compounds. For example, iron forms Fe^{2+} and Fe^{3+} ions resulting in iron(II) and iron(III) compounds. Copper forms Cu$^+$ and Cu^{2+} ions resulting in copper(I) and copper(II) compounds. In contrast, alkali metals form only one stable ion with a charge of 1+.

6 Coloured compounds. Transition metals usually have coloured compounds with coloured solutions. In contrast, alkali metals have white salts with colourless solutions. The coloured compounds of transition metals can be seen in pottery glazes, 'weathered' copper and rust.

7 Catalytic properties. Transition metals and their compounds can act as **catalysts** (see Unit J5). Iron or iron(III) oxide (Fe$_2$O$_3$) is used as a catalyst in the Haber process to manufacture ammonia (NH$_3$) (Unit J7). Nickel is used as a catalyst in the production of margarine from oils (Unit I5). Platinum is used as a catalyst in the manufacture of sulphuric acid (Unit G1) and in catalytic converters (Unit J5).

Study Questions

1 What are the transition metals?
2 Make a list of the characteristic properties of transition metals.
3 Make a table contrasting the properties of transition metals with those of alkali metals.
4 Write equations with symbols for the following word equations:
   a) iron + oxygen → iron(III) oxide
   b) iron + chlorine → iron(III) chloride
   c) iron + hydrogen chloride → iron(II) chloride + hydrogen.
5 What is: (i) an alloy; (ii) brass; (iii) bronze?
6 a) Make a list of the important uses of: (i) iron; (ii) copper.
   b) Explain these uses in terms of the properties of iron and copper.

The Halogens

The elements in group 7 of the periodic table are called **halogens** (Figure 1). They are a group of reactive non-metals. The common elements in the group are fluorine (F), chlorine (Cl), bromine (Br) and iodine (I). The final element, astatine (At), does not occur naturally. It is an unstable radioactive element which was first synthesised in 1940.

6	7	0
		He
O	F	Ne
S	Cl	Ar
	Br	Kr
	I	Xe
	At	Rn

Figure 1

Sources of the halogens

The halogens are so reactive that they never occur naturally as elements. They are usually found combined with metals in salts such as sodium chloride ($NaCl$) and magnesium bromide ($MgBr_2$). This gives rise to the name 'halogens' which means 'salt formers'.

The most widespread compound containing fluorine is fluorspar or fluorite (CaF_2). The commonest chlorine compound is sodium chloride ($NaCl$) which occurs in seawater and in rock salt. Each kilogram of seawater contains about 30 g of sodium chloride. Seawater also contains small amounts of bromides and traces of iodides. Certain seaweeds also contain iodine.

Laminaria *is a type of seaweed which contains iodine. You can often find* Laminaria *at low tide on rocky beaches around Britain. Some types of seaweed are edible*

Patterns in physical properties

The halogens are typical of non-metals – soft when solid, like iodine, poor conductors of heat and electricity with low melting points and boiling points. Table 1 lists some physical properties of chlorine, bromine and iodine. Look at the table and note how their properties change as relative atomic mass increases.

1 State at room temperature changes from gas to liquid to solid.

2 Colour of vapour becomes darker.

3 Melting points increase (Figure 2).

4 Boiling points increase (Figure 2).

Table 1 *Physical properties of chlorine, bromine and iodine*

Element	Relative atomic mass	Colour and state at room temperature	Colour of vapour	Structure	M.pt./°C	B.pt./°C
Chlorine	35.5	Pale green gas	Pale green	Cl_2 molecules	−101	−35
Bromine	79.9	Red brown liquid	Orange	Br_2 molecules	−7	58
Iodine	126.9	Dark grey solid	Purple	I_2 molecules	114	183

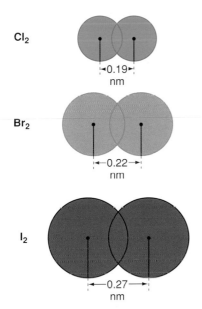

Cl_2

◄0.19►
nm

Br_2

◄0.22►
nm

I_2

◄0.27►
nm

Figure 3

All the halogens exist as simple molecules containing two atoms – F_2, Cl_2, Br_2 and I_2. These are called **diatomic molecules**. Strong bonds hold the two atoms together as a molecule, but the bonds between separate molecules are weak. This means that the molecules are easily separated, so they have low melting points and low boiling points. The relative sizes of these molecules (Figure 3) explain the changes in melting point and boiling point with increasing relative atomic mass.

Moving down the group, the halogen molecules get larger and heavier. The larger the molecule, the harder it is to break up the orderly arrangement within the solid and form a liquid. It is also more difficult to separate larger molecules and form the gas. This is because there are stronger intermolecular forces between the larger molecules than the smaller ones (Unit H4). Thus, more energy is needed to melt and to boil the larger molecules. Hence the melting points and boiling points increase with relative molecular mass. F_2 and Cl_2, the smallest halogen molecules, are gases at room temperature. Br_2 is a liquid and I_2 is a solid.

Study Questions

1 What are the halogens?
2 What are the most important sources of: (i) chlorine; (ii) bromine; (iii) iodine?
3 List the characteristic physical properties of the halogens.
4 Use the information in this unit to predict the following properties of fluorine and astatine:
   colour; state at room temperature; structure; melting point; boiling point.
5 Explain the meaning of the following terms which are used in this unit:
   unstable radioactive element, synthesised, diatomic molecule, intermolecular forces.

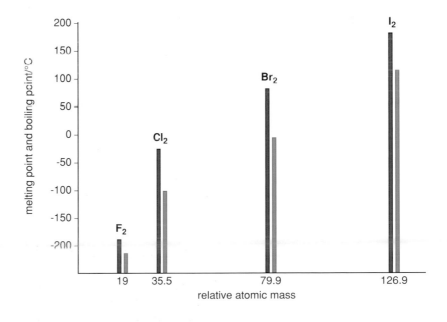

Figure 2 *Melting points and boiling points of the halogens*

7 Reactions of Chlorine and the Halogens

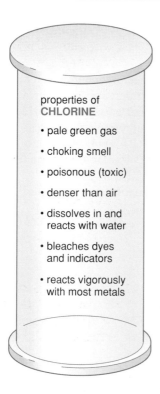

properties of
CHLORINE

• pale green gas

• choking smell

• poisonous (toxic)

• denser than air

• dissolves in and reacts with water

• bleaches dyes and indicators

• reacts vigorously with most metals

Figure 1

Fluorides are added to toothpaste to help in the development of strong teeth

Chlorine is the most important element in group 7. Chlorine and its compounds have far more uses than all the other halogens (Unit E8). However, iodine solution can be used as a mild antiseptic and fluorides are added to toothpastes and to water supplies in the prevention of tooth decay.

The important properties of chlorine are summarised in Figure 1.

Tests for chlorine

The best test for chlorine is to show that it will bleach moist litmus paper. If blue litmus paper is used, this turns red at first, because chlorine reacts with water to form an acidic solution. Then, the paper turns white.

Reactions with water

When chlorine is bubbled into water, it reacts to form a mixture of hydrochloric acid and chloric(I) acid.

$$\text{chlorine} + \text{water} \rightarrow \text{hydrochloric acid} + \text{chloric(I) acid}$$
$$Cl_2 + H_2O \rightarrow HCl + HClO$$

The solution produced is very acidic. It is also a strong bleach which quickly turns litmus paper or universal indicator paper white. Bromine reacts less easily, but in a similar way to chlorine. The solution produced is orange-red and acidic. It bleaches less rapidly than chlorine water.

Iodine dissolves in water only very slightly. The solution is a pale yellow colour. It is only slightly acidic and it bleaches very slowly.

Household bleaches, like *Domestos*, usually contain chlorine compounds similar to those in chlorine water. These compounds are so reactive that they remove coloured stains by reacting with them to make colourless substances.

Reactions with metals

The halogens react with metals to form ionic compounds. These ionic compounds are salts, like sodium chloride ($NaCl$, common salt) and calcium fluoride (CaF_2). The halogens occur as negative ions in salts – fluoride (F^-), chloride (Cl^-), bromide (Br^-) and iodide (I^-). Because of this, the salts are sometimes called **halides**.

Reactions with sodium

Sodium will burn fast and vigorously in chlorine (Figure 2). The product is sodium chloride.

$$\text{sodium} + \text{chlorine} \rightarrow \text{sodium chloride}$$
$$2Na + Cl_2 \rightarrow 2NaCl$$

Sodium also burns in bromine vapour, but much less vigorously. The product is sodium bromide.

$$\text{sodium} + \text{bromine} \rightarrow \text{sodium bromide}$$
$$2Na + Br_2 \rightarrow 2NaBr$$

Reactions with iron

When iron is heated in chlorine, it reacts with a bright glow forming brown iron(III) chloride (Figure 3).

$$\text{iron} + \text{chlorine} \rightarrow \text{iron(III) chloride}$$
$$2Fe + 3Cl_2 \rightarrow 2FeCl_3$$

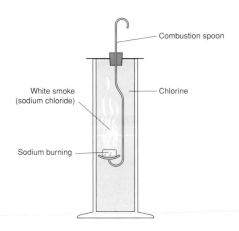

Figure 2 *Sodium burning in chlorine*

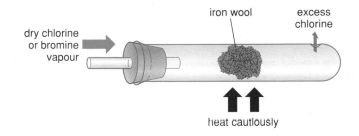

Figure 3 *Iron reacting with chlorine*

When iron is heated in bromine vapour, the reaction is less vigorous forming iron(III) bromide. With iodine vapour, the iron reacts very slowly.

These experiments show that the chemical reactions of the halogens are very similar with gradual changes down the group from one element to the next.

Fluorine is the most reactive of all non-metals. Chlorine is also very reactive, then bromine, whilst iodine is only moderately reactive.

So, **the halogens get less reactive as their relative atomic mass increases.** This is opposite to the trend in group 1 where the alkali metals get more reactive with increasing relative atomic mass.

Displacement reactions

The relative reactivity of the halogens is confirmed by **displacement reactions**. A more reactive halogen will displace a less reactive halogen from a solution of its salt. Thus, chlorine will displace yellow/orange bromine from sodium bromide solution. The more reactive chlorine forms sodium chloride, displacing the less reactive yellow–orange bromine.

$$\text{chlorine} + \text{sodium bromide} \rightarrow \text{sodium chloride} + \text{bromine}$$
$$Cl_2 + 2NaBr \rightarrow 2NaCl + Br_2$$

Halogens as oxidising agents

When halogens react with metals, they gain electrons from them, forming negative halide ions. For example,

$$2Na + Cl_2 \rightarrow 2Na^+Cl^-$$

This is like the reaction of oxygen with metals to form oxide ions. For example,

$$2Mg + O_2 \rightarrow 2Mg^{2+}O^{2-}$$

The oxygen acts as an oxidising agent by accepting electrons from the metal (Unit F3). In the same way, chlorine acts as an oxidising agent because it accepts electrons from the metal. Chlorine also acts as an oxidising agent when it:

- bleaches dyes and indicators,

- displaces bromine from sodium bromide solution.

$$Cl_2 + 2Br^- \rightarrow 2Cl^- + Br_2$$

Study Questions

1 Describe experiments which show the relative reactivity of bromine, chlorine and iodine. Write equations for the reactions you describe.

2 Arrange the following pairs of elements in order of decreasing vigour of reaction.
   lithium and iodine, potassium and chlorine, potassium and fluorine, sodium and chlorine, sodium and iodine.

3 The following poem by Vernon Newton is called 'Mistress Fluorine'.
   Fervid Fluorine, though just nine,
   Knows her aim in life: combine!
   In fact, of things that like to mingle,
   None's less likely to stay single.
   a) Find the meaning of 'fervid' (line 1) and 'mingle' (line 3).
   b) Why is fluorine described as (i) 'fervid'? (ii) 'just nine'?
   c) What does the poem say about the properties of fluorine?
   d) Try to write a short poem about any other element.

8 The Uses of Chlorine

Chlorine and its compounds have far more uses than the other halogens. They are important in industry, in medicine and in the home. The most important uses of the element are in purifying our water supplies (Unit A4) and in sterilising the water in swimming pools.

Chlorine is added in very small quantities to our water supplies. The chlorine kills bacteria in the water, but it does not affect us. Larger quantities of chlorine are added to swimming pools. The concentration is carefully controlled but, it can sometimes affect the sensitive tissues in our eyes.

Household bleaches, like Domestos, contain chlorine compounds. As these substances are so reactive, they must be handled with great care

Uses of chlorine compounds

Hydrochloric acid

Large quantities of chlorine are used to make hydrochloric acid. Chlorine is first burnt in hydrogen to form hydrogen chloride.

$$\text{hydrogen} + \text{chlorine} \rightarrow \text{hydrogen chloride}$$
$$H_2 + Cl_2 \rightarrow 2HCl$$

The hydrogen chloride is then dissolved in water to produce hydrochloric acid. This is the cheapest industrial acid. It is used to clean steel articles before galvanising and to produce ammonium chloride.

Bleach

Household bleaches, like *Domestos*, contain a mixture of chlorine compounds. The active 'bleaching' substance is sodium chlorate(I), NaClO. This is so reactive that it combines with dyes in cloth to form colourless compounds. Bleach also kills bacteria and other micro-organisms and is used for cleaning toilets.

PVC plastic

PVC (polyvinyl chloride) is one of the most important plastics. PVC is a polymer made from the monomer, chloroethene (Unit I6). The correct chemical name for PVC is poly(chloroethene) (Figure 1). PVC plastics are used for floor tiles ('vinyl' tiles), coverings for tables and shelves (Fablon), raincoats, toys, upholstery and electrical insulation.

Figure 1 *A section of PVC polymer*

Disinfectants

Two of the most widely used disinfectants are TCP (trichlorophenol – Figure 2) and *Dettol* which is a similar chlorine compound. TCP can be used as an antiseptic for treating cuts and *Dettol* as a cleaner of sinks and drains.

Very, very dilute bleach, containing sodium chlorate(I) is used as a sterilising liquid to soak babies' feeding bottles

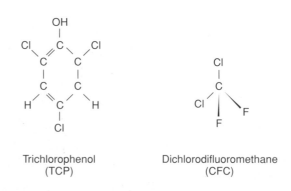

Trichlorophenol (TCP)   Dichlorodifluoromethane (CFC)

Figure 2 *TCP and the common CFC dichlorodifluoromethane*

CFCs – chlorofluorocarbons

Chlorofluorocarbons, usually called CFCs, were used increasingly from the 1960s as the coolant liquids in refrigerators and as the solvent in aerosol sprays (Figure 2). They were ideal for these uses because they were volatile, non-flammable, non-toxic and very unreactive.

During the 1980s, scientists began to realize that CFCs were causing the removal of ozone from the upper atmosphere. Ozone is vitally important in the upper atmosphere because it absorbs ultraviolet radiation from the Sun and prevents it reaching the Earth. This UV radiation can harm plants and animals, including humans. If increasing amounts of harmful UV radiation reaches the Earth, medical problems will increase with greater risks of sunburn, ageing of the skin and skin cancer. There is already evidence to suggest that the increasing occurrence of skin cancers has resulted from the reduced concentrations of ozone in the upper atmosphere. The ozone concentration has been reduced most seriously in the atmosphere above Antarctica and this is sometimes referred to as the 'hole' in the ozone layer.

The problem with CFCs is that they are *too* unreactive. Once in the atmosphere, they stay there for many years. Slowly, the CFC molecules diffuse into the upper atmosphere. Here, intense UV radiation can break the weaker C – Cl bonds to form very reactive, free chlorine atoms. It is these Cl atoms that are causing the removal and depletion of ozone.

The reactive chlorine atoms react with ozone, O_3, to form oxygen and Cl_2O.

$$2Cl + O_3 \rightarrow Cl_2O + O_2$$

Because of these health and environmental problems associated with CFCs, more than 60 countries signed an agreement in 1990 to limit their production and use. Even so, it will be well into the 21st century before the concentration of ozone is restored.

Study Questions

1 Draw a flow diagram for the manufacture of hydrochloric acid.

2 a) Use molecular models to build the structures of the substances in Figures 1 and 2.
b) How do your models differ from the structures drawn on paper?

3 a) What are the main uses of CFCs?
b) How do CFCs reduce the concentration of ozone in the upper atmosphere?
c) Why is it important to maintain the concentration of ozone in the upper atmosphere?

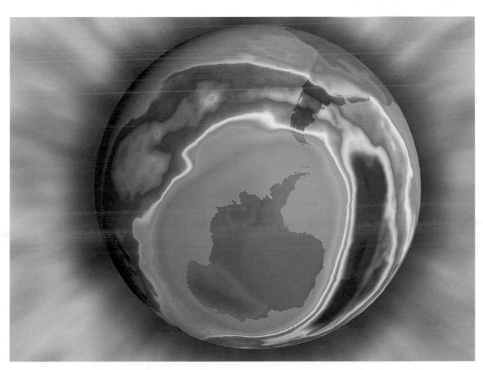

This photo shows concentrations of ozone in the upper atmosphere above Antarctica. Ozone concentrations in the blue area above Antarctica are only about one third of those in the red/orange areas, and about half of those in the yellow/green areas

The Noble Gases

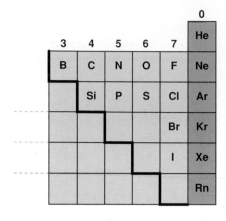

Figure 1

Did you know?

When Mendeléev published his periodic table in 1869, none of the noble gases were included.

At that time, evidence for helium was uncertain and the other noble gases were not discovered until the 1890s.

Figure 1 shows the position of the noble gases in group O of the periodic table. The discovery of the noble gases showed the value of the periodic table in encouraging research.

In 1868, an orange line was noticed in the spectrum of light from around the Sun's atmosphere. This wavelength of light could not be identified, therefore scientists concluded that the Sun's atmosphere contained an element that had not been found on the Earth. The element was named helium which comes from the Greek word *helios* meaning Sun.

In 1890, two scientists called Raleigh and Ramsay, tried to prepare pure nitrogen by removing oxygen, water vapour and carbon dioxide from air. But, the density of this gas was 0.5% greater than that of pure nitrogen. Further experiments on the impure nitrogen from the air showed that it contained another new element, argon, with a relative atomic mass of 40.

In 1894, Ramsay found traces of helium on Earth and showed that it was very similar to argon. These two elements were very different from any of the other elements in the periodic table. This suggested that there was another group in the periodic table. The group was called group O and a search began for the other elements in it.

The fractional distillation of liquid air by Ramsay in 1898 led to the discovery of neon, krypton and xenon. Radon, Rn, was discovered in 1900 as a product from the breakdown of the radioactive element radium.

Table 1 *Properties of the noble gases*

Element	Relative atomic mass	Melting point /°C	Boiling point /°C	Density at 20°C and atm. pressure /g dm^{-3}
Helium	4.0	−270	−269	0.17
Neon	20.2	−249	−246	0.83
Argon	40.0	−189	−186	1.7
Krypton	83.8	−157	−152	3.5
Xenon	131.3	−112	−108	5.5

Properties of the noble gases

Table 1 lists some properties of the noble gases. They are all colourless gases at room temperature with very low melting points and boiling points. As expected, their melting points, boiling points and densities show a steady increase as their relative atomic mass increases. The graph in Figure 2 shows the steady increase in melting point with relative atomic mass.

The noble gases all exist as separate single atoms (i.e. monatomic molecules). Other gaseous elements are also diatomic, e.g. hydrogen, H_2; oxygen, O_2; nitrogen, N_2 and the halogens.

Until 1962, no compounds of the noble gases were known. Chemists thought they were completely unreactive. Because of this, they were called the *inert* gases. Nowadays, several compounds of them are known and the name *inert* has been replaced by *noble*. The word *noble* was chosen because unreactive metals like gold and silver are called *noble metals*.

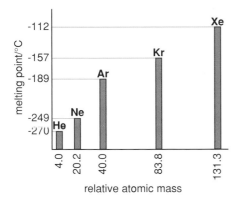

Figure 2 *A graph showing the increase in the melting points of the noble gases as their relative atomic masses increase*

Study Questions

1 a) Which elements make up the noble gases?
  b) Why are they called *noble* gases?
  c) Why were they once called inert gases?

2 Use the values in Table 1 to plot a graph of the boiling points of the noble gases (vertically) against their relative atomic masses (horizontally).
  a) How do the boiling points vary with relative atomic mass?
  b) Explain the pattern shown by the graph.
  c) Use the graph to predict the boiling point of radon (A_r(Rn) = 222).

3 Suppose liquid air contains oxygen (boiling point = −183°C), nitrogen (boiling point = −196°C) water (boiling point = 100°C), neon, argon, krypton and xenon. If liquid air is fractionally distilled, what is the order in which the constituents boil off?

4 Make a summary of the properties of the noble gases.

Obtaining the noble gases

Neon, argon, krypton and xenon are obtained industrially during the fractional distillation of liquid air (Unit B1). There are only minute traces of helium in air. It is more economical to extract helium from the natural gas in oil wells.

Uses of the noble gases

Helium is used in meteorological balloons and airships because of its very low density and because it is non-flammable.

A technician inflates a research balloon with helium. The balloon will carry instruments to measure the levels of ozone in the upper atmosphere over the Arctic

The noble gases will produce coloured glows when their atoms are bombarded by a stream of electrons. The stream of electrons can be produced either from a high voltage across the terminals of a discharge tube or from a laser. Neon and argon are used in discharge tubes to create fluorescent advertising signs (neon – red; argon – blue), whilst krypton and xenon are used in lasers.

Argon and krypton are also used in electric light bulbs. If there is a vacuum inside the bulbs, metal atoms evaporate from the very, very hot tungsten filament. To reduce this evaporation and prolong the life of the filament, the bulb is filled with an unreactive gas which cannot react with the hot tungsten filament.

The bright lights of Las Vegas

Section E Activities

1 Chemistry in verse

Write a short piece of verse (a poem or a limerick) which illustrates some chemistry of an element or some aspect of the periodic table. Your verse should help you and your friends remember something about the element or the periodic table. Here is an example.

Sodium is quite a soft metal,
Not one you'd use in a kettle.
It's not very placid
With water or acid
Under oil, though, it keeps in fine fettle.

Word process your verse and personalise your work using Word Art.

2 Using a spreadsheet to generate a graph of the melting and boiling points of elements in the periodic table

Find the melting and boiling points of the first 20 elements in the periodic table (hydrogen to calcium) and also those of gallium, germanium, arsenic, selenium, bromine and krypton.

1 Open a spreadsheet and in column A list the elements.
2 In columns B and C list the melting and boiling points respectively.
3 In column D use the **Formula** tool to calculate 'B1 + 273'. Copy this formula to rows 1 to 26 of columns D and E. (This converts the temperatures to absolute values so that there are no negative numbers.)
4 Use the **Chart Wizard** to generate 3–D column graphs of the data in columns D and E.
5 What repeating features are there in the graphs?
6 Which data does not fit the patterns produced?
7 Try inserting the same data for the ten elements between calcium and gallium. Alter your chart to include these ten elements.
8 How does this change the pattern you noticed before?

3 Ecology or economics – a mining enquiry

The facts

Geologists working for the mining company *Zinc UK* have discovered large deposits of zinc ore in an attractive coastal area of Southshire (Figure 1). The ore contains up to 24% zinc which is very rich indeed. There is about 50 million tonnes of ore, 40 metres below the surface in an area of land owned by an absentee landlord. This could be mined at a rate of about 2 million tonnes per year. The project would create about 200 new jobs in Southshire.

The issues

(i) Environmental

The area is regarded as one of outstanding natural beauty. It supports many wild plants and animals including deer and otter. It is a tourist attraction for visitors to the small seaside resorts along the coast. Most jobs in the area are related to tourism and farming. Ten miles from the proposed mine there is a new housing estate at Whitford with space for expansion. Whitford has a few shops, a coffee bar, a pub and a primary school. The seaside resorts are small because of the poor road links and because there is no railway. The mining company have, however, promised to build a major road into the area if they are given permission to mine. The road would go directly to the motorway 25 miles away. Mining noise would be kept to a minimum but blasting would occur every other day at 3 pm.

At present there are deer and otters in Southshire. Should wildlife be disturbed in our quest to use the Earth's resources?

Figure 1 *A Map of Southshire*

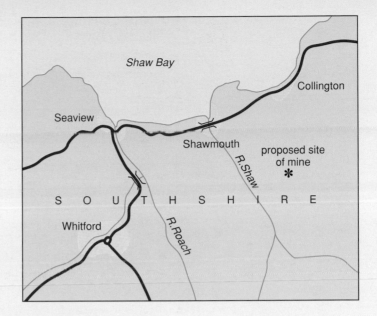

(ii) Economic and social

Unemployment in Southshire is slightly above average for the country. Most of the work in the seaside resorts and farms is seasonal. In the last few years, there has been a decline in the number of holidaymakers.

The people

1 A local councillor from Shawmouth
2 A teenager from Seaview
3 A young mother from Whitford
4 A farm worker
5 The secretary of the local environmental group
6 The absentee landlord
7 A representative of the mining company, *Zinc UK*
8 The owner of a small hotel in Collington

The enquiry

The MP for Southshire has decided to hold a public enquiry to hear the views of the eight people listed above. The enquiry will help to decide whether *Zinc UK* should be allowed to mine the ore. Suppose that you are one of the people named above. List the advantages and disadvantages that the mining operation might bring to you. Then, write out the statement that you would make at the public enquiry.

Section E   Summary

1 During the 19th century, chemists identified families of similar elements (e.g. chlorine, bromine and iodine).

2 In 1869, Mendeléev found **a pattern in the properties of elements and their relative atomic masses** which he summarised in a table. Mendeléev's table of elements led to the modern periodic table.

3 In the modern periodic table, elements are arranged in order of **atomic number**. The horizontal rows are called **periods** and the vertical columns are called **groups**.

4 Each group contains elements with similar properties.

5 The alkali metals in group 1:

  ● are very reactive metals,
  ● have lower melting points, lower boiling points, lower densities and are softer than other metals,
  ● react rapidly with oxygen in the air to form oxides,
  ● react to form ions with one positive charge (e.g. Na^+),
  ● become more reactive with increase in relative atomic mass.

6 The halogens in group 7:

  ● are reactive non-metals,
  ● form diatomic molecules (e.g. Cl_2, Br_2, I_2),
  ● have low melting points and low boiling points,
  ● react to form ions with one negative charge (e.g. Cl^-)
  ● become less reactive with increase in relative atomic mass.

7 The noble gases in group O:

  ● are very unreactive (inert) non-metals,
  ● form monatomic molecules (e.g. He, Ne, Ar),
  ● have very low melting points and very low boiling points,
  ● are all gases at room temperature.

8 The transition metals:

  ● lie between the reactive metals (group 1 and 2) and the poor metals (groups 3 and 4) in the periodic table,
  ● have high melting points, high boiling points and high densities,
  ● are unreactive with cold water,
  ● form coloured compounds (e.g. Cu^{2+} compounds are often blue or green),
  ● act as catalysts as elements and in their compounds,
  ● form more than one stable ion (e.g. Fe forms both Fe^{2+} and Fe^{3+} ions in its compounds).

Section E Exam Questions

1 John Newlands attempted to classify the elements in 1866. He tried to arrange all the known elements in order of their atomic weights. The first 21 elements in Newlands' table are shown below.

	Column						
	a	b	c	d	e	f	g
Symbol	H	Li	Be	B	C	N	O
Atomic weight	1	2	3	4	5	6	7
Symbol	F	Na	Mg	Al	Si	P	S
Atomic weight	8	9	10	11	12	13	14
Symbol	Cl	K	Ca	Cr	Ti	Mn	Fe
Atomic weight	15	16	17	18	19	20	21

Use the periodic table on page 94 to help you answer these questions.

(a) In two of Newlands' columns, the elements match the first three elements in two groups of the modern periodic table.

Which two columns, **a** to **g**, are these?

(b) (i) A group in the modern periodic table is completely missing from Newlands' table. What is the number of this group?

(ii) Suggest a reason why this group of elements is missing from Newlands' table.

(c) Give **one** difference between iron, Fe, and the other elements in column **g** of Newlands' table.

(d) Give the name of the block of elements in the modern periodic table that contains Cr, Ti, Mn and Fe.

(e) Both Newlands and Mendeléev based their tables on atomic weights.

Explain why the modern periodic table is based on proton (atomic) numbers.

(f) The atoms of elements in group 1 of the modern periodic table increase in size going down the group.

Explain, in terms of electrons, how this increase in size affects the reactivity of these elements.

AQA 2000

2 Part of the periodic table which Mendeléev published in 1869 is shown below.

	Group 1	Group 2	Group 3	Group 4	Group 5	Group 6	Group 7
Period 1	H						
Period 2	Li	Be	B	C	N	O	F
Period 3	Na	Mg	Al	Si	P	S	Cl
Period 4	K	Ca	*	Ti	V	Cr	Mn
	Cu	Zn	*	*		As	Se	Br
Period 5	Rb	Sr	Y	Zr	Nb	Mo	*
	Ag	Cd	In	Sn	Sb	Te	I

(a) Name **two** elements in group 1 of Mendeléev's periodic table which are **not** found in group 1 of the modern periodic table.

(b) Which group of elements in the modern periodic table is missing on Mendeléev's table?

(c) Mendeléev left several gaps in his periodic table. These gaps are shown as asterisks(*) on the table above.

Suggest why Mendeléev left these gaps.

(d) Copy and complete the following sentence.

In the **modern** periodic table the elements are arranged in the order of their .... numbers.

Edexcel 1999

3 (a) The diagram below shows a summary of some reactions of the group 1 element, sodium.

The products of the reactions are labelled, **A, B, C,** and **D**.

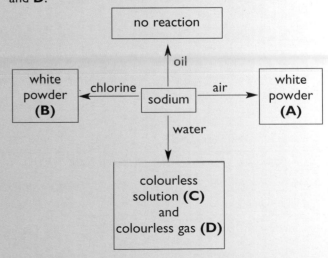

111

(i)   Give the chemical names of the substances labelled **A** to **D**.

(ii) Copy, complete and balance the **symbol** equation for the reaction that occurs when sodium burns in air.

.... Na + ... → .... Na$_2$O

(iii) Which reaction, in the diagram above, shows that sodium is an alkali metal?
Explain your answer.

(b) Explain, **in terms of electronic structure**, why the reactivity of group I elements **increases** down the group.

AQA 2000

4 (a) What is the name given to the block of elements in the middle of the periodic table which includes vanadium?

(b) Some of the properties of vanadium are shown in this list.

- It has a high melting point.
- It is a solid at room temperature.
- It is a conductor of electricity.
- It is a good conductor of heat.
- It forms coloured compounds.
- It forms crystalline compounds.
- It forms compounds that are catalysts.

Select **two** properties, from the list above, which are **not** typical of a group I metal.

(c) One compound of vanadium is vanadium oxide. A sample of vanadium oxide contained 10.2 g of vanadium and 8.0 g of oxygen.
Calculate the formula of this vanadium oxide.
You must show **all** your working to gain full marks.
(Relative atomic masses: V = 51, O = 16).

WJEC 2000

5 This question is about the halogen elements in group 7 of the periodic table.
The reactivity of the elements in group 7 decreases down the group.

(a) Write down the name and symbol of the **most** reactive halogen in group 7.

(b) The table gives information about three halogens.

Halogen	Colour	Melting point in °C	Boiling point in °C	State at room temperature and pressure
Chlorine	greenish-yellow	−101	−34	gas
Bromine	red	−7	60	liquid
Iodine	dark grey	114	185	solid

Astatine is in group 7 of the periodic table. It is below iodine.
Use the information in the table and your knowledge to answer the following.

(i)   Predict the state of astatine at room temperature and pressure.

(ii) Suggest a melting point for astatine. Use the data to explain your choice.

(iii) Predict the colour of astatine.

(iv) What are the name and formula of the compound formed by sodium and astatine?

(c) The table summarises the results of reactions when halogens are added to solutions of sodium halides.

(i)   Copy and then finish the table by adding a tick (✓) if a reaction takes place and a cross (✗) if a reaction does not take place. Some have been done for you.

Halogen added	Solutions of		
	sodium chloride	sodium bromide	sodium iodide
Bromine	✗	✗	✓
Chlorine	✗		
Iodine			✗

(ii) Copy and then finish the sentence by choosing the **best** word from the list.
decomposition; displacement; neutralisation.
The reaction of bromine with sodium iodide is an example of a .... reaction.

(iii) Write an equation for the reaction taking place when bromine, Br$_2$, is added to potassium iodide solution, KI.

(d) Sodium chloride is used as a raw material for producing other sodium compounds.
These include **sodium carbonate; sodium hydrogencarbonate; sodium hydroxide**.
Choose **two** of these. For each one, write down a use of the sodium compound.

AQA 1999

Metals

What properties of metals and alloys made them useful in constructing Concorde?

By the end of this section you should:
- Understand how the properties of metals are related to their structure.
- Appreciate the importance and uses of alloys.
- Be able to use the reactivity series to predict the reactions of metals.
- Understand oxidation and reduction in terms of electrons.
- Be able to predict the method of extracting a metal from its position in the reactivity series.
- Know about the extraction of iron from iron ore and the production of steel from pig-iron.
- Understand the chemical tests used to identify anions and cations.

The Properties of Metals

Blacksmiths rely on the malleability of metals to hammer and bend them into useful shapes

Metals are important and useful materials. Just look around and notice the uses of different metals – cutlery, cars, ornaments, jewellery, pipes, radiators, girders and bridges. The properties of metals lead to these and many other important uses.

In general, metals:

● have high densities,

● have high melting points and high boiling points,

● are good conductors of heat and electricity,

● are malleable (can be hammered into different shapes).

Density

X-ray analysis shows that the atoms in most metals are packed as close together as possible. This arrangement is called **close packing**. Figure 1 shows a few atoms in one layer of a metal crystal.

Notice that each atom in the middle of the crystal touches six other atoms in the same layer. When a second layer is placed on top of the first, atoms in the second layer sink into the dips between atoms in the first layer. This allows atoms in one layer to get as close as possible to those in the next layer. This close packing of atoms in metals helps to explain their high densities.

Melting and boiling points

High melting points and high boiling points suggest that there are strong forces holding the atoms together in metal crystals. Chemists think that the outermost electrons in metal atoms move about freely. So, the metal consists of positive ions surrounded by a 'sea' of moving electrons (Figure 2). The negative 'sea' of electrons attracts *all* the positive ions and cements everything together. These forces of attraction between closely packed atoms result in high melting points and high boiling points.

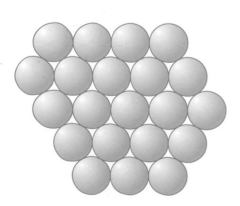

Figure 1 *Close packing of atoms in a metal*

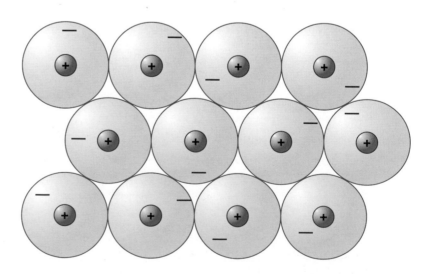

Figure 2 *The outermost electrons of each atom move around freely in the metal structure*

Conductivity

When a metal is heated, energy is transferred to the electrons. The electrons move around even faster and conduct the heat (energy) to other parts of the metal. When a metal is connected in a circuit, freely moving electrons in the metal move towards the positive terminal. At the same time, electrons can be fed into the other end of the metal from the negative terminal (Figure 3). This flow of electrons through the metal forms the electric current.

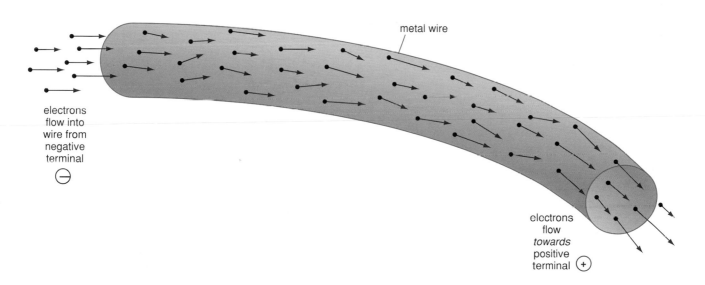

metal wire

electrons
flow into
wire from
negative
terminal
⊖

electrons
flow
towards
positive
terminal ⊕

Figure 3 *Electrons flowing along a metal wire form an electric current*

Study Questions

1 Explain the following terms: *close packing*; *slip*; *malleable*.

2 Explain why metals: (i) have a high density; (ii) have a high melting point; (iii) are good conductors of heat; (iv) are malleable.

3 Answer *true* or *false* to parts A to F. Some reasons for classifying magnesium as a metal are:
  A it burns to form an oxide,
  B it reacts with non-metals,
  C it reacts only with non-metals,
  D it is magnetic,
  E it conducts electricity,
  F it has a high density.

4 a) Why do you think blacksmiths dip red hot steel objects into cold water?
  b) Why do you think sodium has a much lower density and melting point than most metals?

Malleability

The bonds between atoms in a metal are strong, but they are *not* rigid. When a force is applied to a metal, the layers of atoms can 'slide' over each other. This is known as **slip**. After slipping, the atoms settle into position again and the close-packed structure is restored. Figure 4 shows the positions of atoms before and after slip. This is what happens when a metal is hammered into different shapes.

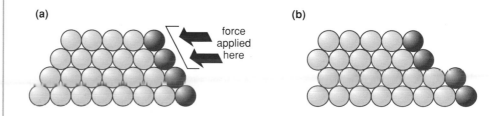

(a)

force
applied
here

(b)

Figure 4 *The positions of atoms in a metal crystal, (a) before and (b) after 'slip' has taken place*

2 Alloys

Metallurgists have found ways of making metals harder and stronger. They do this by preventing slip. If slip cannot occur, then the metal is less malleable. Metals can be made stronger by alloying.

Alloying

Alloying involves adding small amounts of another element to a metal. Brass is made by mixing copper and zinc. This alloy is much stronger than pure copper or pure zinc. The different-sized atoms break up the regular packing of metal atoms. This prevents slip and makes the metal harder and less malleable (Figure 1).

Steel is an alloy. In steel, the lattice of iron atoms is distorted by adding smaller, carbon atoms. These form crystals of iron carbide which are very hard. The regions of iron carbide in the softer iron make steel very strong (Figure 2).

As soon as our ancestors had built furnaces that would melt metals, they began to make alloys. The first alloy to be used was probably bronze, a mixture of copper and tin. Bronze swords, ornaments and coins were being made as early as 1500 BC.

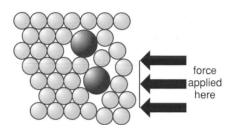

Figure 1 *Slip cannot occur in the alloy because the atoms of different size cannot slide over each other*

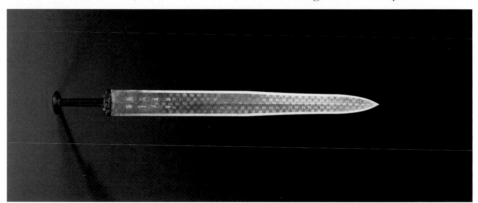

Bronze articles like this sword, were made as early as 1500 BC. Bronze is a mixture of copper and tin

Nowadays, we depend on alloys. Most of the metallic materials we use are alloys and not pure metals. Almost all the metal parts in a car are alloys. If the bodywork and components were pure iron, they would rust very rapidly compared to present-day steels. They would also be very malleable and would buckle under strain.

Using alloys

It is possible to make alloys with very specific properties. Some are made for hardness, some are resistant to wear and corrosion. Other alloys have special magnetic or electrical properties. Usually alloys are made by mixing the correct amounts of the constituents in the molten state. For example, solder is made by melting lead, mixing in tin and then casting the alloy into sticks. Solder melts at only 183°C. It is used to join electrical wires.

The most important alloys are those based on steel. The constituents, properties and uses of various steels are shown in Table 1.

During the last 30 years, aluminium alloys have been used more and more. These include *duralumin* which contains 4% copper. Aluminium alloys are light, strong and corrosion resistant, but they may cost six times as much as steel. They are used for aircraft bodywork, window frames and lightweight tubing.

Our coins are alloys of copper. 2p coins are 97% copper, 2.5% zinc and 0.5% tin. 50p coins are 75% copper and 25% nickel

The best-known alloys of copper are brass and bronze. Coins are also copper alloys.

Table 1 *The constituents, properties and uses of various steels*

Type of steel	Constituents	Properties	Uses
Mild steel	99.8% Fe, 0.2% C	Easily pressed into shape	Car bodies
High carbon steel	98% Fe, 1.7% C, 0.3% Mn	Hard but brittle	Tools
Manganese steel	85% Fe, 1.2% C, 13% Mn	Very hard	Railway lines, safes, rock breaking machines
Stainless steel	74% Fe, 0.3% C, 18% Cr, 8% Ni	Corrosion resistant and hard	Cutlery

Study Questions

1 Why are alloys often harder than pure metals?

2 Make a table showing the elements present in the following alloys and the main uses of each alloy: *brass*; *bronze*; *stainless steel*; *solder*; *duralumin*.

3 Look at Figure 3
  a) Which process produces the strongest alloy – chill casting (i.e. rapid cooling) or sand casting (i.e. slow cooling) of the liquid alloy?
  b) What percentage of aluminium produces the strongest alloy?
  c) How many times stronger is this alloy than pure copper?
  d) What percentage of aluminium produces a sand-cast alloy twice as strong as pure copper?
  e) Why do you think the strength of the alloy increases at first and then decreases as more aluminium is added?

4 Describe an experiment that you could carry out to compare the strengths of two wires made of copper/aluminium alloy.

A slab of red hot steel being quenched with a spray of cold water. Quenching helps to harden steel

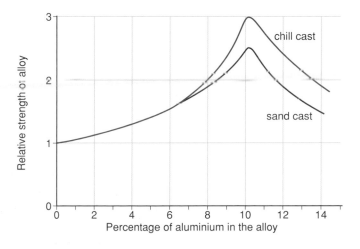

Figure 3 *The effect of aluminium on the strength of copper alloys*

3 The Reactions of Metals

Which of these foodstuffs contain acids?

One of these spoons has been left in lemon juice for several days. Citric acid in the juice has attacked metals in the spoon

Metals and acids

Various foods, including vinegar and citrus fruits, contain acids. These acids attack pans and cutlery made of certain metals.

Table 1 shows what happens when different metals are added to dilute hydrochloric acid at room temperature (21°C). This acid is more reactive than those in foods, but it shows how different metals are attacked by acids. **Wear safety spectacles** if you try this experiment.

Notice in Table 1 that aluminium does not react at first. This is because its surface is protected by a layer of aluminium oxide. The oxide reacts slowly with the acid. This exposes aluminium, which reacts more vigorously.

The metals used most commonly for pans and cutlery are aluminium, copper and iron (steel). Copper is the only one which does not react with the acids in food. But copper is so expensive that aluminium and steel are used in most of the saucepans sold today. A thin oxide coating on aluminium protects it from most of the weak acids in foods. However, acetic acid (ethanoic acid) in vinegar does react with aluminium and this 'cleans' the saucepan during cooking. Iron (steel) which is used in cutlery is also attacked very slowly by acids in food.

Foods containing acids are best stored in unreactive containers made of glass or plastic. Tin cans are also used to store acidic foods like pineapples and grapefruit. Tin cans are made of steel coated on both sides with tin and then lacquered on the inside. The lacquer forms an unreactive layer between the tin and its contents.

Table 1 *Reactions of metals with dilute hydrochloric acid*

Metal used	Reaction with dilute hydrochloric acid	Highest temperature recorded
Aluminium	No reaction at first, but hydrogen is produced rapidly after a time	85°C
Copper	No reaction. No bubbles of hydrogen	21°C
Iron	Slow reaction, bubbles produced slowly from iron	35°C
Lead	Very slow reaction, a few bubbles appear on the lead	23°C
Magnesium	Very vigorous reaction, hydrogen is produced rapidly	95°C
Zinc	Moderate reaction, bubbles of hydrogen are produced steadily	55°C

Look at the results in Table 1.

1 Write an order of reactivity for the metals in the table.

2 Is the order of reactivity with acid similar to that with water?

3 Use the results in Table 1 to draw up a reactivity series.

All the metals except copper in Table 1 react with dilute hydrochloric acid. The products of the reaction are hydrogen and the chloride of the metal.

metal + hydrochloric acid → metal chloride + hydrogen

Using M as a symbol for the metal and assuming M forms M^{2+} ions, we can write a general equation as:

$$M(s) + 2HCl(aq) \rightarrow MCl_2(aq) + H_2(g)$$

A similar reaction occurs between metals and dilute sulphuric acid. This time the products are hydrogen and a metal sulphate. We can summarise these reactions as:

> metal   +   acid   →   metal compound   +   hydrogen
> (above copper)

From these reactions of metals with dilute acids and the reactions of metals with air (oxygen) and water, we can draw up an overall **reactivity series**. This is shown in Figure 1.

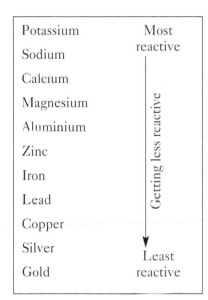

Potassium	Most reactive
Sodium	
Calcium	
Magnesium	
Aluminium	Getting less reactive
Zinc	
Iron	
Lead	
Copper	
Silver	Least
Gold	reactive

Figure 1 *The reactivity series of metals*

Copper is so unreactive that a copper pan will last for more than a lifetime

Summarising the reactions of metals

The order of reactivity of metals is the same with air (oxygen), with water and with acids. This is not really surprising because metal atoms react to form metal ions in each case. The higher the metal in the reactivity series, the more easily it forms its ions.

$$M \rightarrow M^{2+} + 2e^-$$

Reaction with air (oxygen)

Metals lose electrons to form metal ions. The electrons are taken by oxygen molecules (O_2) forming oxide ions (O^{2-}).

$$\text{metal + oxygen} \rightarrow \text{metal oxide}$$
$$2M \;+\; O_2 \;\rightarrow\; 2M^{2+}O^{2-}$$

Reaction with water

Here again, the metals lose electrons to form ions. The electrons are taken by water molecules which form oxide ions (O^{2-}) and hydrogen (H_2).

$$\text{metal} + \text{water} \rightarrow \text{metal oxide} + \text{hydrogen}$$
$$M + H_2O \rightarrow M^{2+}O^{2-} + H_2$$

Reaction with acids

This time, the metals give up electrons to H^+ ions in the acids and hydrogen (H_2) is produced.

$$\text{metal} + \text{acid} \rightarrow \text{metal compound} + \text{hydrogen}$$
$$M + 2H^+ \rightarrow M^{2+} + H_2$$
$$\text{(above copper)}$$

The reactivity series is a very useful summary of the reactions of metals. Metals at the top of the series want to lose electrons and form ions. Metals at the bottom of the series are just the opposite. Ions of these metals want to gain electrons and form atoms.

What is the disadvantage of using iron (steel) for the boiler in a steam train?

Oxidation, reduction and redox

When elements react with oxygen, they form products called **oxides**. These reactions in which elements and other substances gain oxygen are called **oxidations**.

So, when metals react with oxygen or water to form oxides, the process involves oxidation.

Sometimes, it is possible to remove oxygen from an oxide. For example, if mercury oxide is heated strongly, it will decompose to mercury and oxygen.

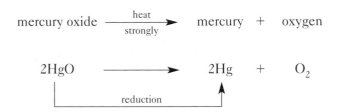

$$\text{mercury oxide} \xrightarrow[\text{strongly}]{\text{heat}} \text{mercury} + \text{oxygen}$$

$$2HgO \xrightarrow{\hspace{2cm}} 2Hg + O_2$$

$$\underbrace{\hspace{5cm}}_{\text{reduction}}$$

Reactions like this in which a substance loses oxygen are called **reductions**.

> So, oxidation is *gain* of oxygen,
> reduction is *loss* of oxygen.

When magnesium reacts with oxygen, the product is magnesium oxide (MgO).

$$2Mg + O_2 \rightarrow 2Mg^{2+}O^{2-}$$

During this reaction, each magnesium atom (Mg) loses two electrons ($2e^-$) to form a magnesium ion Mg^{2+}. This means that four electrons are lost by the two magnesium atoms in the last equation.

$$2Mg \rightarrow 2Mg^{2+} + 4e^-$$

These four electrons are gained by the two oxygen atoms in the oxygen molecule (O_2) to form two oxide ions (O^{2-}).

$$O_2 + 4e^- \rightarrow 2O^{2-}$$

Now we know that magnesium is oxidised in this reaction and oxygen is reduced. So, instead of defining oxidation in terms of oxygen, we can also define it in terms of electrons. Magnesium which loses electrons in the reaction is oxidised and oxygen which gains electrons is reduced.

> In general, oxidation is the *loss* of electrons,
> reduction is the *gain* of electrons.

By defining oxidation as the loss of electrons and reduction as the gain of electrons, it is easy to see that oxidation and reduction must always occur together. If one substance loses electrons in a reaction, then another substance must gain them.

Because **Red**uction and **Ox**idation always occur together, these reactions are often called **Redox** reactions.

When oxidation and reduction are defined in terms of electrons, many more reactions can be classified and understood as redox reactions. These include the reactions of metals with water and with acids. When metals react with water, the products are the metal oxide and hydrogen.

$$M + H_2O \rightarrow M^{2+}O^{2-} + H_2$$

In this reaction, the metal (M) loses electrons and is oxidised to its ions (M^{2+}). The water (H_2O) gains electrons and is reduced to hydrogen (H_2).

When metals react with acids containing hydrogen ions (H^+), the products are a metal compound containing ions of the metal (M^{2+}) and hydrogen (H_2).

$$M + 2H^+ \rightarrow M^{2+} + H_2$$

In this case, the metal (M) loses electrons again and is oxidised to its ions (M^{2+}). The hydrogen ions (H^+) in the acid gain electrons and are reduced to hydrogen (H_2).

Study Questions

1. Look at the photographs of the hot water tank and the steam train. Answer the questions in the captions to the photos.
2. Plan an experiment that you could do to find the position of lithium in the reactivity series. Say what you would do and how you would ensure that your test is fair.
3. a) **X** is a metal which reacts with dilute hydrochloric acid but not with water.
   What metal could **X** be?
   b) Metal **P** will remove oxygen from the oxide of metal **Q**, but not from the oxide of metal **R**. Write **P**, **Q** and **R** in their order in the reactivity series (most reactive first).
4. Write word equations and balanced symbolic equations for the reactions of:
   a) copper with oxygen,
   b) aluminium with oxygen,
   c) calcium with water,
   d) zinc with dilute nitric acid,
   e) magnesium with dilute sulphuric acid.
5. a) Why is copper better for saucepans than aluminium?
   b) Why is copper not used for most pans today?
   c) Why is aluminium less reactive than expected with acidic foods?
   d) How are tin cans protected from acids in their contents?

4 Extracting Metals

From rocks to metals

Most metals are too reactive to exist on their own in the Earth. They are usually found in rocks as compounds with non-metals and mixed with other substances.

> Rocks containing metals or metal compounds from which it is economic to extract the metal are called **ores**.

A few metals, like gold and silver, are very unreactive. They occur in the Earth as the metal itself. So, separating and extracting these metals need not involve a chemical process.

Gold is so unreactive that it occurs in the Earth as the metal itself. Look at the vein of gold in this rock

> Extracting metals from their ores usually involves three stages.
> 1 Mining and concentrating the ore.
> 2 Reducing the ore to the metal
> 3 Purifying the metal.

An aerial view of a copper mine in Arizona, USA. The ore being mined is copper pyrites, a mixture of copper(II) sulphide and iron(II) sulphide

Let's look at the three stages in extracting metals in more detail.

1 Mining and concentrating the ore

Mining metal ores involves either quarrying, tunnelling or open-cast digging. After the ore has been mined, it must be separated from impurities. This is called concentrating the ore.

All the Earth's resources, including metal ores, are finite. The ores of some metals are in very limited supply. Others are more plentiful, but even the richest ores are impure. The ore is mixed with soil and rocks which must be removed. First, the rock is crushed. The ore can then be separated from the waste because of their difference in density.

2 Reducing the ore to the metal

Table 1 shows the ores from which we get some important metals.

Table 1 *The ores from which we get some important metals*

Metal	Name of the ore	Name and formula of metal compound in the ore
Sodium	rock salt	sodium chloride, $NaCl$
Aluminium	bauxite	aluminium oxide, Al_2O_3
Zinc	zinc blende	zinc sulphide, ZnS
Iron	iron ore (haematite)	iron(III) oxide, Fe_2O_3
Copper	copper pyrites	copper (II) sulphide, CuS and iron (II) sulphide, FeS

Notice in Table 1 that metal ores are often oxides, sulphides and chlorides. These ores contain metal ions (say M^{2+}) and non-metal ions (O^{2-}, S^{2-} or Cl^-).

Obtaining the metal involves converting the metal ions (M^{2+}) to metal atoms. This process involves gain of electrons which is reduction.

$$M^{2+} + 2e^- \rightarrow M$$

> The actual method used to get a metal from its ore depends on two factors:
> - the position of the metal in the reactivity series,
> - the cost of the process.

(i) Heating the ore in air

This is the cheapest way to extract a metal. But it only works with the compounds of metals at the bottom of the reactivity series. These compounds can be reduced to the metal fairly easily.

For example, copper is extracted from copper pyrites (copper sulphide) by heating the ore in a limited supply of air. If there is too much air (oxygen), the copper produced is oxidised to copper oxide.

$$\text{copper sulphide} + \text{oxygen} \rightarrow \text{copper} + \text{sulphur dioxide}$$
$$CuS + O_2 \rightarrow Cu + SO_2$$

Abandoned tin mine buildings in Cornwall. Tinstone (tin(IV) oxide, SnO$_2$) was once mined in Cornwall and reduced to tin in furnaces near the mines. The tin ore is now virtually used up and the furnaces are derelict

(ii) Reduction with carbon and carbon monoxide

Metals in the middle of the reactivity series, like zinc, iron and lead, cannot be obtained simply by heating their ores in air. But, they can be obtained by reducing their oxides with carbon (coke) or carbon monoxide.

In these cases, carbon and carbon monoxide are more reactive than the metals. So, carbon or carbon monoxide can remove oxygen from the metal oxide, leaving the metal. For example:

$$\text{zinc oxide} + \underset{\text{(coke)}}{\text{carbon}} \rightarrow \text{zinc} + \text{carbon monoxide}$$
$$ZnO + C \rightarrow Zn + CO$$

Sometimes, these metals exist as sulphide ores. These ores must be converted to oxides before reduction. This is done by heating the sulphides in air.

$$\text{zinc sulphide} + \text{oxygen} \rightarrow \text{zinc oxide} + \text{sulphur dioxide}$$
$$2ZnS + 3O_2 \rightarrow 2ZnO + 2SO_2$$

Later in this section, we will study the extraction of iron from iron ore.

(iii) Electrolysis of molten compounds

Metals at the top of the reactivity series, like sodium, magnesium and aluminium cannot be obtained by reduction of their oxides with carbon or carbon monoxide. This is because the temperature needed to reduce their oxides is too high. These metals are obtained from their ores using electricity. The process is called **electrolysis**. But the process cannot use *aqueous* solutions. This is because electrolysis would decompose the water in the solution and *not* the metal compound.

So, the only way to extract these reactive metals is by electrolysis of their molten (melted) compounds. Potassium, sodium, calcium and magnesium are obtained by electrolysis of their molten chlorides. Aluminium is obtained by electrolysis of its molten oxide. This is described in Unit D5.

Table 2 summarises the methods used to extract different metals. Notice how the method used depends on the position of the metal in the reactivity series.

Table 2 *Summarising the methods used to extract metals*

Reactivity series of metals	Method of extraction
Potassium Sodium Calcium Magnesium Aluminium	Electrolysis of molten ore
Zinc Iron Lead	Reduction of ore with carbon or carbon monoxide
Copper	Heat ore in limited supply of air
Silver Gold	Metals occur uncombined in the Earth

Study Questions

1. a) List the three stages involved in extracting a metal from its ore.
   b) Describe what happens in these three stages when steel is manufactured from iron ore.

2. Magnesium is extracted by electrolysis of molten magnesium chloride ($MgCl_2$).
   a) What ions are present in molten $MgCl_2$?
   b) Write an ionic equation to show the production of magnesium.
   c) Explain why this extraction of magnesium involves reduction.

3. Titanium is a transition metal with a relatively low density. It is resistant to corrosion and forms very strong alloys with aluminium. Titanium is extracted from the ore, rutile, which contains titanium(IV) oxide. This oxide is first converted to titanium(IV) chloride, $TiCl_4$. The $TiCl_4$ is then reacted with a more reactive metal, such as sodium, to form titanium metal. This reaction is carried out in an atmosphere of argon.
   a) Why are titanium alloys used for replacement hip joints?
   b) Suggest another possible use for titanium.
   c) Write the formula of titanium(IV) oxide.
   d) Write an equation for the reaction of titanium(IV) chloride with sodium to form titanium.
   e) Why is this reaction carried out in an atmosphere of argon?

Mining bauxite, impure aluminium oxide. Aluminium is extracted from the purified oxide using electrolysis

3 Purifying the metal

The copper which comes straight from the furnace contains about 3% impurities. Sheets of this copper are purified by electrolysis with copper sulphate solution (Unit D5).

Similarly, iron obtained directly from the furnace contains about 7% impurities. This impure iron is called pig-iron. The purification of pig-iron is described in the next unit.

Extracting Iron from Iron Ore

Iron is the most important metal. Most of it is made into steel and used for machinery, tools, vehicles and large girders in buildings and bridges.

The main raw material for making iron is iron ore (haematite). This ore contains iron(III) oxide. The best quality iron ore is found in Scandinavia, North America, Australia, North Africa and Russia.

Iron ore is converted to iron in special furnaces called **blast furnaces** (Figure 1). These furnaces are built as towers about 15 metres tall. Blasts of hot air are blown into the bottom of the furnace. This hot air reacts with coke and keeps the temperature high. Figure 1 shows a diagram of a blast furnace with a summary of the process involved.

Figure 1 *Extracting iron from iron ore in a blast furnace*

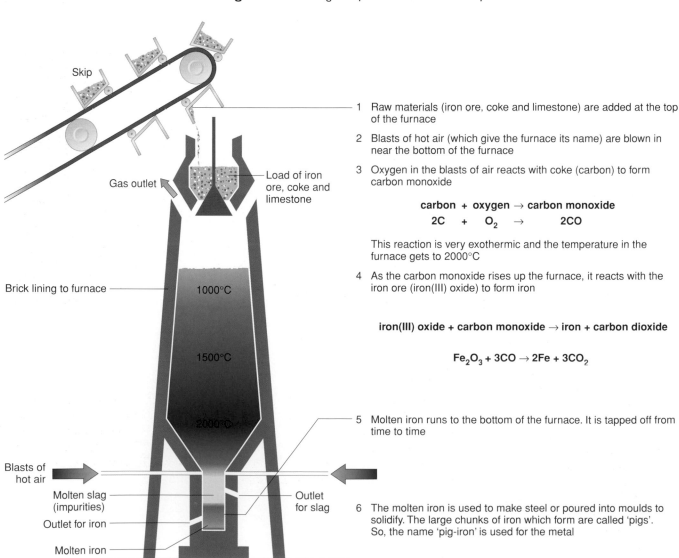

1 Raw materials (iron ore, coke and limestone) are added at the top of the furnace

2 Blasts of hot air (which give the furnace its name) are blown in near the bottom of the furnace

3 Oxygen in the blasts of air reacts with coke (carbon) to form carbon monoxide

carbon + oxygen → carbon monoxide
2C + O$_2$ → 2CO

This reaction is very exothermic and the temperature in the furnace gets to 2000°C

4 As the carbon monoxide rises up the furnace, it reacts with the iron ore (iron(III) oxide) to form iron

iron(III) oxide + carbon monoxide → iron + carbon dioxide

$$Fe_2O_3 + 3CO \rightarrow 2Fe + 3CO_2$$

5 Molten iron runs to the bottom of the furnace. It is tapped off from time to time

6 The molten iron is used to make steel or poured into moulds to solidify. The large chunks of iron which form are called 'pigs'. So, the name 'pig-iron' is used for the metal

Labels on figure: Skip; Gas outlet; Load of iron ore, coke and limestone; Brick lining to furnace; 1000°C; 1500°C; 2000°C; Blasts of hot air; Molten slag (impurities); Outlet for iron; Molten iron; Outlet for slag

Why is limestone used in the furnace?

Iron ore usually contains impurities like earth and sand (silicon dioxide, SiO_2). Limestone helps to remove these impurities. The limestone decomposes at the high temperatures inside the furnace to form calcium oxide and carbon dioxide.

$$\text{calcium carbonate} \rightarrow \text{calcium oxide} + \text{carbon dioxide}$$
$$CaCO_3 \rightarrow CaO + CO_2$$

The calcium oxide then reacts with sand (SiO_2) and other substances in the impurities to form 'slag' containing calcium silicate.

$$\text{calcium oxide} + \text{silicon dioxide} \rightarrow \text{calcium silicate}$$
$$CaO + SiO_2 \rightarrow CaSiO_3$$

The molten 'slag' falls to the bottom of the furnace and floats on the molten iron. It is tapped off from the furnace at a different level from the molten iron. The 'slag' is used for building materials and cement manufacture.

Blast furnaces work 24 hours a day. Raw materials are continually added at the top of the furnace and hot air is blasted in at the bottom. At the same time, molten slag and molten iron are tapped off from time to time as they collect. This process goes on all the time for about two years. After this time, the furnace has to be closed down so that the lining can be repaired.

Molten pig-iron being poured into a steel-making furnace

From pig-iron to steel

Pig iron contains about 7% of impurities. The main impurity is carbon. This makes pig-iron very hard and brittle compared to iron and steel. Unlike steel, both pig-iron and pure iron have very few uses. To make pig-iron into mild steel, the amount of carbon must be reduced to about 0.2%. This is done by blowing oxygen under pressure onto the hot, molten pig-iron. The oxygen converts carbon to carbon dioxide which escapes as a gas.

Study Questions

1. a) Why are furnaces used to make iron called *blast furnaces*?
   b) Why are blast furnaces usually built near coal fields?
   c) What materials are added to a blast furnace?
   d) What materials come out of a blast furnace?
2. a) The prices of metals are given in the 'commodities' section of the more serious daily papers, on Teletext or on the Internet. Look up the prices for iron (steel), aluminium, copper and zinc. How does the price of iron (steel) compare with other metals?
   b) Suggest three reasons why iron is the cheapest of all metals.
   c) Suggest three reasons why iron is used in greater quantities than any other metal.

6 Metal Compounds

Lime (calcium oxide) has been produced since the 18th century by heating limestone. This photo shows a lime burning kiln in the Middle East

Some of the reactions of metal compounds can be linked to the reactivity series like the reactions of metals themselves. If you try any of the reactions or tests in this unit, **you must wear safety spectacles**.

Heating metal compounds

The effect of heat on metal compounds can be related to the reactivity series. The equations below summarise what happens when copper hydroxide, zinc hydroxide, copper carbonate and zinc carbonate are heated. The distinctive colour changes can be used to help in the identification of these substances.

$$Cu(OH)_2(s) \rightarrow CuO(s) + H_2O(g)$$

blue   black

$$Zn(OH)_2(s) \rightarrow ZnO(s) + H_2O(g)$$

white   yellow when hot, white when cold

$$CuCO_3(s) \rightarrow CuO(s) + CO_2(g)$$

green

$$ZnCO_3(s) \rightarrow ZnO(s) + CO_2(g)$$

white

These reactions are examples of **thermal decomposition**. Notice how similar the equations are. In each case, the metal compound decomposes to a solid metal oxide and a gaseous non-metal oxide.

$$\text{metal compound} \xrightarrow{\text{heat}} \text{metal oxide} + \text{non-metal oxide}$$

Other common metal compounds, such as sulphates, sulphides and chlorides, are more stable than hydroxides and carbonates and they do not decompose so readily on heating.

The action of heat on metal hydroxides and carbonates is summarized in Table 1. Notice from Table 1 that the metal compounds fall into three groups.

1 The most reactive metals, such as potassium and sodium, have stable hydroxides and carbonates.

2 Metals in the middle of the reactivity series, from calcium to copper, form less stable compounds. Their hydroxides and carbonates decompose to give the metal oxide on heating.

3 The least reactive metals, like silver and gold, are so unreactive that their compounds decompose very easily. Their hydroxides and carbonates are too unstable to exist even at room temperature.

> In general, the lower a metal is in the reactivity series, the easier it is to decompose its compounds.

Identifying anions

The action of heat on metal compounds can be used to identify most carbonates (CO_3^{2-}) and nitrates (NO_3^-).

Test for carbonate

Heat the substance and pass any gases produced on heating through lime water (Figure 1). If the solid is a carbonate, carbon dioxide may be produced. This turns lime water milky.

Table 1 *The action of heat on metal hydroxides and carbonates*

Metal	Action of heat on hydroxide	Action of heat on carbonate
K Na	stable	stable
Ca Mg Al Zn Fe Pb Cu	decompose to oxide + H_2O e.g. $Ca(OH)_2 \rightarrow CaO + H_2O$	decompose to oxide + CO_2 e.g. $CaCO_3 \rightarrow CaO + CO_2$
Ag Au	hydroxides are too unstable to exist	carbonates are too unstable to exist

In order to make sure that the substance is a carbonate, add dilute nitric acid to the solid. Carbon dioxide should be produced.

$$CO_3^{2-}(s) + 2H^+(aq) \rightarrow CO_2 + H_2O$$

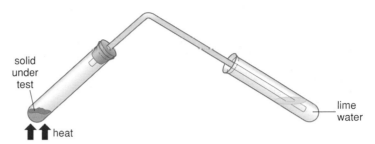

Figure 1 *Testing for carbonate*

Test for sulphite

Add dilute hydrochloric acid to the solid under test. If the substance is a sulphite, bubbles of sharp, pungent sulphur dioxide are produced.

$$\underset{\text{sulphite}}{SO_3^{2-}(s)} + 2H^+(aq) \rightarrow \underset{\text{sulphur dioxide}}{SO_2(g)} + H_2O$$

Test for nitrate

Most nitrates give brown fumes of nitrogen dioxide (NO_2) on heating (Figure 2). This is good evidence for a nitrate.

$$Cu(NO_3)_2(s) \xrightarrow{\text{heat}} CuO(s) + 2NO_2(g) + \tfrac{1}{2}O_2(g)$$

To check for a nitrate, add dilute sodium hydroxide solution plus a little aluminium powder to the substance under test. Then heat **carefully**. Ammonia gas is produced if the substance is a nitrate. Ammonia turns damp red litmus paper blue.

Test for chloride, bromide and iodide

Add dilute nitric acid to a solution of the substance. Then add silver nitrate solution.

Chlorides (Cl^-) give a white precipitate of silver chloride which turns purple-grey in sunlight.

$$Ag^+(aq) + Cl^-(aq) \rightarrow AgCl(s)$$

Bromides (Br^-) give a cream precipitate of silver bromide which turns green-yellow in sunlight.

$$Ag^+(aq) + Br^-(aq) \rightarrow AgBr(s)$$

Iodides (I^-) give a yellow precipitate of silver iodide which does not change in sunlight.

$$Ag^+(aq) + I^-(aq) \rightarrow AgI(s)$$

Test for sulphate

Add dilute nitric acid to a solution of the substance. Then add barium nitrate solution. If the substance contains sulphate (SO_4^{2-}), a thick white precipitate of barium sulphate ($BaSO_4$) forms.

$$Ba^{2+}(aq) + SO_4^{2-}(aq) \rightarrow BaSO_4(s)$$

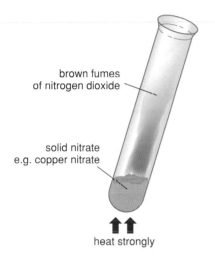

brown fumes
of nitrogen dioxide

solid nitrate
e.g. copper nitrate

heat strongly

Figure 2 *Testing for nitrate*

Study Questions

1 How is the decomposition of metal carbonates related to the reactivity series?

2 Write equations for the action of heat on the following compounds. If decomposition does not occur, say so.
$Zn(OH)_2$; KOH; Ag_2O; Rb_2CO_3; $PbCO_3$; $Mg(NO_3)_2$

3 Find out about the manufacture of lime from limestone. What are the uses of (i) limestone, (ii) lime?

4 Two fertilisers are labelled 'sulphate of potash' and 'nitrate of potash'. How would you check which was which?

7 Identifying Cations

We can identify different substances using tests for the atoms and ions in them. The best way to identify a substance is to find a property or a reaction which is shown only by that substance and is easy to see.

Two of the best tests for cations use flame tests and sodium hydroxide solution. **You must wear eye protection** if you try any of the tests in this unit.

Flame tests

When substances are heated strongly, the electrons in them absorb extra energy. We say that the electrons are **excited**. The excited electrons soon release this excess energy as light and they become stable again. Different cations emit different colours of light when substances are heated (Table 1).

Check the flame test for a potassium or a copper compound using the following method.

Dip a nichrome wire in concentrated hydrochloric acid and then heat it in a roaring Bunsen until it gives no colour to the flame. The wire is now clean. Dip it in hydrochloric acid again, and then in the substance to be tested. Heat the wire in the Bunsen and note the flame colour.

Chemists have developed special instruments called emission spectroscopes which can measure the wavelengths of light emitted during flame tests. This allows them to identify the substance under test. Emission spectroscopes enable chemists to identify certain ions very accurately and very rapidly, even when the amount of the substance to be tested is very small.

Emission spectroscopes are used to monitor substances in the environment, in the water we drink and in the food we eat.

Table 1 *The flame colours from some cations*

Cation present in substance	Flame colour
K^+	lilac
Na^+	yellow
Li^+	red
Ca^{2+}	red
Ba^{2+}	pale green
Cu^{2+}	blue/green

Carrying out a flame test for potassium

Tests using sodium hydroxide solution

The hydroxides of all metals (except those in group 1) are insoluble. So, these insoluble hydroxides form solid precipitates when aqueous sodium hydroxide, containing hydroxide ions (OH^-), is added to a solution of metal ions. For example:

$$Cu^{2+}(aq) + 2OH^-(aq) \rightarrow Cu(OH)_2(s)$$

blue precipitate

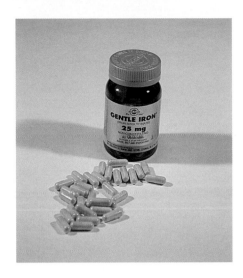

What tests would you carry out to see whether iron tablets contain Fe^{2+} or Fe^{3+} ions?

Table 2 shows what happens when:
  (i)   a little sodium hydroxide solution, NaOH(aq) and then,
  (ii) excess sodium hydroxide solution is added to solutions of some common cations.
  Look carefully at Table 2.

Table 2 *Testing for cations with sodium hydroxide solution*

Cation in solution	3 drops of NaOH(aq) added to 3 cm³ of solution of cation	10 cm³ of NaOH(aq) added to 3 cm³ of solution of cation
K^+	no precipitate	no precipitate
Na^+	no precipitate	no precipitate
Ca^{2+}	a white precipitate of $Ca(OH)_2$ forms $Ca^{2+} + 2OH^- \rightarrow Ca(OH)_2$	white precipitate remains
Mg^{2+}	a white precipitate of $Mg(OH)_2$ forms $Mg^{2+} + 2OH^- \rightarrow Mg(OH)_2$	white precipitate remains
Al^{3+}	a white precipitate of $Al(OH)_3$ forms $Al^{3+} + 3OH^- \rightarrow Al(OH)_3$	white precipitate dissolves to give a colourless solution
Fe^{2+}	a green precipitate of $Fe(OH)_2$ forms $Fe^{2+} + 2OH^- \rightarrow Fe(OH)_2$	green precipitate remains
Fe^{3+}	a brown precipitate of $Fe(OH)_3$ forms $Fe^{3+} + 3OH^- \rightarrow Fe(OH)_3$	brown precipitate remains
Cu^{2+}	a blue precipitate of $Cu(OH)_2$ forms $Cu^{2+} + 2OH^- \rightarrow Cu(OH)_2$	blue precipitate remains

1 Which cations give no precipitate with sodium hydroxide solution?
   How can you tell the difference between these cations using flame tests?

2 Which cations give a white precipitate which does *not* dissolve in excess sodium hydroxide solution?
   How can you tell the difference between these cations using flame tests?

3 Which cations give a coloured (non-white) precipitate with sodium hydroxide solution? How can you tell the difference between these cations from the colour of their hydroxides?

4 The ammonium cation, NH_4^+ can also be identified by warming with sodium hydroxide solution. This produces ammonia gas (NH_3) which turns damp red litmus paper blue.

$$NH_4^+\,(aq) + OH^-\,(aq) \xrightarrow{\text{warm}} NH_3(g) + H_2O(l)$$
$$\text{ammonia}$$

Study Questions

1 a) How would you carry out a flame test on a sample of chalk?
  b) What colour should the flame test give?
  c) Why must eye protection be worn during flame testing?
  d) What causes flame colours from certain cations?

2 a) A garden pesticide is thought to contain copper sulphate. Describe two tests that you would do to find out whether it contains Cu^{2+} ions.
  b) How would you show that the pesticide contains sulphate?

3 A metal has become coated with a layer of oxide. How would you check whether the metal is aluminium or magnesium?

Section F Activities

The Eiffel Tower is made of steel. Why is steel used? What other important structural materials do we have for large buildings and bridges?

1 The importance of iron and steel

Iron is the most important metal for industry and society. There are four reasons for this.

● **It is strong.** Although pure iron is weak, it can be alloyed with carbon to make steel, which is very strong. Steel has a high tensile strength. This means that it does not crack, break, stretch or bend easily. Large forces can deform steel, but it returns to its original shape when the force is removed.

● **It is easy to work.** Iron is very malleable when it is hot. This makes it very useful for manufacturing different articles.

● **It forms alloys.** Iron can form a large range of alloys with a wide variety of different properties.

● **It is cheap.** Iron is the cheapest of all metals.

Because of these factors, iron is used in greater quantity than any other metal.

1 List the factors which make iron more important than any other metal.

2 What do the following mean:
   (i) tensile strength,   (ii) malleable?

3 The prices of metals are given in the 'commodities' section of some daily papers, on Teletext and also on the Internet. Look up the prices for iron (steel), aluminium, copper and zinc. How does the price of iron (steel) compare with the other metals?

4 Suggest three reasons why iron is the cheapest of all metals.

5 List five important uses of iron (steel).

2 Panning for gold

Look closely at the photo of the 'prospector' panning for gold.

1 Why does the gravel in the bed of the stream contain gold?

2 Why is the gold found as the element and not as compounds of gold?

3 What method will the 'prospector' use to separate gold from other materials in the gravel?

4 Why did the method in question 3 separate the gold?

5 What problems do you think the early gold prospectors in California faced from day to day?

3 Mining and producing copper

Look carefully at the information below.
What is the main ore?
Copper pyrites (chalcopyrites), a mixture of CuS and FeS forming $CuFeS_2$.
How is it found?
Underground, mixed with other copper ores such as chalcocite (Cu_2S). About 0.5% of the ore is copper.
Where is it mined?
About half of all copper ores *mined* in the world comes from Chile and the USA. The other major mining countries are Indonesia, Canada, Peru, Australia, China and Russia.
How is it mined?
By open pit mining or underground mining.

Panning for gold

What is the world production of copper?

See Table 1. About one tenth of the copper produced is recycled from scrap. This is called **secondary copper**. Copper produced from its ores is called **primary copper**.

1 What are the chemical names for
   a) CuS and FeS   b) Cu_2S?
2 What percentage of the ore is copper?
3 What mass of the ore is needed to produce 1 kg of copper?
4 Only a small percentage of the ore is copper. Suggest 3 problems that this causes.
5 The copper ore mined in Chile in 2000 was sufficient to produce nearly 4 670 000 tonnes of copper.
   a) How much copper did Chile actually produce in 2000?
   b) How do you account for the difference between the actual copper produced and the possible production of 4 670 000 tonnes?
6 What is the difference between primary copper and secondary copper?
7 a) Look at the countries where copper is mined. Which countries are surprisingly absent from the major producers of the metal in Table 1?
   b) What do you think happens to most of the ore mined in these countries?
8 Make a bar chart showing the copper production in 2000 for the nine most important producers shown in Table 1.

Table 1 *The major copper-producing countries shown in order for the year 2000*

Country	Production in tonnes
Chile	2,670,000
USA	1,803,000
Japan	1,437,000
China	1,325,000
Russia	790,000
Germany	710,000
Canada	551,000
Poland	485,000
South Korea	470,000

4 Using *Word* to identify an ionic compound

a) Look at the tests for cations in Unit F7 and the tests for anions in Unit F6 of this section.
b) Use *Word* to write a flow chart or a key which would allow you to identify one cation from amongst the following using the cation tests in Unit F7:

$$Al^{3+}, Ba^{2+}, Ca^{2+}, Cu^{2+}, Fe^{2+}, Fe^{3+}, K^+, Li^+, Mg^{2+}, Na^+, NH_4^+$$

c) Use *Word* to write a flow chart or a key which would allow you to identify one anion from amongst the following using the anion tests in Unit F6:

$$Br^-, Cl^-, CO_3^{2-}, I^-, NO_3^-, SO_4^{2-}, SO_3^{2-}$$

5 Using *PowerPoint* to present a metal

Produce a *PowerPoint* presentation on the history, reactions and uses of a metal of your choice.

1 In general, metals:

- have high densities,
- have high melting points and high boiling points,
- are good conductors of heat and electricity,
- are malleable.

The properties of metals can be explained using the idea that metals have a close-packed structure of atoms in which the outer electrons move about freely.

2 Metals can be made harder, stronger and more useful by alloying. An **alloy** is a mixture of elements containing at least one metal.

3 The reactions of metals related to the reactivity series are summarised in the following table. You must learn the order of metals in the reactivity series.

Table 1 *A summary of the reactions of metals based on the reactivity series*

Reactivity series	Reaction with oxygen when heated in air	Reaction in water	Reaction with dilute acids	Reaction with solutions of metal compounds	Symbol
Potassium Sodium Calcium Magnesium	burn with decreasing reactivity down the series to form their oxide	react with water with decreasing reactivity down the series forming hydrogen	react with dilute HCl and dilute H_2SO_4, less and less vigorously down the series, producing hydrogen	a more reactive metal (higher in the series) displaces less reactive metals from their compounds	K Na Ca Mg
Aluminium Zinc Iron		react with steam, but not water, forming hydrogen			Al Zn Fe
Lead Copper	only form a layer of oxide	do not react with water or steam	do not react with dilute acid		Pb Cu
Silver Gold	do not react with oxygen				Ag Au
General equation	$2M + O_2 \rightarrow 2MO$	$M + H_2O \rightarrow MO + H_2$	$M + 2HCl \rightarrow MCl_2 + H_2$ $M + H_2SO_4 \rightarrow MSO_4 + H_2$	$M_h + M_l^{2+} \rightarrow M_h^{2+} + M_l$	

4 **Reduction** and **oxidation** always occur together. These reactions are often called **redox reactions**.

Oxidation Is Loss of electrons. } Think of '*Oil Rig*' to
Reduction Is Gain of electrons. } remember this!

When metals react, they form ions and lose electrons: $M \rightarrow M^{2+} + 2e^-$

So, all the reactions of metals involve oxidation.

5 Rocks containing metals or metal compounds from which it is economic to extract the metal are called **ores**.

6 The extraction of metals from their ores involves three stages.

- Mining and concentrating the ore.
- Reducing the ore to the metal (i.e. converting metal ions in the ore to the metal), $M^{2+} + 2e^- \rightarrow M$
- Purifying the metal.

7 The method used to extract a metal from its ore depends on the position of the metal in the reactivity series.

- Metals at the top of the reactivity series are extracted by electrolysis of the molten ore or by reacting the purified ore with a more reactive metal.
- Metals in the middle of the reactivity series are extracted by reducing their oxides with carbon (coke) or carbon monoxide.
- Metals at the bottom of the reactivity series are extracted by heating the ore in a limited supply of air.

8 Metal hydroxides, metal carbonates and metal nitrates **decompose** on heating. They form the metal oxide plus a non-metal oxide.

Section F   Exam Questions

1 By observing the reactions of metals with water and dilute sulphuric acid it is possible to put metals in order of their reactivity.
(a) A, B, C and D represent four metals.

Metal	Reaction with water	Reaction with dilute sulphuric acid
A	no reaction	reacts slowly at first
B	no reaction	no reaction
C	little or no reaction	reacts quickly
D	vigorous reaction	violent – dangerous reaction

(i)   Put metals A, B, C and D in order of their reactivity from most reactive to least reactive.
(ii) The metals used were copper, magnesium, sodium and zinc. Use the information in the table to identify which of these metals was A, B, C and D.

(b) A student tried to make some magnesium sulphate. Excess magnesium was added to dilute sulphuric acid. During this reaction fizzing was observed due to the production of a gas.

magnesium   sulphuric acid

(i)   Copy and then complete and balance the chemical equation for this reaction.
.... + H_2SO_4 → .... + ...
(ii) At the end of the reaction the solution remaining was filtered. Why was the solution filtered?
(iii) The filtered solution was left in a warm place.

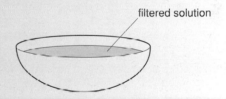

filtered solution

Explain why the filtered solution was left in a warm place.

AQA 2000

2 (a) Magnesium is manufactured by electrolysis of magnesium chloride.
(i)   Explain why this process is expensive to operate.
(ii) Copy and complete the word equation for the electrolysis of magnesium chloride.
magnesium chloride → magnesium + ...
(b) (i)   Draw a diagram to show the electronic structure of an **atom** of magnesium.
(ii) How does a magnesium atom (Mg) change when it forms a magnesium ion (Mg^{2+})?
(c) Magnesium (Mg) burns in oxygen to form magnesium oxide (MgO).
(i)   Write a balanced equation for this reaction.
(ii) Explain why magnesium is said to be oxidised in this reaction.

(d) The reaction between magnesium and dilute sulphuric acid is exothermic.
  (i) State what is meant by the term **exothermic**.
  (ii) Describe how you could show that this reaction is exothermic.

Edexcel 1999

3 The diagram shows the arrangement of atoms in an *alloy*.

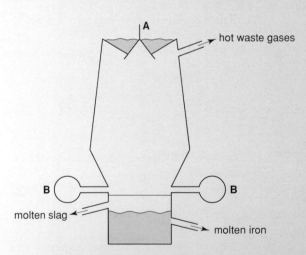

Key

○ iron atoms

● carbon atoms

(a) What is meant by an *alloy*?
(b) Name the alloy represented in the diagram.
(c) Give **one** advantage of using this alloy instead of pure iron.
(d) Which elements are used to make brass?

AQA 2000

4 Iron is extracted from its ore in a blast furnace.

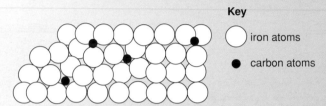

  (i) Three solid raw materials are added to the furnace at **A**. Iron ore is one of these raw materials.
  Name the other **two** solids.
  (ii) What is forced into the furnace at **B**?
  (iii) Describe how the furnace is heated.
  (iv) Iron oxide is **reduced** to iron in the furnace.
   I. Copy and complete the **word** equation below which represents this reaction.
   iron oxide + ... → iron + ...
   II. What is meant by the term **reduced**?
  (v) State one method of conserving the iron ore.

WJEC 2000

5 Most of the cans used for drinks are made from aluminium.
  (a) (i) Aluminium is an element. What does this mean?
   (ii) Metals are malleable and this makes them suitable to make drinks cans. What does malleable mean?
  (b) The arrangement of electrons in an aluminium atom is:

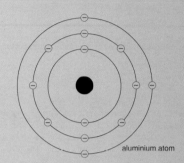

aluminium atom

  (i) On the diagram, label the nucleus of the aluminium atom.
  (ii) How many protons does an aluminium atom have?
  (iii) To which group of the periodic table does aluminium belong?
  (iv) To which period of the periodic table does aluminium belong?
  (c) The reaction between aluminium and iron oxide is used to join lengths of railway track. It is called the thermit reaction.
   $Fe_2O_3(s) + 2Al(s) \rightarrow Al_2O_3(s) + 2Fe(l)$
   (i) Why does aluminium react with iron oxide?
   (ii) What does the (l) after Fe in the chemical equation mean?
   (iii) Suggest why the thermit reaction can be used to join lengths of railway track.

AQA 1999

6 Molten, impure iron is made from iron ore in the blast furnace.
  (a) In the blast furnace, reducing agents change iron ore into iron.
  Give the name of ONE substance which can act as a reducing agent in the blast furnace.
  (b) The main impurity in iron ore is silicon dioxide (SiO_2).
  Describe how this is removed.
  Give the name of the raw material which must be present to remove this impurity and describe the reactions involved, naming the waste product formed. You should include equations for the chemical reactions taking place.

Edexcel 2000

Acids, Bases and Salts

Oranges and other fruits contain citric acid. This gives them a sharp taste

By the end of this section you should:
- Know how acids react with metals, bases and carbonates.
- Be able to recall the importance of acids and neutralisation in everyday life.
- Understand neutralisation in terms of ions.
- Appreciate the importance of sulphuric acid and limestone for industry.
- Understand the concepts of concentration and strength as applied to acids and alkalis.
- Know how solubility affects the preparation of salts.
- Be able to use indicators as a measure of acidity and alkalinity and in the preparation of some soluble salts.
- Appreciate that our understanding of acids, bases and alkalis has changed and developed.
- Understand how hard water forms and how it can be softened.

1 Introducing Acids

The most convenient method of testing for acids is to use **indicators**, like litmus and universal indicator. Indicators are substances which change colour depending on how acidic or how alkaline a solution is.

- Acidic solutions turn litmus red and give an orange or red colour with universal indicator (Figure 1).

- Alkaline solutions turn litmus blue and give a green, blue or violet colour with universal indicator.

It would be awkward to use the colour of an indicator to describe how acidic or how alkaline something is. So, chemists use a scale of numbers called the **pH scale**. The pH of a solution gives a measure of its acidity or alkalinity. On this scale:

- Acidic solutions have a pH below 7.

- Alkaline solutions have a pH above 7.

- Neutral solutions have a pH of 7.

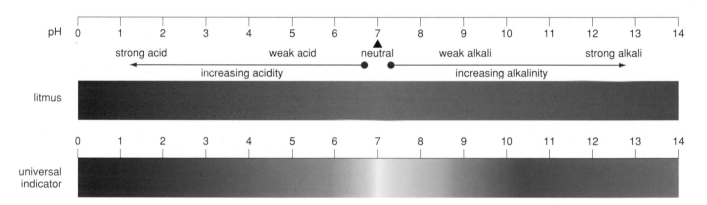

Figure 1 *The colours of litmus and universal indicator with solutions of different pH*

Making acids

- **From non-metal oxides and water**

When non-metal oxides are added to water, acids are produced. For example:

$$\text{sulphur dioxide} + \text{water} \rightarrow \text{sulphurous acid}$$
$$SO_2 + H_2O \rightarrow H_2SO_3$$

Sulphuric acid is manufactured via sulphur dioxide. The raw materials are sulphur, air (oxygen) and water. Most of the sulphur is shipped to the UK from North America. There are three stages in the manufacture of sulphuric acid.

1 First, sulphur dioxide is made by burning sulphur in air (oxygen).

$$S + O_2 \rightarrow SO_2$$

2 The sulphur dioxide is then converted to sulphur trioxide. This is called the **contact process**. The sulphur dioxide is mixed with air (oxygen) and passed over a catalyst of vanadium(V) oxide at 450°C.

$$\text{sulphur dioxide} + \text{oxygen} \rightarrow \text{sulphur trioxide}$$
$$2SO_2 + O_2 \rightarrow 2SO_3$$

What precautions is this technician taking to protect himself from the acid he is pipetting?

3 Finally, the sulphur trioxide is converted to sulphuric acid. Sulphur trioxide does not dissolve very easily in water. If the sulphur trioxide is added directly to water, an acid mist forms and this is difficult to contain. So, the sulphur trioxide is dissolved in 98% sulphuric acid and then water is added.

$$\text{sulphur trioxide} + \text{water} \rightarrow \text{sulphuric acid}$$
$$SO_3 + H_2O \rightarrow H_2SO_4$$

A sulphuric acid plant. The hot gas filter removes unburnt sulphur dust from sulphur dioxide produced in the first stage of the process. What do you think happens in the converter? The heat exchanger uses the heat produced in the contact process to warm up the reactant gases. Why is this sensible?

Study Questions

1 a) How would you check the pH of toothpaste?
   b) Why is the pH of toothpaste important?
2 Why are acids important?
3 This question is about the manufacture of sulphuric acid.
   a) Write equations for the three stages in the manufacture of sulphuric acid.
   b) The first two stages in the manufacture involve oxidation. Which substances are oxidised?
   c) What is the contact process?
   d) Suggest two reasons why a catalyst is used in the contact process.
   e) 450°C is an optimum temperature for the contact process. What do you think the term 'optimum temperature' means?
   f) Most of the sulphuric acid plants in the UK are situated near large ports. Suggest reasons for this.

Sulphur being mined in an open pit in North America. Most sulphur for the manufacture of sulphuric acid in the UK is imported from North America

● **By combining hydrogen with reactive elements**

The most important acid to be manufactured in this way is hydrochloric acid. Hydrogen chloride is first made by burning hydrogen in chlorine.

$$H_2 + Cl_2 \rightarrow 2HCl$$

The hydrogen chloride is then passed up a tower packed with stones (or some other unreactive substance) over which water trickles. The gas dissolves in the water to form hydrochloric acid.

2 | Acids in Everyday Life

Many foods, especially sauces and pickles, contain acetic acid from vinegar

Acids are important in everyday life and in industry. They are present in our foods and in our bodies. They are used to make our clothes and our medicines. They are present in acid rain and are responsible for acidity in the soil.

Acids in our foods

Many foods and drinks contain acids. Citrus fruits, such as oranges, lemons, pineapples and grapefruit, all contain citric acid. Tomato sauce, brown sauce and mint sauce get their sharp taste from vinegar which contains ethanoic (acetic) acid.

One of the simplest and cheapest drinks is soda water. This is made by dissolving carbon dioxide in water under pressure. Some of the carbon dioxide reacts with the water to form carbonic acid. When soda water is poured from the bottle, it fizzes because the pressure is lower, which causes carbon dioxide to form as bubbles in the drink. Other fizzy drinks, like Coke and lemonade, also contain carbonic acid.

Acids in our bodies

The stomach wall produces hydrochloric acid. This gives a very acidic pH of about 2 in the stomach. The acidic conditions help us to digest (break down) foods, particularly proteins. Proteins are broken down into smaller molecules, called peptides and amino acids. These small molecules can pass through the lining of our intestines into the bloodstream. The blood carries these small molecules round the body to where they are needed.

The pH of our blood is 7.4 (slightly alkaline). Most reactions in our bodies can only take place within a narrow range of pH. A change in the pH in your stomach might give you indigestion, but a pH change of only 0.5 in the blood would probably kill you. In order to prevent changes in pH, our bodies contain substances that counteract the effects of acids and alkalis.

Acids in the air – acid rain

When fuels burn, carbon dioxide and smaller amounts of sulphur dioxide are produced. Because of this, city air may contain five times as much sulphur dioxide as fresh air. Sulphur dioxide and carbon dioxide react with rain and water vapour in the air to form sulphurous acid, H_2SO_3, and carbonic acid, H_2CO_3.

$$SO_2 + H_2O \rightarrow H_2SO_3$$
$$\text{(sulphurous acid)}$$

$$CO_2 + H_2O \rightarrow H_2CO_3$$
$$\text{(carbonic acid)}$$

These acids make the rain acidic, which is why we use the term 'acid rain' (Unit B6).

Acids in the soil

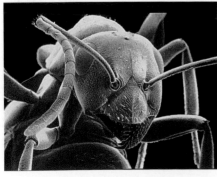

Ants kill other insects by biting them and then spraying formic acid onto the wound

The pH of soil can vary from about 4 to 8, but most soils have a pH between 6.5 and 7.5. In chalk or limestone areas, the soil is usually alkaline, but in moorland, sandstone and forested areas it is generally acidic. Peat bogs and clay soils are also normally acidic. For general gardening and farming purposes, the best results are obtained from a neutral or slightly acidic soil of pH 6.5 to 7.0.

Acid rain, caused by fumes from industry has had drastic effects on the natural environment in parts of the Czech Republic. Trees have been stunted or killed and the acidic pH of lakes has wiped out entire food chains

Only a few plants, including rhododendrons and azaleas, can grow well in soils which are more acidic than pH 6.5. In areas where the soil is too acidic, it can be improved by treatment with powdered limestone (calcium carbonate) or slaked lime (calcium hydroxide). These substances which react with and neutralise acids in the soil are called **bases**.

Study Questions

1. a) Describe how you would check the pH of soil samples.
    b) Why do you think that forested and peaty areas have acid soils?
    c) Why is it important for gardeners to know the pH of their garden soil?

2. Make a list of six different foodstuffs which contain acids and say what acids they contain.

3. a) Why is soda water both fizzy and acidic?
    b) Would you expect mineral water to be: (i) fizzy, (ii) acidic? Explain your answers.

4. Design an experiment to compare the fizziness and pH of different soda waters and mineral waters.

5. Find out more about acid rain. Here are some questions to consider.
    a) When did acid rain first become a problem?
    b) Why did this problem not arise earlier?
    c) What are the major factors causing acid rain?
    d) What steps might be taken to reduce acid rain?
    Prepare a short report for your class.

Most heather grows best in acid soil

These beech trees grow best in slightly alkaline soil

3 The Properties of Acids

What citrus fruits does this photo show? What acid is present in citrus fruits?

These gravestones are made from limestone. Their worn and pitted appearance has been caused by the action of carbonic acid, sulphurous acid, sulphuric acid and nitric acid in 'acid rain'

We know a lot about acids already.

- **Acids have a sharp taste** – some of them kill the cells in our bodies and are described as corrosive.
- **Acids give characteristic colours with indicators.** They give a red colour with litmus and an orange or red colour with universal indicator.
- **Acids react with metals** above copper in the reactivity series to form a salt and hydrogen.

$$\text{metal} \;+\; \text{acid} \;\rightarrow\; \text{salt} \;+\; \text{hydrogen}$$

For example, $\quad Mg \;+\; H_2SO_4 \rightarrow MgSO_4 \;+\; H_2$

Nearly all salts contain a metal and at least one non-metal. They are ionic compounds with a cation (e.g. Cu^{2+}, Mg^{2+}) and an anion (Cl^-, SO_4^{2-}). Sodium chloride (Na^+Cl^-) is known as common salt.

- **Acids react with bases** (such as metal oxides and hydroxides) to form a salt and water. These reactions are called **neutralisations**. Neutralisation is studied in detail in the next unit.

$$\text{base} + \text{acid} \rightarrow \text{salt} + \text{water}$$

For example, when black copper oxide is added to warm dilute sulphuric acid, the black solid disappears and a blue solution of copper sulphate forms.

$$\text{copper oxide} \;+\; \text{sulphuric acid} \;\rightarrow\; \text{copper sulphate} \;+\; \text{water}$$
$$CuO \;+\; H_2SO_4 \;\rightarrow\; CuSO_4 \;+\; H_2O$$

- **Acids react with carbonates** to give a salt plus carbon dioxide and water.

$$\text{carbonate} + \text{acid} \rightarrow \text{salt} + CO_2 + H_2O$$

This explains why sulphuric acid in acid rain 'attacks' buildings made of limestone (calcium carbonate).

$$\text{calcium} \;+\; \text{sulphuric} \;\rightarrow\; \text{calcium} \;+\; \text{carbon} \;+\; \text{water}$$
$$\text{carbonate} \qquad \text{acid} \qquad \text{sulphate} \qquad \text{dioxide}$$
$$CaCO_3 \;+\; H_2SO_4 \;\rightarrow\; CaSO_4 \;+\; CO_2 \;+\; H_2O$$

Notice that carbonates neutralise acids like metal oxides and hydroxides. So, we must also classify carbonates as bases.

- **Acid solutions conduct electricity and are decomposed by it.** This shows that solutions of acids contain ions (Table 1). All acids produce hydrogen at the cathode during electrolysis. This shows that all acids contain H^+ ions. Because of this:

Acids are defined as substances which donate (give) H^+ ions.

Table 1: Some acids and the ions which they form in solution

Name of acid	Formula	Ions produced from acid
Acetic acid	CH_3COOH	$H^+ + CH_3COO^-$
Carbonic acid	H_2CO_3	$2H^+ + CO_3^{2-}$
Hydrochloric acid	HCl	$H^+ + Cl^-$
Nitric acid	HNO_3	$H^+ + NO_3^-$
Sulphuric acid	H_2SO_4	$2H^+ + SO_4^{2-}$

Concentrated and dilute acids

Concentrated acids contain a lot of acid in a small amount of water. Concentrated sulphuric acid has 98% sulphuric acid and only 2% water.

Dilute acids have a small amount of acid in a lot of water. Dilute sulphuric acid has about 10% sulphuric acid and 90% water.

Concentration tells us how much substance is dissolved in a certain volume of solution. It is usually given as the number of grams or the number of moles of solute per dm^3 of solution. Dilute acids usually have concentrations of 1.0 mole per dm^3 of solution or less.

For example, a solution of sulphuric acid containing 1.0 mole per dm^3 has 1 mole of sulphuric acid (98 g H_2SO_4) in 1 dm^3 (1000 cm^3) of solution. This is sometimes written as 1.0 M H_2SO_4.

0.1 M H_2SO_4 (i.e. 0.1 mole dm^{-3} H_2SO_4) contains 9.8 g H_2SO_4 in 1000 cm^3 of solution.

The following examples will help you to understand concentrations in grams per dm^3 and moles per dm^3 of solution.

Some vinegar contains 3 g of ethanoic acid ($C_2H_4O_2$) in 100 cm^3 of the liquid. What is the concentration of ethanoic acid in the vinegar in:
(i) grams per dm^3 (g dm^{-3}), (ii) moles per dm^3 (mol dm^{-3})?

(i) 100 cm^3 of the vinegar contains 3 g ethanoic acid

$\Rightarrow$ 1 cm^3 of vinegar contains $\dfrac{3}{100}$ g ethanoic acid

$\Rightarrow$ 1000 cm^3 (1 dm^3) of vinegar contains $\dfrac{3}{100} \times 1000$ g ethanoic acid

$\therefore$ concentration of ethanoic acid in the vinegar = 30 g/dm^3

(ii) The relative formula mass of ethanoic acid, $M_r(C_2H_4O_2)$
$= 2 \times A_r(C) + 4 \times A_r(H) + 2 \times A_r(O)$
$= (2 \times 12) + (4 \times 1) + (2 \times 16)$ $= 60$ g
$\therefore$ 1 mole of ethanoic acid $= 60$ g
concentration of the ethanoic acid $= 30$ g per dm^3
$= \dfrac{30}{60}$ moles per dm^3
$= 0.5$ moles per dm^3 or 0.5 M

Strong and weak acids

When different acids with the same concentration in moles per dm^3 are tested with the same indicator, they give different pHs (Figure 1)

The different pH values mean that some acids produce H^+ ions more readily than others. The results in Figure 1 show that hydrochloric acid, nitric acid and sulphuric acid produce more H^+ ions than the other acids. We say that they **ionise** (split up into ions) more easily. We call them **strong acids** and the others **weak acids**. Strong acids and weak acids also show a difference in their reactions with metals. Strong acids react much, much faster than weak acids.

We can show the difference between strong and weak acids in the way we write equations for their ionisation.

Hydrochloric acid: $HCl(aq) \rightarrow H^+(aq) + Cl^-(aq)$
Ethanoic acid: $CH_3COOH(aq) \rightleftharpoons H^+(aq) + CH_3COO^-(aq)$

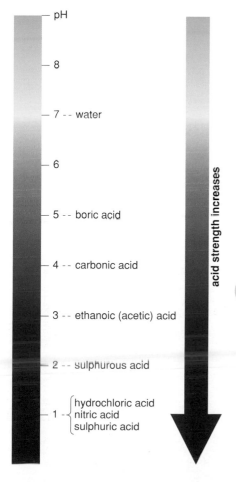

Figure 1 *The pH of solutions of various acids (all solutions have a concentration of 0.1 mole per dm^3)*

A single arrow, in the hydrochloric acid equation shows that *all* the HCl has formed H^+ and Cl^- ions in aqueous solution. The arrows in opposite directions for ethanoic acid show that some of the CH_3COOH molecules have formed H^+ and CH_3COO^- ions, but most of it remains as CH_3COOH molecules.

> ● *Strong* acids are *completely* ionised in water.
> ● *Weak* acids are *only partly* ionised in water.

Notice the difference between the terms 'concentration' and 'strength'.

● **Concentration** tells us how much solute is dissolved in solution, and we use the words 'concentrated' and 'dilute'.

● **Strength** tells us the extent to which the acid is ionised and we use the words 'strong' and 'weak'.

We can distinguish between strong and weak acids by using the pH scale or by their rate of reaction with metals.

All vinegars contain ethanoic acid (acetic acid)

Formic acid is used to descale kettles. Notice the 'Corrosive' hazard label. Formic acid is a weak acid. Why is hydrochloric acid not used as a descaler?

Study Questions

1 Make a table to summarise the properties and chemical reactions of acids.

2 a) Why can vinegar (which contains ethanoic acid) be used to descale kettles?
   b) Why is sulphuric acid *not* used to descale kettles?
   c) Classify vinegar (1.0 M CH_3COOH) and battery acid (4.0 M H_2SO_4) as
       (i) concentrated or dilute,
       (ii) strong or weak.

3 Alkalis, like acids, can be strong or weak.
   a) Sodium hydroxide (NaOH) is a strong alkali. Write an equation for its ionisation.
   b) How would you test to decide whether calcium hydroxide is a strong or weak alkali?

4 Complete the following word equations and then write balanced chemical equations for the following reactions.
   a) zinc + hydrochloric acid →
   b) aluminium oxide + sulphuric acid →
   c) copper carbonate + nitric acid →

5 Concentrated sulphuric acid is 12.0 M. Acid in car batteries (battery acid) is 4.0 M sulphuric acid.
   a) What is the concentration of battery acid in: (i) moles per dm^3 (ii) grams per dm^3 of H_2SO_4?
   b) Battery acid can be made by diluting concentrated sulphuric acid with water. How much concentrated sulphuric acid and how much water are needed to make 6 dm^3 of battery acid?

Adverts for indigestion cures usually talk of 'acid stomach and 'acid indigestion'. Medicines which ease stomach ache (such as Milk of Magnesia and Rennies) are called antacids because they neutralise excess acid in the stomach.

- Substances which neutralise acids are called **bases**.
- Bases which are soluble in water are called **alkalis**.
- The reactions between acids and bases are called **neutralisations**.

The bases in indigestion tablets include magnesium hydroxide and calcium carbonate. In the last unit we learnt that farmers use slaked lime (calcium hydroxide) and limestone (calcium carbonate) to neutralise acid soils.

Neutralisation is also important in other situations.

Dental care

Toothpaste neutralises the acids produced when food breaks down in the mouth (Figure 1).

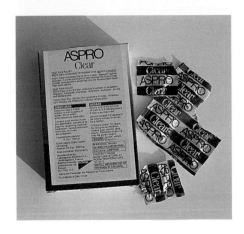

What substances in Aspro help to neutralise acids in the stomach?

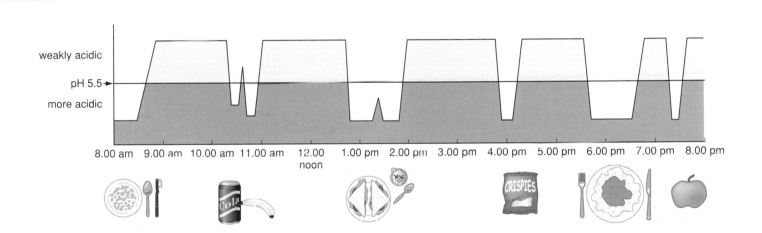

Figure 1 *This shows how the pH in your mouth changes during the day. Notice how the pH becomes lower and more acidic during and just after meals. This is because sugars in your food are broken down into acids. These acids react with tooth enamel when the pH falls below 5.5*

Treating stings from plants and animals

The stings from certain plants and animals contain acids or bases so they can be treated by neutralisation. For example, nettle stings and wasp stings contain complex bases like histamine. They are treated with acidic substances called antihistamines. Unlike wasp stings, bee stings are acidic. So, they are treated with bases.

Making fertilisers such as ammonium nitrate ('Nitram')

This is a very important industrial application of neutralisation. Ammonium nitrate is manufactured by neutralising nitric acid (HNO_3) with ammonia (NH_3). Fertilisers are studied in detail in Unit J9.

Treating splashes of acid or alkali on people's skin or clothing.

How much acid and base react?

When an acid is neutralised by a base, the pH of the solution changes. We can follow this pH change using an indicator to find out how much base (e.g. sodium hydroxide solution) just reacts with the acid (e.g. hydrochloric acid). The reaction produces a neutral salt solution.

If you try the following experiment, **wear eye protection**.

Measure 25 cm³ of sodium hydroxide solution containing 1.0 mole per dm³ (1.0 M NaOH(aq)) into a conical flask using a pipette (Figure 2).

Add 5 to 10 drops of universal indicator and note the colour.

Then add 5 cm³ of 1.0 M hydrochloric acid from a burette (Figure 3), mix well and record the colour again. Record the colour also when 10, 15 and 20 cm³ of hydrochloric acid have been added.

Now add 1 cm³ of hydrochloric acid and record the colour again. Repeat the addition of 1 cm³ nine more times and note the colour each time.

Table 1 shows the results that you should get. Notice that the indicator shows a neutral pH colour (yellow) when 25 cm³ of hydrochloric acid have been added. So, 25 cm³ of 1.0 M hydrochloric acid just neutralise 25 cm³ of 1.0 M sodium hydroxide.

> This method of adding one solution from a burette to another solution in order to find out how much of the two solutions will *just* react with each other is called a **titration**. When the two solutions just react and neither is in excess, we have found the **neutral point** or **end point** of the titration.

25 cm³ of 1.0 M HCl *just* react with 25 cm³ of 1.0 M NaOH.
Now, 1000 cm³ of a 1.0 M solution contains 1 mole, so

25 cm³ of 1.0 M HCl contains $\dfrac{25}{1000} \times 1 = 0.025$ moles of HCl and

25 cm³ of 1.0 M NaOH contains $\dfrac{25}{1000} \times 1 = 0.025$ moles of NaOH

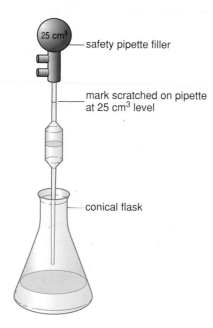

Figure 2 *Measure 25 cm³ of 1.0 M NaOH(aq) using a pipette*

Table 1

Volume of 1.0 M HCl(aq) added/cm³	Colour of indicator
0	purple
5	purple/blue
10	blue
15	blue
20	blue
21	blue
22	blue
23	blue
24	blue/green
25	yellow
26	pink
27	pink
28	pink
29	pink
30	pink

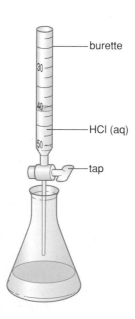

Figure 3 *Adding 1.0 M HCl from a burette to 1.0 M NaOH*

Table 2 *The names of salts*

Base	Name of salt
Magnesium oxide	magnesium–
Potassium hydroxide	potassium–
Zinc oxide	zinc–

Acid	Name of salt
Sulphuric	–sulphate
Sulphurous	–sulphite
Nitric	–nitrate
Nitrous	–nitrite
Carbonic	–carbonate
Hydrochloric	–chloride

$\therefore$ 0.025 moles of HCl react with 0.025 moles of NaOH

$\Rightarrow$ 1 mole of HCl reacts with 1 mole of NaOH

We can write the left-hand side of the equation as:

$$HCl(aq) + NaOH(aq) \rightarrow$$

If all the water from the end-point solution is evaporated, the only product which remains is sodium chloride, $NaCl(s)$. The complete equation is therefore:

$$HCl(aq) + NaOH(aq) \rightarrow NaCl(aq) + H_2O(l)$$

$\therefore$ 1 mole of HCl reacts with 1 mole of NaOH to give 1 mole of NaCl and 1 mole of H_2O.

Substances like sodium chloride which form when acids react with bases are called **salts**. Sodium chloride is usually known as common salt. Other important salts include copper sulphate ($CuSO_4$), potassium chloride (KCl) and ammonium nitrate (NH_4NO_3).

Explaining neutralisation in terms of ions

Hydrochloric acid contains equal numbers of H^+ ions and Cl^- ions. So, we can write $H^+(aq) + Cl^-(aq)$ in place of HCl(aq) in equations. (See Table 1 in Unit G3.)

Similarly, sodium hydroxide, NaOH(aq) and sodium chloride, NaCl(aq), also consist of ions. They can be written as:

$$Na^+(aq) + OH^-(aq) \text{ and } Na^+(aq) + Cl^-(aq)$$

Water does not consist of ions so it must be written as H_2O.

We can now rewrite our initial equation:

$$HCl(aq) + NaOH(aq) \rightarrow NaCl(aq) + H_2O(l)$$

in terms of ions as:

$$H^+(aq) + Cl^-(aq) + Na^+(aq) + OH^-(aq) \rightarrow Na^+(aq) + Cl^-(aq) + H_2O(l)$$

Notice that $Na^+(aq)$ and $Cl^-(aq)$ appear on both sides of the last equation. These two ions do not really react. They are just the same after the reaction as they were before. If we cancel $Na^+(aq)$ and $Cl^-(aq)$ on both sides of the equation, we get:

$$H^+(aq) + OH^-(aq) \rightarrow H_2O(l)$$

This final equation shows clearly what happens during the reaction. H^+ ions in the acid have reacted with OH^- ions in the base to form water. Na^+ and Cl^- ions have not changed. They have just 'stood by and watched' the reaction like spectators at a sports event. Ions like Na^+ and Cl^- in this reaction, which are present in the mixture but take no part in the reaction, are called **spectator ions**.

Naming salts

Look at Table 2. This shows how the name of a salt comes from its parent base and acid. So, magnesium oxide and nitric acid would produce magnesium nitrate. Notice also in Table 2 that:

● Acids with names ending in '**–ic**' form salts with names ending in '**–ate**'. (Hydrochloric acid is an exception – its salts are called chlorides.)

● Acids with names ending in '**–ous**' form salts with names ending in '**–ite**'.

Study Questions

1 Design an experiment to compare the effectiveness of indigestion tablets. Which tablets are best at neutralising acid? Which tablets are the best buy?

2 a) What causes indigestion?
   b) How do indigestion cures like Rennies work?

3 Complete the following.
   a) magnesium oxide + sulphuric acid → _____ + _____
   b) potassium hydroxide + _____ → _____ nitrate + water
   c) _____ + hydrochloric acid → zinc _____ + _____

4 Explain the following:
   base; indicator; titration; neutral point

5 30 cm³ of 2.0 M NaOH *just* react with 10 cm³ of 3.0 M H_2SO_4.
   a) How many moles of NaOH react?
   b) How many moles of H_2SO_4 react?
   c) How many moles of NaOH react with 1 mole of H_2SO_4?
   d) Write an equation for the reaction.

The manufacture of sulphuric acid was described in Unit 1 of this section. About 2.5 million tonnes of sulphuric acid are manufactured each year in the UK. Figure 1 shows its main uses and its economic importance.

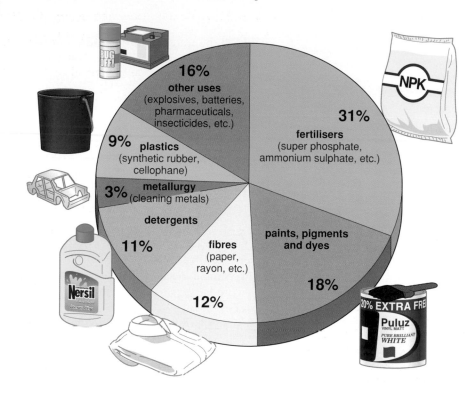

Figure 1 *The uses of sulphuric acid*

Reaction with water

Concentrated sulphuric acid contains about 98% H_2SO_4 and only 2% water. **It must be handled carefully wearing eye protection.** Concentrated sulphuric acid is an oily, corrosive liquid which reacts with water producing a lot of heat. Because of this, **always add concentrated H_2SO_4 to a large volume of water when mixing the two. Never add water to acid.** If water is added to concentrated H_2SO_4, the heat produced can boil the water and spit out drops of acid.

Pure H_2SO_4 and pure water are both poor conductors of electricity. They contain simple molecules *not* ions. But, a solution of sulphuric acid in water is a good conductor of electricity, so it *must* contain ions. The ions are formed when the H_2SO_4 reacts with water. H_2SO_4 is a strong acid so it reacts with water and ionises completely.

$$H_2SO_4(l) \xrightarrow{\text{water}} 2H^+(aq) + SO_4^{2-}(aq)$$

Notice that each molecule of H_2SO_4 can produce two H^+ ions.

Reactions as an acid

Always **wear eye protection** if you are handling sulphuric acid. Dilute sulphuric acid contains H^+ ions. So, it reacts like a typical acid (Unit G3) with:

• **indicators,**

Concentrated sulphuric acid attacks skin, clothing, metals and other materials. Because of these hazards, containers for concentrated sulphuric acid must carry the 'corrosive' warning sign

- **metals** above copper in the reactivity series, forming a metal sulphate and hydrogen:

$$Mg + H_2SO_4 \rightarrow MgSO_4 + H_2$$

- **bases** (metal oxides and hydroxides), forming a metal sulphate and water.

$$MgO + H_2SO_4 \rightarrow MgSO_4 + H_2O$$

- **carbonates** forming a metal sulphate, carbon dioxide and water:

$$MgCO_3 + H_2SO_4 \rightarrow MgSO_4 + CO_2 + H_2O$$

Reactions as a dehydrating agent

Concentrated sulphuric acid reacts violently with water. It absorbs water very rapidly and can be used to dry gases. It is a **dehydrating agent**.

Because of this concentrated sulphuric acid will remove water from:

- hydrated salts such as blue copper(II) sulphate ($CuSO_4.5H_2O$),

- carbohydrates such as sugar ($C_{12}H_{22}O_{11}$),

- compounds in clothes and skin containing hydrogen and oxygen. This is why it burns and chars clothing and skin.

Dilute sulphuric acid contains lots of water and does *not* react as a dehydrating agent.

When concentrated H_2SO_4 is added to sugar and warmed gently, the reaction gets very hot. The mixture froths up into a steaming black mass of carbon.

$$C_{12}H_{22}O_{11} \xrightarrow[H_2SO_4]{concentrated} 12C + \underset{\substack{\text{water removed by} \\ \text{concentrated } H_2SO_4}}{11H_2O}$$

Sugar, like other carbohydrates, contains carbon plus hydrogen and oxygen atoms in the ratio 2:1 as in water. Hence the name *carbohydrate*. Our flesh also contains carbohydrates. Concentrated H_2SO_4 removes the water from these carbohydrates.

Study Questions

1 a) What is a dehydrating agent?
  b) What uses do dehydrating agents have?
  c) Accurate clocks sometimes have silica crystals (as a dehydrating agent) placed near their working parts. Why is this?

2 a) Write the formula for blue copper(II) sulphate crystals.
  b) What colour will these crystals become when concentrated sulphuric acid is added?
  c) Write an equation for the reaction.

3 Why does dilute sulphuric acid *not* react as a dehydrating agent?

4 a) Why is concentrated sulphuric acid a poorer conductor of electricity than dilute sulphuric acid?
  b) Why does concentrated sulphuric acid burn the skin but dilute sulphuric acid does not?

5 Which of the following are carbohydrates:
  ethanol, C_2H_6O; glucose, $C_6H_{12}O_6$; ethene, C_2H_4; glycerine, $C_3H_8O_3$?

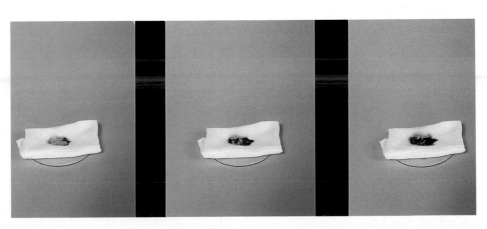

Concentrated sulphuric acid will attack cotton cloth by removing water molecules from carbohydrates in the cotton fibres

6

Bases and Alkalis

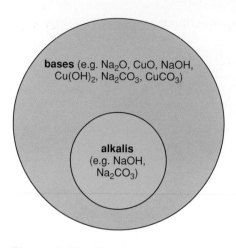

Figure 1 *This Venn diagram shows the relationship between bases and alkalis. All alkalis are bases, but not all bases are alkalis*

Bases are substances which neutralise acids. They are the chemical opposites to acids. The largest group of bases are metal oxides, hydroxides and carbonates such as sodium oxide, copper oxide, sodium hydroxide and copper carbonate.

> A special sub-set of bases are called **alkalis**. Alkalis are bases which are soluble in water. Their solutions have a pH above 7. They turn litmus blue and give a green, blue or purple colour with universal indicator.

The most common alkalis are sodium hydroxide (NaOH), calcium hydroxide ($Ca(OH)_2$) and ammonia (NH_3). Calcium hydroxide is much less soluble than sodium hydroxide. A solution of calcium hydroxide in water is often called 'limewater'. Sodium oxide (Na_2O), potassium oxide (K_2O) and calcium oxide (CaO) react with water to form their hydroxides. So, the reactions of these three metal oxides with water produces alkalis. For example,

$$Na_2O(s) + H_2O(l) \rightarrow 2NaOH(aq)$$

$$CaO(s) + H_2O(l) \rightarrow Ca(OH)_2(aq)$$

Most other metal oxides and hydroxides are insoluble in water. These insoluble metal oxides and hydroxides are bases but *not* alkalis. The relationship between bases and alkalis is shown in a Venn diagram in Figure 1.

Like acids, alkalis can be classified by the extent of their ionisation in water. Strong alkalis, such as sodium hydroxide and calcium hydroxide, are completely ionised in water.

$$\text{i.e. } NaOH(aq) \rightarrow Na^+(aq) + OH^-(aq)$$

Weak alkalis, such as ammonia are only partly ionised in water.

$$NH_3(aq) + H_2O(l) \rightleftharpoons NH_4^+(aq) + OH^-(aq)$$

Did you know?

Generally, alkalis are more dangerous to the eyes than acids of the same concentration.

So, you must **always wear eye protection** when using alkalis.

More about acids, bases and neutralization

During the 19th century, the Swedish chemist Svante Arrhenius put forward new ideas about acids and bases. Arrhenius suggested that *acids were substances which split up into ions (ionised) in water to produce hydrogen ions, H^+*.

For example, $HCl \rightarrow H^+ + Cl^-$

At the same time, Arrhenius said that *bases were substances which reacted with H^+ ions from acids to form water*. For example,

	base	+	acid	→	salt	+	water
	sodium hydroxide	+	hydrochloric acid	→	sodium chloride	+	water
	$NaOH(aq)$	+	$HCl(aq)$	→	$NaCl(aq)$	+	$H_2O(l)$
	copper oxide	+	sulphuric acid	→	copper sulphate	+	water
	$CuO(s)$	+	$H_2SO_4(aq)$	→	$CuSO_4(aq)$	+	$H_2O(l)$

According to Arrhenius's theory, bases contained either oxide ions (O^{2-}) like copper oxide or hydroxide ions (OH^-) like sodium hydroxide. During neutralisation, these ions react with H^+ ions in the acids to form water.

$$2H^+ + O^{2-} \rightarrow H_2O$$
$$H^+ + OH^- \rightarrow H_2O$$

These ideas helped chemists to understand neutralisation and to see that bases were the chemical opposites of acids.

A worker checks a bleached sample of wood pulp during the manufacture of paper

But, Arrhenius's ideas were unsatisfactory to some chemists because they only applied to:

● reactions involving acids in aqueous solution,

● bases reacting with H^+ ions to form water.

In order to overcome these problems and widen the scope of acid–base reactions, Brønsted and Lowry independently suggested the following definitions in 1923.

> Acids are substances which donate H^+ ions.
> Bases are substances which accept H^+ ions.

Using this definition, carbonates can also act as bases by accepting H^+ ions.

$$CO_3^{2-} + 2H^+ \rightarrow CO_2 + H_2O$$
carbonate　acid　　carbon dioxide　water

The reaction between the gases hydrogen chloride and ammonia is also an acid–base reaction.

$$HCl(g) + NH_3(g) \rightarrow NH_4^+Cl^-(s)$$

In this reaction, HCl has donated H^+ to NH_3 leaving NH_4^+ and Cl^- ions.

So, these last two reactions are clearly acid–base reactions. But they are *not* neutralisations which are restricted to reactions of acids with bases to form a salt and water only.

Alkalis in industry

The most important industrial alkalis are sodium hydroxide (caustic soda) and calcium hydroxide (slaked lime). Calcium hydroxide is made by adding water to quicklime (calcium oxide). It is used to treat acid soils, in cement and in the manufacture of sodium hydroxide and bleaching powder. Large amounts of sodium hydroxide are used to make soap, paper, rayon and ceramics.

Paper and rayon are both made from the cellulose fibres in wood. The wood is first made into pulp and soaked in sodium hydroxide solution. This removes gums and resins and leaves the natural fibres of cellulose. The cellulose fibres are then bleached and squashed into thin white sheets which look like blotting paper. This purified pulp can be used to make paper and rayon.

Soaps and soap powders are made by boiling fats and oils with sodium hydroxide in large vats (Figure 2).

Study Questions

1 Suppose your best friend has missed the last few lessons and asks you for help. How would you explain to him or her what the difference is between (i) acids and bases; (ii) bases and alkalis; (iii) bases and salts?

2 Explain the following:
   a) All alkalis are bases, but all bases are *not* alkalis.
   b) Sodium hydroxide is used in oven cleaners to remove fat and grease.
   c) Limestone, slaked lime and quicklime are all bases, but only slaked lime is an alkali.

3 Write word equations and then balanced equations for the following reactions:
   a) the action of heat on limestone (calcium carbonate),
   b) the reaction of quicklime (calcium oxide) with water,
   c) the reaction of zinc oxide with hydrochloric acid.

4 a) Why is it important to recycle paper?
   b) What are the main stages in recycling paper?
   c) Paper can be made from certain rags. Why is this?

oil or fat molecule　　　　　　　　soap　　　　glycerine (glycerol)

(⋀⋀⋀⋀ = long chain of carbon, hydrogen and oxygen atoms)

Figure 2

Salts are formed when acids react with metals, bases or carbonates. Most salts contain a positive metal ion and a negative ion composed of one or two non-metals.

> Salts:
> - are ionic compounds,
> - have high melting points and boiling point,
> - are electrolytes,
> - are often soluble in water.

The best known salt is sodium chloride, NaCl, which is often called common salt. Many ores and minerals are composed of salts. These include chalk and limestone (calcium carbonate), gypsum (calcium sulphate) and iron pyrites (a mixture of copper sulphide and iron sulphide).

Salt crystals, like those of sodium chloride, are often formed by crystallisation from aqueous solution. When this happens, water molecules sometimes form part of the crystal structure. This occurs in Epsom Salts ($MgSO_4.7H_2O$), gypsum ($CaSO_4.2H_2O$) and washing soda ($Na_2CO_3.10H_2O$). The water which forms part of the crystal structure is called **water of crystallisation**. Salts containing water of crystallisation are called **hydrates** or hydrated salts.

Did you know?

Silver chloride is so insoluble that it would need all the water in an Olympic-sized swimming pool (and a very big stirring spoon) to dissolve just one gram!

Soluble and insoluble salts

If you are using a salt or making a salt, it is important to know whether it is soluble or insoluble.

Table 1 shows the solubilities of various salts in water at 20°C. Notice the wide range in solubilities from potassium nitrite (300 g per 100 g water) to silver chloride (0.000 000 1 g per 100 g water). It is useful to divide salts into two categories – soluble and insoluble.

Salts with a solubility greater than 1 g per 100 g water are classed as soluble; salts with a solubility less than 1 g per 100 g water are classed as insoluble.

Table 2 summarises the general rules for the **solubilities of common salts**.

Purple cubic crystals of fluorite (calcium fluoride). Calcium fluoride is a salt. It is added to toothpaste so that we take in small amounts. It helps to make our teeth and bones stronger

Table 1 *The solubilities of various salts*

Salt	Formula	Solubility /g per 100 g water at 20°C
Barium chloride	$BaCl_2$	36.0
Barium sulphate	$BaSO_4$	0.000 24
Calcium chloride	$CaCl_2$	74.0
Calcium sulphate	$CaSO_4$	0.21
Copper(II) sulphate	$CuSO_4$	20.5
Copper(II) sulphide	CuS	0.000 03
Lead(II) sulphate	$PbSO_4$	0.004
Potassium chlorate	$KClO_3$	7.3
Potassium nitrite	KNO_2	300.0
Silver chloride	$AgCl$	0.000 000 1
Silver nitrate	$AgNO_3$	217.0
Sodium chloride	$NaCl$	36.0
Sodium nitrate	$NaNO_3$	87.0

Table 2 *Solubilities of common salts*

All	sodium potassium ammonium	salts are soluble	
All	nitrates	are soluble	
All	ethanoates	are soluble	
All	sulphates	are soluble except	Ag_2SO_4, $CaSO_4$ $BaSO_4$, $PbSO_4$
All	chlorides	are soluble except	$AgCl$, $PbCl_2$
All	carbonates hydroxides sulphides	are **insoluble** except	those of Na^+, K^+ and NH_4^+

Study Questions

1 Explain the following:
hydrated; *water of crystallisation*;
precipitation; *insoluble*.

2 What units are used for: (i)
concentration; (ii) solubility?

3 a) Summarise the stages in
preparing an insoluble salt.
b) Describe how you would
prepare a pure sample of
insoluble barium sulphate.
c) Write an equation for the
reaction which occurs.

4 Make a table to show whether
the following salts are soluble or
insoluble:
$Pb(NO_3)_2$; Ag_2S; $CuCO_3$; K_2SO_4;
NH_4Cl; $FeSO_4$.

5 Epsom Salts have the formula
$MgSO_4.7H_2O$. What does this tell
you about Epsom Salts?

Preparing insoluble salts

The method used to prepare a salt depends on whether the salt is soluble or
insoluble. Methods for soluble salts are described in the next unit. Insoluble salts,
like lead chloride, silver chloride, calcium carbonate and barium sulphate, are
prepared by making the salt as a precipitate.

Suppose you are making insoluble silver chloride, AgCl. You will need to mix a
soluble Ag^+ salt and a soluble chloride.

1 Which Ag^+ salt is certain to be soluble? Look at Table 2.

2 Which chloride is certain to be soluble? Look at Table 2.

These questions show that you can precipitate any insoluble salt (say **XY**) by
mixing solutions of NaY and XNO_3. Both NaY and XNO_3 are soluble, since all
sodium salts and all nitrates are soluble. Figure 1 shows how an insoluble salt is
precipitated and then purified.

1 **Mix** two solutions, one containing the positive ion in the insoluble salt and the
other containing the negative ion.

2 **Filter** off the precipitate of the insoluble salt.

3 **Wash** the precipitate with water.

4 Leave the precipitate to **dry** at room temperature.

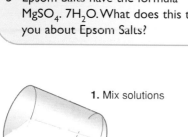

1. Mix solutions

solution containing
positive ion

solution containing
negative ion

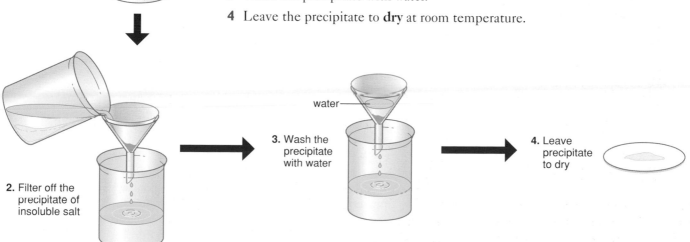

**2. Filter off the
precipitate of
insoluble salt**

water

**3. Wash the
precipitate
with water**

**4. Leave
precipitate
to dry**

Figure 1 *Preparing an insoluble salt*

8

Preparing Salts

When you are making a salt, the first question to ask is 'Is the salt soluble or insoluble?'.

> If the salt is **insoluble**, it is usually prepared by **precipitation**, described in the last unit.
> If the salt is **soluble**, it is usually prepared by **reacting an acid with a metal, a base or a carbonate** (see Unit G3).

$$\text{metal} + \text{acid} \rightarrow \text{salt} + H_2$$
$$\text{base} + \text{acid} \rightarrow \text{salt} + H_2O$$
$$\text{carbonate} + \text{acid} \rightarrow \text{salt} + CO_2 + H_2O$$

Wear eye protection if you try any of the experiments in this unit.

Preparing soluble salts

Method 1: Using metals, insoluble bases and insoluble carbonates.

Figure 1 shows the main stages in this method.

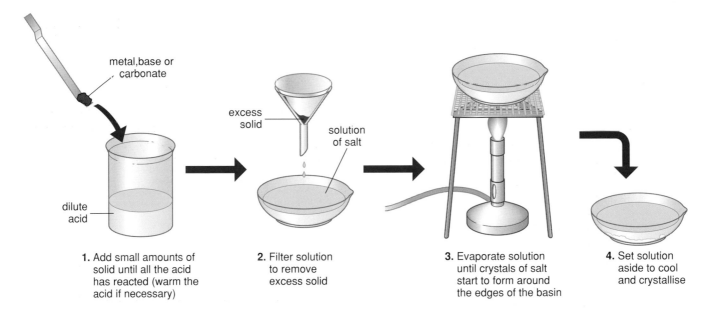

metal, base or carbonate

excess solid

solution of salt

dilute acid

1. Add small amounts of solid until all the acid has reacted (warm the acid if necessary)

2. Filter solution to remove excess solid

3. Evaporate solution until crystals of salt start to form around the edges of the basin

4. Set solution aside to cool and crystallise

Figure 1

Zinc sulphate can be made by this method using sulphuric acid with either zinc, zinc oxide or zinc carbonate.

$$Zn + H_2SO_4 \rightarrow ZnSO_4 + H_2$$
$$ZnO + H_2SO_4 \rightarrow ZnSO_4 + H_2O$$
$$ZnCO_3 + H_2SO_4 \rightarrow ZnSO_4 + CO_2 + H_2O$$

Method 2: Using soluble bases and carbonates.

In method 1, we can tell when the acid has been used up because unreacted metal, base or carbonate remains in the liquid as undissolved, *insoluble* solid. But, if the base or carbonate is *soluble* (like sodium hydroxide or sodium carbonate), we cannot tell when the acid has been used up because excess solid will dissolve even after the acid has been neutralised. To get round this, we must use an indicator to tell us when we have added just enough base or carbonate to neutralise the acid. Figure 2 shows the main stages involved.

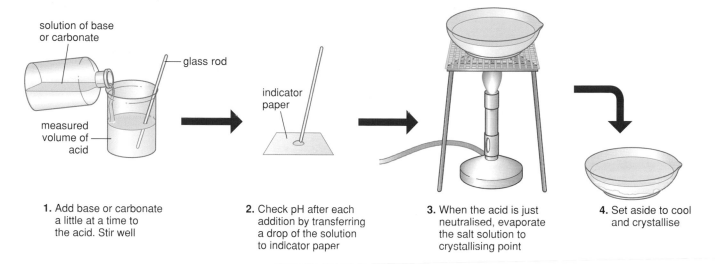

1. Add base or carbonate a little at a time to the acid. Stir well

2. Check pH after each addition by transferring a drop of the solution to indicator paper

3. When the acid is just neutralised, evaporate the salt solution to crystallising point

4. Set aside to cool and crystallise

Figure 2

Study Questions

1. Look at method 1 for preparing soluble salts.
   a) Explain why this method will not work using metals below hydrogen in the activity series.
   b) Why is this method not used with sodium?
   c) How can you tell when all the acid is used up if the solid is: (i) zinc; (ii) copper oxide; (iii) copper carbonate?
   d) Why is the salt produced not contaminated with: (i) the acid used; (ii) the solid added?
   e) Why is method 1 no good for insoluble salts?
   f) Why is method 1 no good if the solid added dissolves in water?

2. Look at method 2 for preparing salts.
   a) Why is the pH of the solution tested using indicator paper rather than putting indicator solution into the acid?
   b) Describe how you would make sodium nitrate by this method.
   c) Write a word equation and a balanced symbolic equation for the reaction in b).

Potassium chloride can be made by this method using hydrochloric acid with either potassium hydroxide or potassium carbonate.

$$KOH + HCl \rightarrow KCl + H_2O$$
$$K_2CO_3 + 2HCl \rightarrow 2KCl + CO_2 + H_2O$$

Method 2 is used to make the salts of sodium, potassium and ammonium because the bases and carbonates containing sodium, potassium and ammonium are all soluble. Other soluble salts are usually made by method 1.

Figure 3 is a flowchart showing how you can prepare a particular salt.

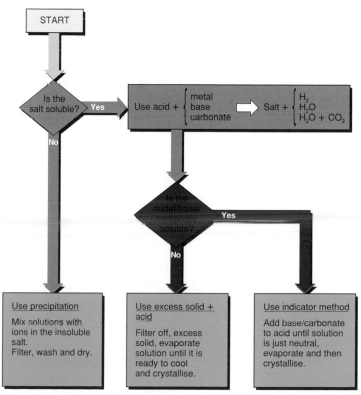

Figure 3 *How to prepare a salt*

9

Limestone for Industry

A limestone quarry near Castleton, Derbyshire. The quarrying of limestone is big business because it has so many commercially valuable products

Limestone is one of the most important raw materials for the chemical and building industries. The main substance in limestone rock is calcium carbonate ($CaCO_3$). Quicklime (calcium oxide, CaO) and slaked lime (calcium hydroxide, $Ca(OH)_2$) are easily manufactured from limestone, which makes it even more important.

The uses of limestone and its products are shown in Figure 1. Notice:

● The main uses of limestone itself are in building and construction, in neutralising acid soil, in fertilisers such as nitro-chalk and in making iron and steel (Unit E5).

● The main substances made from limestone are calcium oxide (quicklime), calcium hydroxide (slaked lime), cement and glass.

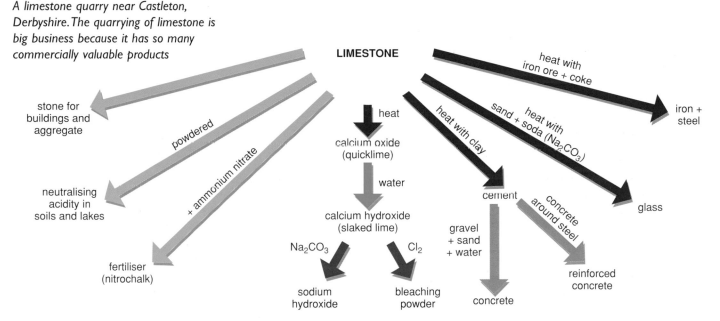

Figure 1 *Important uses and products of limestone*

● **Calcium oxide (quicklime)** is made by the thermal decomposition of limestone (calcium carbonate) in lime kilns (Figure 2).

$$CaCO_3(s) \rightarrow CaO(s) + CO_2(g)$$

The quicklime is then reacted with water to make calcium hydroxide (slaked lime).

$$CaO(s) + H_2O(l) \rightarrow Ca(OH)_2(s)$$

● **Calcium hydroxide (slaked lime)** is the cheapest industrial alkali. It is used to make sodium hydroxide and bleaching powder. Powdered calcium hydroxide is also used to control acidity in the soil. Calcium hydroxide is only slightly soluble in water. The dilute alkaline solution which it forms is called **limewater**.

● **Cement** is made by heating limestone with clay. It contains a mixture of calcium silicate and aluminium silicate. This mixture reacts with water to form hard, interlocking crystals as the cement sets. When cement is used, it is normally mixed with two or three times as much sand as well as water.

● **Concrete** is a mixture of cement, sand and water with gravel (aggregate), broken stones or bricks. As the mixture of cement, sand and water sets around the aggregate, it produces a hard, stone-like building material.

Reinforced concrete is made by allowing concrete to set around a steel framework. It is used in building large structures like office blocks and buildings.

Reinforced concrete is an example of a **composite material**. Composite materials contain two different materials, but the particles in the materials do not mix. Reinforced concrete contains concrete and steel. Because of this, it has the hardness of concrete and the flexibility and tensile strength of steel.

Study Questions

1 Chalk, marble and limestone are different natural forms of calcium carbonate.
   a) Why are there three different forms?
   b) Look at the classification of rocks as 'sedimentary', 'metamorphic' and 'igneous' in Unit L2. Which classes of rocks do chalk, marble and limestone belong to?

2 Various mixtures of sand and cement (by volume) are used in building. Plan an experiment to find out which mixture (ratio of sand to cement 2:1, 3:1 or 4:1) gives the *hardest* product.

3 Try to explain the following. Write balanced equations where appropriate.
   a) Finely ground limestone is used to neutralise acids in the soil.
   b) Limewater is used to test for carbon dioxide.

4 'Wattle and daub' might be described as the medieval equivalent of reinforced concrete as a composite material. Find out about 'wattle and daub'. Why is it a composite material? What was the advantage of 'wattle and daub' over just 'wattle' or just 'daub'?

5 a) What problems are associated with the large-scale quarrying of chalk and limestone?
   b) What steps can be taken to overcome or reduce these problems?

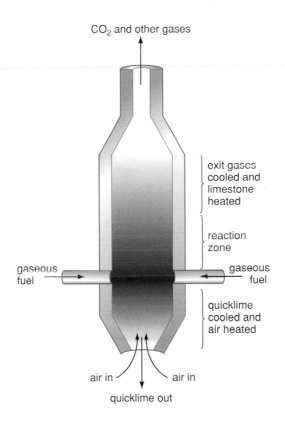

Figure 2 *A gas-fuelled lime kiln*

Chalk, limestone and marble

Calcium carbonate occurs naturally as chalk and marble, as well as limestone. In fact, calcium carbonate is the second most abundant material in the Earth's crust after silicates like clay, sand and sandstone.

Chalk is the softest form of calcium carbonate. Deposits of chalk have formed from the shells of dead sea creatures that lived millions of years ago. In some places, the chalk was covered with other rocks and put under great pressure. This changed the soft chalk into harder rock – **limestone**. In other places, the chalk was under pressure *and heat*. This changed the soft chalk into **marble**, the hardest form of calcium carbonate.

Malham Cove in the Yorkshire Dales. Water once poured from the top of the rocks. Over many years, carbonic acid in the water has reacted with the limestone rock and formed caves. The water now flows through these caves and finally emerges at the bottom of the cove

In chalk and limestone regions, the water does not easily form a lather with soap. The water also forms a **scum** when it is mixed with soap. This kind of water is known as **hard water**.

Which ions cause hard water?

Table 1 shows what happens when 10 cm³ of each of the solutions listed are shaken with 1.0 cm³ of soap solution.

Table 1 *The reactions of some solutions with soap*

Solution used	Ions present	Reaction with hard water
Sodium chloride	Na^+, Cl^-	No scum, lots of lather
Calcium chloride	Ca^{2+}, Cl^-	Lots of scum, little lather
Potassium nitrate	K^+, NO_3^-	No scum, lots of lather
Magnesium nitrate	Mg^{2+}, NO_3^-	Lots of scum, little lather
Sodium sulphate	Na^+, SO_4^{2-}	No scum, lots of lather
Iron(II) sulphate	Fe^{2+}, SO_4^{2-}	Lots of scum, little lather

Just look at the scum which has formed with this hard water. Notice also that there is no lather

Look closely at Table 1.

1 Which solutions cause hard water?

2 Which of the following ions cause hard water: Na^+; Cl^-; Ca^{2+}; K^+; NO_3^-; Mg^{2+}; SO_4^{2-}; Fe^{2+}?

3 Which ions are most likely to cause hard water in the UK?

Why does scum form?

The main cause of hard water in the UK are calcium ions, Ca^{2+}. Some hardness in the UK is also caused by magnesium ions, Mg^{2+}. Soaps contain salts such as sodium palmitate and sodium stearate. When hard water is mixed with soap, Ca^{2+} ions in the hard water react with palmitate and stearate ions in the soap forming an insoluble precipitate of calcium stearate and calcium palmitate. This precipitate is scum.

$$Ca^{2+}(aq) \quad + \quad 2X^-(aq) \quad \rightarrow \quad CaX_2(s)$$
(calcium ions in hard water)   (stearate/palmitate ions in soap)   (scum)

Soaps and detergents are both used for cleaning, but they differ in *one* important way. Detergents, like washing-up liquid, do *not* give scum with hard water. Unlike soaps, they do not contain ions which react with Ca^{2+} and Mg^{2+} ions in hard water to form a precipitate.

How does hard water form?

When rain falls, it reacts with carbon dioxide in the air to form carbonic acid, H_2CO_3.

$$H_2O(l) + CO_2(g) \rightarrow H_2CO_3(aq)$$

When this dilute solution of carbonic acid flows over limestone or chalk, it reacts with calcium carbonate in the rocks to form calcium hydrogencarbonate, $Ca(HCO_3)_2$.

$$CaCO_3(s) \quad + \quad H_2CO_3(aq) \quad \rightarrow \quad Ca(HCO_3)_2(aq)$$
(in limestone)   (in rain water)   (in hard water)

Unlike calcium carbonate, calcium hydrogencarbonate is soluble in water and the calcium ions make the water hard.

Calcium carbonate in chalk and limestone is the main cause of hard water. In some areas, magnesium carbonate ($MgCO_3$) and calcium sulphate which occurs as gypsum ($CaSO_4.2H_2O$) and anhydrite ($CaSO_4$) also cause hardness. Calcium sulphate is only slightly soluble in water, but enough will dissolve to make the water hard.

Carbonic acid in rain water has helped to dissolve the limestone in the cracks of this limestone pavement

Study Questions

1 Explain the following:
   hard water; scum; soap; detergent.
2 a) Why does scum form?
   b) Write an equation for the reaction involved.
   c) Why is scum a nuisance?
3 What is the big advantage of detergents over soaps?
4 Plan an experiment to compare the hardness of two different samples of tap water.
5 Design and make a poster to show some of the geological features in limestone areas that have resulted from the effects of dissolved carbon dioxide on limestone.

11 Softening Hard Water

'Fur' inside a kettle is a deposit of calcium carbonate from hard water

Hard water usually tastes better than soft water. The dissolved substances in hard water also produce stronger teeth and bones and help to reduce the chance of heart diseases. But hard water does have several disadvantages.

- It uses more soap than soft water.

- It produces scum, which looks unsightly.

- It results in the formation of 'scale' in water pipes and 'fur' in kettles. The 'scale' may block pipes and 'fur' will reduce the efficiency of kettles, washing machines and hot water systems.

- It is sometimes necessary to remove the hardness from the water and this can be an expensive undertaking.

When hard water is warmed up or boiled, the calcium hydrogencarbonate in it is decomposed to calcium carbonate, water and carbon dioxide.

$$Ca(HCO_3)_2(aq) \rightarrow CaCO_3(s) + H_2O(l) + CO_2(g)$$

The calcium carbonate is insoluble and forms a deposit inside the kettle or pipe. This reaction is the reverse of that which forms hard water. The reaction also explains the formation of stalagmites and stalactites in limestone caves. The temperature inside the cave is just warm enough for some of the hard water to decompose and leave a tiny deposit of calcium carbonate. More water drips down and the deposit gets larger. A deposit also forms where the drops hit the ground. After hundreds of years, the deposits will grow into large stalagmites and stalactites.

Did you know?

With stalagmites and stalactites – 'mites' mount and 'tites' tilt!

Stalagmites and stalactites in Black Spring Cave, South Wales

How is hard water softened?

Sometimes, substances that cause hardness in the water must be removed. This is called **water softening**. In order to soften hard water, Ca^{2+} and Mg^{2+} ions must be removed. This is done in various ways.

By boiling

Boiling decomposes calcium hydrogencarbonate forming an insoluble deposit of calcium carbonate.

$$Ca(HCO_3)_2(aq) \rightarrow CaCO_3(s) + H_2O(l) + CO_2(g)$$

This removes the hardness caused by calcium hydrogencarbonate, but boiling does not remove the hardness caused by calcium sulphate. Because of this, the hardness from calcium sulphate is called **permanent hardness**. The hardness caused by calcium hydrogencarbonate (which is removed by boiling) is called **temporary hardness**.

By distillation

Distillation produces pure water, removing both permanent and temporary hardness.

By adding sodium carbonate

Washing soda and bath salts contain sodium carbonate (Na_2CO_3). Adding these to hard water removes all the Ca^{2+} and Mg^{2+} ions as a precipitate of calcium and magnesium carbonates.

$$\underset{\text{(in hard water)}}{Ca^{2+}(aq)} + \underset{\text{(in washing soda)}}{CO_3^{2-}(aq)} \rightarrow CaCO_3(s)$$

By ion-exchange

The most convenient way of softening water is to use an ion-exchange column. The water passes through a column containing a special substance called a **resin** (Figure 1). The resin contains sodium ions which are displaced by calcium and magnesium ions as hard water passes through the column. Na^+ ions do not cause hardness, so the water is now 'soft'.

$$\underset{\text{(in hard water)}}{Ca^{2+}(aq)} + \underset{\text{(on resin)}}{2Na^+(s)} \rightarrow \underset{\text{(on resin)}}{Ca^{2+}(s)} + \underset{\text{(in the water)}}{2Na^+(aq)}$$

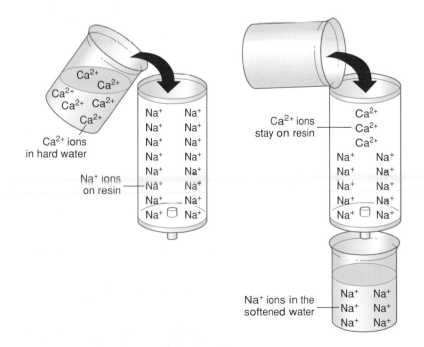

Figure 1 *Using an ion-exchange column*

Study Questions

1 Explain the following:
   water softening; permanent hardness; temporary hardness; ion-exchange resin.

2 a) What are the advantages of hard water?
   b) What are the disadvantages of hard water?

3 a) How do stalagmites and stalactites form?
   b) Write an equation for the reaction involved in a).

4 a) List the main methods of softening water.
   b) For each method, write an equation to summarise the reaction involved.

5 Tap water in London is much harder than tap water in Manchester. Why is this?

6 Limescale often forms on taps in hard water areas. Usually, there is more scale on the hot tap than on the cold tap.
   a) How does limescale form?
   b) Why is there usually more on the hot tap?

7 During the 1950s, tooth decay was worse in the North West of England than in the South East. Why was this?

8 Design an experiment to compare the hardness of a water sample before and after softening by boiling.
   a) Say what you would do.
   b) List the measurements you would make.
   c) Say what methods and precautions you would take to get an accurate result.

Section G Activities

1 Limestone – quarrying or countryside?

There are important economic, social and environmental issues in the mining and quarrying of rocks and ores. These issues lead to both advantages and disadvantages – benefits and problems. This is well illustrated in the UK by the quarrying of limestone. Limestone areas in the Yorkshire Dales, the Derbyshire Peak District, the Chiltern Hills in Buckinghamshire and the Sussex Downs are so picturesque and we don't want to see them spoilt. The limestone industry can cause environmental problems. Quarrying damages the countryside, destroys wildlife habitats and creates pollution.

But limestone is a very useful raw material for industry and agriculture. We need it to neutralise acidity in soils and lakes, for making quicklime and slaked lime and for manufacturing steel, cement and glass. Every year about 90 million tonnes of limestone is quarried in Britain.

The limestone industry provides important products for society, it creates jobs and increases the wealth of the community.

So, how do we balance the benefits it brings against the problems it causes?

The quarry near Littleham

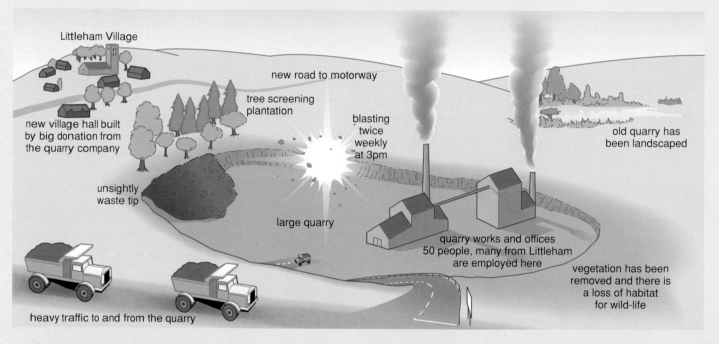

Littleham Village

new road to motorway

tree screening plantation

new village hall built by big donation from the quarry company

blasting twice weekly at 3pm

old quarry has been landscaped

unsightly waste tip

large quarry

quarry works and offices 50 people, many from Littleham are employed here

vegetation has been removed and there is a loss of habitat for wild-life

heavy traffic to and from the quarry

Look carefully at the drawing above showing the quarry near Littleham.

1 Suppose you are a resident in Littleham. Make a list of the advantages and disadvantages that affect you now that quarrying is happening near your home.

2 Suppose you are the Chairman of the Littleham Residents' Association. At last week's meeting of the Resident's Association, complaints were made about the problems that the quarry was creating for the people and the area around the town.

   Write a letter to the Chief Executive of *Limestone UK*, the quarry operators, expressing the views of members of the Residents' Association.

3 Suppose you are the Chief Executive of *Limestone UK*. For some time now you have been aware of the anxieties of residents in Littleham regarding the quarry.

Write a letter to the Chairman of the Littleham Residents' Association explaining how you are trying to reduce the problems that the quarry might cause and the improvements and advantages it has created for the area and the people of Littleham.

2 Ammonium phosphate fertiliser

The reaction of ammonia (NH_3) with phosphoric acid (H_3PO_4) to form ammonium phosphate, $(NH_4)_3PO_4$ involves neutralisation.

a) Write a word equation and then a balanced equation for the reaction.

b) How many grams of phosphoric acid react with 17 g (1 mole) of ammonia? ($H = 1$, $N = 14$, $P = 31$, $O = 16$)

c) How many tonnes of phosphoric acid are needed to react with 100 tonnes of ammonia?

3 pH changes after eating a sweet

Using a special instrument called a pH meter, Dr Razell measured the pH in Lee's mouth after he had eaten a sugary sweet.
The results are shown in Table 1.

a) Open up a new spreadsheet on your computer.

b) Enter the times and pHs as in Table 1.

c) From the spreadsheet, plot a line graph of pH (y-axis) against time (x-axis). (If you can't plot graphs directly from the spreadsheet, draw the graph by hand.)

d) Print a copy of your line graph.

Sugary foods are converted to acids in our mouths. These acids attack the enamel on our teeth and cause tooth decay. Tooth decay occurs when the pH is lower than 5.5.

e) What does pH measure?

f) Describe how the pH changes in Lee's mouth after eating the sweet.

g) How many minutes after eating the sweet does tooth decay start?

h) How many minutes after eating the sweet does tooth decay stop?

i) How many minutes after eating the sweet is tooth decay at its worst? Explain you answer.

j) Use your graph to explain why dentists advise against eating sweets between meals.

k) What should the pH of toothpaste be? Explain your answer.

l) Dental decay can be prevented by strengthening the enamel of teeth. This is often done using a chemical in drinking water or in toothpaste. Find out more about this.

Table 1 *How the pH changed in Lee's mouth after eating a sweet*

Time after eating sweet /minutes	pH
0	6.6
2	5.6
4	5.2
6	5.0
8	4.9
10	4.9
12	5.1
14	5.3
16	5.5
18	5.6
20	5.8

4 Using *Word* to report on a salt

1 Choose a salt and find out about its:
(i) occurrence, (ii) uses; (iii) chemistry.

2 Write a report on the salt you have chosen using *Word*. Make the report as interesting as possible using icons and diagrams.

3 Try highlighting sections with a different border and/or shading.

Section G   Summary

1 Properties of acids

Acids:
- have a sour taste and are corrosive
- have a pH less than 7
- turn litmus red
- turn universal indicator red or orange.

2 Important reactions of acids

$$\text{metal} + \text{acid} \rightarrow \text{salt} + \text{hydrogen}$$

e.g. $\quad Zn + 2HCl \rightarrow ZnCl_2 + H_2$

$$\text{metal oxide} + \text{acid} \rightarrow \text{salt} + \text{water}$$

e.g. $\quad ZnO + 2HCl \rightarrow ZnCl_2 + H_2O$

$$\text{carbonate} + \text{acid} \rightarrow \text{salt} + \text{carbon dioxide} + \text{water}$$

e.g. $\quad ZnCO_3 + 2HCl \rightarrow ZnCl_2 + CO_2 + H_2O$

- Acids are substances which donate H^+ ions.
- Bases are substances which accept H^+ ions.

The largest group of bases are metal oxides, hydroxides and carbonates (e.g. Na_2O, $NaOH$, Na_2CO_3, CuO, $Cu(OH)_2$, $CuCO_3$).

3 Sulphuric acid is manufactured as shown by the flow scheme below.

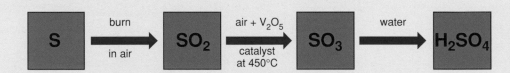

Dilute sulphuric acid reacts as a typical strong acid. Concentrated sulphuric acid is a strong dehydrating agent.

4 Concentration and strength

- The **concentration** of a solution tells us how much solute is dissolved in a solution.

- Concentration is usually given in moles of solute per dm^3 ($mol\ dm^{-3}$) or grams of solute per dm^3 ($g\ dm^{-3}$) of solution.

- The **strength** of a solution tells us how much of the solute has ionised. In aqueous solution:

Strong acids and alkalis are completely ionised.
Weak acids and alkalis are only partly ionised.

5 Neutralisation is the reaction:

$$\text{acid} + \text{base} \rightarrow \text{salt} + \text{water}$$

e.g. $\quad HCl + NaOH \rightarrow NaCl + H_2O$

$\quad\quad 2HCl + CaO \rightarrow CaCl_2 + H_2O$

During neutralisation, H^+ ions in acids are neutralised by OH^- ions or O^{2-} ions in bases.

$$H^+ + OH^- \rightarrow H_2O, \quad 2H^+ + O^{2-} \rightarrow H_2O$$

Carbonate ions (CO_3^{2-}) can also act as bases. They react with acids to form carbon dioxide and water, but this reaction is *not* classed as neutralisation.

6 Alkalis

Alkalis are bases which are soluble in water. The commonest alkalis are sodium hydroxide ($NaOH$), calcium hydroxide ($Ca(OH)_2$) and ammonia (NH_3).

7 Salts

Salts are ionic substances (like $NaCl$, $CuSO_4$ and $CaCO_3$) containing anions and cations.

- They have high melting points and boiling points.
- They are electrolytes.

Preparing salts

The method of preparing a salt depends on whether it is soluble or insoluble.
Insoluble salts are prepared by precipitation.
Soluble salts are prepared by the reaction of an acid with a metal, a base or a carbonate.

8 Limestone

Limestone is an important raw material for the chemical and building industries. It is used in constructing roads and buildings, in neutralising acid soils and in the manufacture of quicklime, slaked lime, steel, cement and glass.

9 Hardness of water

- Hard water is water that does not readily give a lather with soap.
- The main cause of hard water in the UK are Ca^{2+} ions.
- Hard water is caused either by the action of carbonic acid in rainwater on limestone and chalk (calcium carbonate) or by the dissolving of calcium sulphate.
- Hardness in water can be removed by boiling, by distillation, by adding sodium carbonate or by using ion exchange.

The hardness caused by calcium hydrogencarbonate is removed by boiling and is called **temporary hardness**.
The hardness caused by calcium sulphate is *not* removed by boiling and is called **permanent hardness**.

Section G   Exam Questions

1 The three main stages in the manufacture of sulphuric acid are:

stage 1   formation of sulphur dioxide
stage 2   formation of sulphur trioxide
stage 3   formation of sulphuric acid

(i) Copy out and complete the **word** equation for
I. Stage 1,
.... + oxygen → ....
II. Stage 2,
.... + oxygen ⇌ ....

(ii) Name the substance into which sulphur trioxide is absorbed in stage 3.

(iii) I. Which stage 1, 2 or 3 uses a catalyst?
II. Name the catalyst used in the manufacture of sulphuric acid.

(iv) Stage 2 is exothermic. Give **one** way this reduces the cost of the process.

(v) Give **one** hazard in handling concentrated sulphuric acid.

WJEC 2001

2 Acids and bases are commonly found around the home.
(a) Baking powder contains sodium hydrogencarbonate mixed with an acid.
(i) When water is added, the baking powder releases carbon dioxide. How could you test the gas to show that it is carbon dioxide?
(ii) Copy out, complete and balance the chemical equation for the reaction of sodium hydrogencarbonate with sulphuric acid.

$NaHCO_3 + H_2SO_4 \rightarrow$ .... + ... + ...

(b) Indigestion tablets contain bases which cure indigestion by neutralising excess stomach acid.

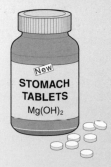

(i) One type of indigestion tablet contains magnesium hydroxide. This base neutralises stomach acid as shown by the balanced chemical equation.

$Mg(OH)_2 + 2HCl \rightarrow MgCl_2 + 2H_2O$

Write a balanced **ionic** equation for the neutralisation reaction.

(ii) How does the pH in the stomach change after taking the tablets?

(c) Ammonium sulphate is used as a lawn fertiliser. Using ammonia solution, describe how you would make the fertiliser ammonium sulphate.

AQA 2000

3 Dilute hydrochloric acid was added slowly to dilute sodium hydroxide solution in a beaker. The graph below shows how the pH of the solution in the beaker changed as the acid was added.

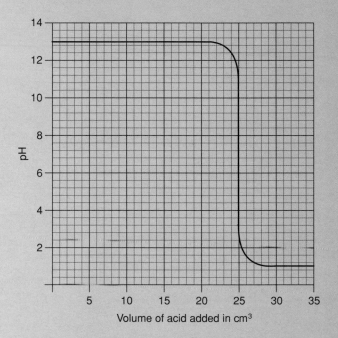

Volume of acid added in cm³

(a) What is the pH of the solution in the beaker when 30 cm³ of dilute hydrochloric acid has been added?

(b) The dilute sodium hydroxide solution in the beaker contained universal indicator. What colour was the solution in the beaker when the following volumes of dilute hydrochloric acid had been added?
(i) 30.0 cm³;   (ii) 10.0 cm³.

(c) (i) What is the pH of a neutral solution?
(ii) What volume of dilute hydrochloric acid was added to neutralise the sodium hydroxide solution in the beaker?
(iii) The neutral solution was evaporated to dryness to leave a solid salt. What is the name of the salt which is formed?
(iv) Describe what the salt looks like.
(v) State the type of bonding that is present in this salt.
(vi) Copy and complete the word equation for the reaction of sodium hydroxide with hydrochloric acid.

sodium   hydrochloric   ....
hydroxide +   acid   .... + ...
                                ....

Edexcel 1999

4 Kay is making sodium chloride from sodium hydroxide solution and dilute hydrochloric acid.

(a) Copy out and finish the symbol equation

NaOH + HCl → .... + ...

(b) She measures out exactly 25.0 cm³ of sodium hydroxide solution into a conical flask.

She adds a few drops of an indicator to the sodium hydroxide solution. Then she adds small volumes of hydrochloric acid until the solution changes from colourless to pink.

The solution is now neutral and contains no sodium hydroxide or hydrochloric acid.

She evaporates the solution using the apparatus in the diagram.

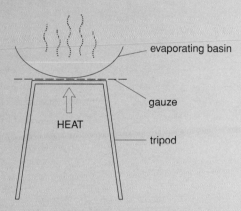

- evaporating basin
- gauze
- HEAT
- tripod

Describe how she could now make some **pure** sodium chloride in a similar experiment

(c) She tests the sodium chloride to make sure it contains chloride ions. She dissolves a sample in water and tests it.

Which test A, B, C, D or E should she carry out?

A Add universal indicator.
B Add sodium hydroxide solution.
C Add hydrochloric acid.
D Add nitric acid and silver nitrate solution.
E Add hydrochloric acid and barium chloride solution.

(d) Kay then carries out a similar experiment to produce sodium sulphate using sodium hydroxide solution and dilute sulphuric acid.

The equation is

$2NaOH + H_2SO_4 \rightarrow Na_2SO_4 + 2H_2O$

She finds that 25.0 cm³ of 0.1 mol/dm³ sodium hydroxide solution reacts with 20.0 cm³ of the sulphuric acid.

(i) Calculate the number of moles of sodium hydroxide in 25.0 cm³ of 0.1 mol/dm³ sodium hydroxide solution.

You **must** show your working.

(ii) How many moles of sulphuric acid react with one mole of sodium hydroxide?

Use the equation to help you.

(iii) How many moles of sulphuric acid react with 25.0 cm³ of 0.1 mol/dm³ sodium hydroxide solution?

You **must** show your working.

(iv) Calculate the concentration of the solution of sulphuric acid used.

You **must** show your working.

OCR 2001

5 (i) The relative molecular mass (M_r) of sodium hydroxide, NaOH, is 40. If 8.0 g of sodium hydroxide are present in 1000 cm³ (1 dm³) of aqueous solution

I.   what is the concentration of this solution in mol.dm^{-3}?

II. how many moles would be present in 25 cm³ of the sodium hydroxide solution?

(ii) Ethanoic acid, CH_3COOH, and sodium hydroxide react in a 1:1 ratio. When ethanoic acid was neutralised by sodium hydroxide solution, it was found that 25 cm³ of the sodium hydroxide solution required 20 cm³ of ethanoic acid solution.

I.   How many moles of ethanoic acid are present in 20 cm³ of ethanoic acid solution?

II   How many moles would be present in 1 dm³ of ethanoic acid solution?

(iii) If the relative molecular mass (M_r) of ethanoic acid is 60, calculate the number of **grams** of ethanoic acid present in 1 dm³ of the solution.

WJEC 2000

6 Portland cement was invented by Joseph Aspdin, a builder from Leeds. The flow diagram shows how cement is made.

limestone →

raw material **X** → MIXER → KILN → cement powder

(a) (i) Name the raw material **X** used to make cement.

(ii) In the kiln the raw materials are heated to about 1500°C. The limestone (calcium carbonate) is broken down at this temperature.

Copy and complete the word equation for this reaction.

calcium carbonate → ....
+ carbon dioxide

(iii) Suggest **one** major cost of this process other than the cost of the raw materials.

(b) Cement can be used to make concrete.
Name **two** substances that must be mixed with cement to make concrete.

AQA 1999

7   A sample of natural hard water contains the following ions.
calcium; chloride; hydrogencarbonate; magnesium; sodium; sulphate.
(a) Which **two** of these ions make the water hard?
(b) Some of these ions can be identified using a flame test. Name **one** of these ions and state the colour it produces in the flame test.
(c) A sample of the hard water was shaken with ten drops of soap solution. Scum was formed but no lather.
An equal volume of the hard water was boiled, then shaken with ten drops of soap solution. A lather was formed.
  (i)   Why did the boiled water form a lather?
  (ii) What substance, other than soap, could be added to both samples of water to form a lather?
  (iii) A sample of hard water was passed through an ion exchange column. What would you **see** when the treated water was shaken with soap solution?
(d) Hard water can form deposits called scale inside water pipes.
  (i)   Explain why these deposits may cause problems in hot water pipes.
  (ii) Explain why these deposits may be beneficial in lead water pipes.

Edexcel 2001

8   (a) (i)   Cement is an important building material.
          Describe how cement is made.   (3)
     (ii) When cement is mixed with water, sand and crushed rock, a slow chemical reaction takes place which produces another important building material.
          Name this important building material.   (1)
    (b) Mortar is used to hold bricks and stonework in position. It is a much older building material than cement and has been used since Roman times.
Mortar is made by mixing calcium hydroxide (slaked lime), sand and water into a paste. Mortar hardens over many years on standing in air. This is due to two processes.
   ● The water evaporates.
   ● The slaked lime reacts **slowly** with carbon dioxide in the air to form calcium carbonate.
$$Ca(OH)_2(s) + CO_2(g) \rightarrow CaCO_3(s) + H_2O(l)$$

  (i)   Suggest why the calcium carbonate forms very slowly.
  (ii) Use your answer to part (b) (i) to help you answer this question.
An archaeologist found two pieces of mortar. One piece was very old and from a Roman villa built about 300 AD. The other piece was from a modern cottage built in 1995.
Describe and give the result of an experiment the archaeologist could do which would prove that one of the pieces of mortar was much older then the other piece.
  (iii) The outer layer of mortar slowly changes. The calcium carbonate reacts with carbon dioxide and water in the air to form calcium hydrogencarbonate.
$$CaCO_3(s) + H_2O(l) + CO_2(g) \rightarrow Ca(HCO_3)_2(aq)$$
Rainwater removes the calcium hydrogencarbonate from between the bricks. The gaps then need to be filled in (pointed) with new mortar or cement.
Use the equation to suggest why calcium hydrogencarbonate is easily removed by rainwater.

AQA 2000

9   Potassium chloride can be made from potassium hydroxide solution and hydrochloric acid. A titration is used to find the exact volumes of the solutions which react together. In this titration the hydrochloric acid is added to the potassium hydroxide solution.
(a) Name the **two** pieces of apparatus used to measure the volumes of solutions accurately in a titration.
(b) The reaction is complete when all the potassium hydroxide solution has been neutralised by hydrochloric acid.
How can you tell when you have reached this point?
(c) The equation for the reaction is:
$$KOH + HCl \rightarrow KCl + H_2O$$

Calculate the maximum mass of potassium chloride which can be made from 11.2 g of potassium hydroxide.
(Relative atomic masses: K = 39; O = 16; H = 1; Cl = 35.5)

Edexcel 2000

The Structure of Materials

Mica has a structure in which the particles are arranged in layers. These layers can be separated very easily

By the end of this section you should:

- Appreciate how the structures of solids can be studied using X rays.
- Be able to classify substances and their structures as; giant metallic, giant covalent (giant molecular), simple molecular or giant ionic.
- Understand how giant ionic and giant covalent lattices are held together.
- Understand how substances with covalent bonds can form simple molecular or giant structures.
- Know how the physical properties of substances with giant structures differ from those with simple molecular structures.
- Appreciate that the bonding in a substance determines its properties which, in turn, determine its uses.
- Know about the variety of useful substances that can be made from rocks and minerals, particularly chlorine and sodium hydroxide from salt and glass from sand.

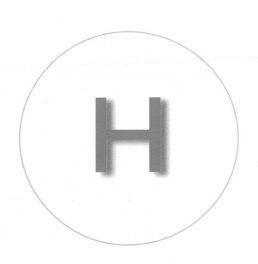

1 Studying Structures

Crystals of impure rock salt. Even in this impure sample you can see the cubic shape of sodium chloride crystals

Impure dolomite crystals on white quartz crystals. Quartz is silicon dioxide. Dolomite is a mixture of calcium carbonate and magnesium carbonate

Look at the crystals of rock salt and quartz in the photos above. What do you notice about the shapes of the salt crystals? What do you notice about the shapes of the quartz crystals? All the salt crystals are roughly the same cubic shape. All the quartz crystals have pointed tops like pyramids.

Detailed studies show that the crystals of one substance have *similar shapes.*

This suggests that the particles in the crystals of a substance are always packed in the same way to give the same overall shape.

Sometimes, crystals grow unevenly and their shapes are not perfect. Even so, it is usually easy to see their general shape.

Solids which have a regular packing of particles are described as **crystalline**.

The particles may be atoms, ions or molecules. Figure 1 shows how cubic crystals and hexagonal crystals can form. If the particles are always placed in parallel lines or at 90° to each other, the crystal will be cubic. If the particles are placed at 120° in the shape of a hexagon, the final crystal will be hexagonal.

Figure 1

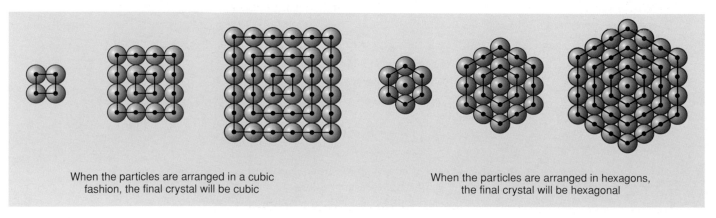

When the particles are arranged in a cubic fashion, the final crystal will be cubic

When the particles are arranged in hexagons, the final crystal will be hexagonal

We can compare the way in which a crystal grows to the way in which a bricklayer lays bricks. If the bricklayer always places the bricks in parallel lines or at 90° to each other, then the final buildings will be like cubes or boxes. If some bricks are laid at 120° to make hexagons, then the final buildings will be hexagonal.

The shape of a crystal only gives a clue to the way in which the particles are arranged. X-rays give much better evidence.

Using X-rays to study crystals

Look through a piece of thin stretched cloth at a small bright light. You will see a pattern. This pattern is caused by the deflection of the light by regularly spaced threads of the fabric.

> This deflection of the light is called **diffraction** and the patterns produced are **diffraction patterns**.

If the cloth is stretched so that the threads in the fabric get closer, then the pattern spreads further out. From the diffraction pattern which we *can* see, it is possible to work out the pattern of the threads in the fabric which we *cannot* see. The same idea is used to work out how the particles are arranged in a crystal.

A narrow beam of X-rays is directed at a crystal of the substance being studied (Figure 2). Some of the X-rays are diffracted by particles in the crystal onto X-ray film. When the film is developed, a regular pattern of spots appears. This is the diffraction pattern for the crystal. From the diffraction pattern which we *can* see, it is possible to work out the pattern of particles in the crystal which we *cannot* see. A regular arrangement of spots on the film indicates a regular arrangement of particles in the crystal.

> The regular arrangement of particles in a crystal is called a **lattice**.

X-rays have been used in this way to study the structure of thousands of different solids. An X-ray diffraction photograph is shown in Figure 3. Photos like this give us accurate information about the structure of different substances.

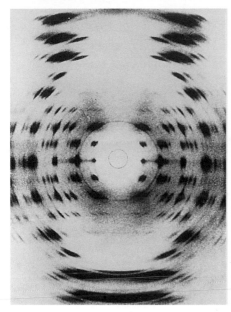

Figure 3 *An X-ray diffraction photo of DNA. DNA is the substance that makes up our genes. Notice the general pattern in the dots*

Snowflake crystals. How do you think the particles are arranged in snowflakes?

Study Questions

1 Explain the words:
  crystal; lattice; diffraction.
2 Look at the snowflake crystals in the photo above.
  a) What substance makes up snowflakes?
  b) What particles do snowflakes contain?
3 How are X-rays used to give evidence for the arrangement of particles in a crystal?
4 Why do all crystals of one substance have roughly the same shape?

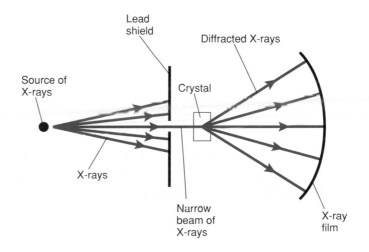

Figure 2 *Diffraction of X-rays by a crystal*

2 The Structure of Substances

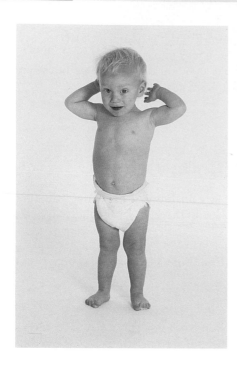

What properties must the material in nappies have? What do you think the structure of nappy material is like?

Metal was used to make suits of armour in the Middle Ages. Why do you think metal was used?

The uses of materials depend on their properties. For example, copper is used for electrical wires and cables because it can be drawn into wires and it is a good conductor of electricity. Clay is used for pots and crockery because it is soft and easily moulded when wet, but becomes hard and rigid when heated (fired) in a furnace.

All substances are made up of particles. If we know how these particles are arranged (the **structure**) and how the particles are held together (the **bonding**), we can explain the **properties** of substances. For example, copper is a good conductor because its metallic bonding allows electrons to move through the structure when it is connected to a battery. It can be drawn into wires because copper atoms can slide over each other in the close-packed structure (Unit F1).

Wet clay is soft and easily moulded because water molecules can get between its flat two-dimensional structure. When clay is fired, all the water molecules are driven out. Atoms in one layer bond to those in the layers above and below. This gives the clay a three dimensional structure, making it hard, rigid and useful for pots and crockery.

Notice how:

- the structure and bonding of a substance determine its properties,

- the properties of a substance determine its uses.

So, the links from structure and bonding to properties help us to explain the uses of materials. They explain why metals are used as conductors, why graphite is used in pencils and why clay is used to make pots.

Using X-ray analysis, we can find out how the particles are arranged in a substance (its structure), but it is more difficult to study the forces between these particles (its bonding).

From Section C, you will know that:

> All substances are made up from only three kinds of particle – atoms, ions and molecules.

These three particles give rise to four different solid structures.

● Giant metallic structures

● Giant covalent (giant molecular) structures

● Simple molecular structures

● Giant ionic structures

Table 1 shows the particles in these four structures, the types of substances they form and examples of these substances.

A large natural diamond embedded in volcanic igneous rock. How do the structure and properties of diamond lead to its use in jewellery?

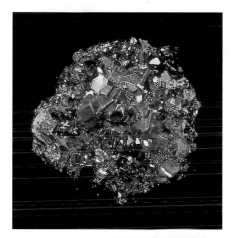

A sample of lead sulphide (galena) crystals. What particles will lead sulphide contain? How do you think the particles are arranged?

Table I *The four types of solid structure and the particles they contain*

Type of structure	Particles in the structure	Types of substance	Examples
Giant metallic (see section F)	atoms	metals and alloys (mixtures of metals)	Na, Fe, Cu, steel, brass
Giant covalent (giant molecular)	very large molecules containing thousands of atoms	non-metals, or non-metal compounds	diamond graphite, polythene, sand (silicon dioxide, SiO_2)
Simple molecular	small molecules containing a few atoms	non-metals, or non-metal compounds	I_2 (iodine) O_2 (oxygen) H_2O (water) CO_2 (carbon dioxide)
Giant ionic	ions	compounds of metals with non-metals	Na^+Cl^- (salt) $Ca^{2+}O^{2-}$ (lime) $Cu^{2+}SO_4^{2-}$ (copper sulphate)

Study Questions

1 Get into a small group with two or three others. Look at the photos in this unit and discuss the questions in the captions.

2 a) What are the particles in metal structures?
b) Why are most metal structures described as close-packed?

c) How are the particles arranged in most metal structures?

3 What type of structure will the following substances have: *chlorine, limestone (calcium carbonate), silver, air, rubber, polyvinylchloride (PVC), brass, wood?*

4 Conductivity tests can give evidence for the particles in a substance and its type of structure. Describe: (i) the tests you would carry out, (ii) the results you would expect, (iii) the conclusions you would make from your results. (*Hint:* See Section D, Units 2 and 3.)

3 Diamond and Graphite – Giant Covalent Structures

Diamond and graphite are both made of pure carbon but these two solids have very different properties and uses. Diamond is hard and clear, whereas graphite is soft and black. Diamonds are used to cut stone and engrave glass, but graphite in pencils is used by artists to achieve a soft, shaded effect.

Diamonds which are not good enough for jewellery are used in glass cutters and in diamond-studded saws. This photo shows an engraver using a diamond-studded wheel to make patterns in a glass vase

Did you know?

Diamond and graphite are both made of pure carbon. Diamond is the hardest natural substance. Graphite is soft and slippery.

These different forms of solid carbon are called **allotropes**. A few other elements also have allotropes. Oxygen has two allotropes – oxygen (O_2) and ozone (O_3). Sulphur has three allotropes – rhombic sulphur, monoclinic sulphur and plastic sulphur.

Allotropes are different forms of the same element in the same state.

Diamond and graphite have different properties and different uses because *they have different structures*. They both contain carbon, but the carbon atoms are packed in different ways.

The arrangement of carbon atoms in diamond and graphite has been studied by X-ray analysis.

Diamond

In diamond, carbon atoms are joined to each other by strong covalent bonds (Unit H4). *Inside* the diamond structure (Figure 1), each carbon atom forms a covalent bond with four other carbon atoms. Check this for yourself in Figure 1. The strong covalent bonds extend through the whole diamond, forming a three-dimensional giant structure.

Because of this, diamond is described as a **giant covalent structure** or a **giant molecular structure**. Every perfect diamond is a giant molecule with covalent bonds linking one carbon atom to the next.

Only a small number of atoms are shown in the model in Figure 1. In a real diamond, this arrangement of carbon atoms is extended millions and millions of times.

Figure 1 *An 'open' model of the diamond structure. Each black ball represents a carbon atom and each stick is a covalent bond.*

The properties and uses of diamond

- **Diamonds are very hard** because the carbon atoms are linked by very strong covalent bonds. Another reason for its hardness is that the atoms are not arranged in layers so they cannot slide over one another like the atoms in metals. Most industrial uses of diamond depend on its hardness. Diamonds which are not good enough for gems are used in glass cutters and in diamond studded saws. Powdered diamonds are also used as abrasives for smoothing very hard materials.

- **Diamond has a very high melting point.** Carbon atoms in diamond are held in the giant structure by very strong covalent bonds. This means that the atoms cannot vibrate fast enough to break away from their neighbours until very high temperatures are reached. So, the melting point of diamond is very high.

- **Diamond does not conduct electricity.** Unlike metals, diamond has no free electrons. All the electrons in the outer shell of each carbon atom are held firmly in covalent bonds. So there are no free electrons in diamond to form an electric current.

Graphite

Figure 2 shows a model of part of the structure of graphite. Notice that the carbon atoms are arranged in parallel layers. Each layer contains millions and millions of carbon atoms arranged in hexagons. Each carbon atom is held strongly in its layer by strong covalent bonds to three other carbon atoms. So every layer is a **giant molecule** and graphite is a **giant covalent structure**, like diamond. The distance between neighbouring carbon atoms in the same layer is only 0.14 nm, but the distance between the layers is 0.34 nm.

A can of lubricating oil containing graphite. Graphite has a layered structure. The layers slip and slide over one another very easily. This makes graphite an excellent material to improve the lubricating action of oils

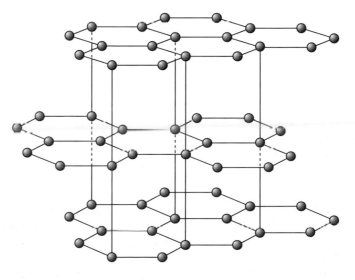

Figure 2 *A model of the structure of graphite. Notice the layers of hexagons, one on top of the other*

The properties and uses of graphite

- **Graphite is a lubricant.** In graphite, each carbon atom is linked by strong covalent bonds to three other atoms in its layer. But, the layers are 2½ times further apart than carbon atoms in the same layer. This means that the forces between the layers are weak. If you rub graphite, the layers slide over each other and onto your fingers. This property has led to the use of graphite as the 'lead' in pencils and as a lubricant. The layers of graphite slide over each other like a pile of wet microscope slides (Figure 3).

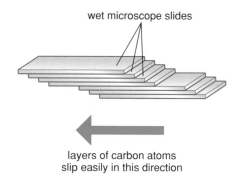

wet microscope slides

layers of carbon atoms
slip easily in this direction

Figure 3 *The layers in graphite slide over each other like wet microscope slides. The wet slides stick together and it is difficult to pull them apart. But, a force parallel to the slides pushes them over each other easily and smoothly*

- **Graphite has a high melting point.** Although the layers of graphite move over each other easily, it is difficult to break the strong covalent bonds between carbon atoms within one layer. Because of this, graphite does not melt until 3730°C and it does not boil until 4830°C. So, it is used to make crucibles for molten metals. The bonds between carbon atoms in the layers of graphite are so strong that graphite fibres with the layers arranged along the fibre are stronger than steel. These fibres are used to reinforce metals and broken bones.

- **Graphite conducts electricity.** The bonds *between* the layers of graphite are fairly weak. The electrons in these bonds can move along the layers from one atom to the next when graphite is connected to a battery. So graphite will conduct electricity, unlike diamond and other non-metals. Because of this unusual property, graphite is used for electrodes in industry and as the positive terminals in dry cells.

Graphite fibres have been used to reinforce the shaft of this badminton racket

Oxygen and water are good examples of **simple molecular** substances. They have simple molecules containing a few atoms. Their formulas and structures are shown near the top of Table 1. Most non-metals and non-metal compounds are also made of simple molecules. For example, hydrogen is H_2, chlorine is Cl_2, carbon dioxide is CO_2 and methane in natural gas is CH_4. Sugar ($C_{12}H_{22}O_{11}$) has much larger molecules than these substances, but it still counts as a simple molecule.

In these simple molecular substances, the atoms are held together in each molecule by strong covalent bonds (see Unit K6). But there are only weak forces between the separate molecules (Figure 1).

> These weak forces between separate molecules are called **intermolecular bonds** or **Van der Waals forces**.
> ('inter' means between. 'Waal' is pronounced 'Vaal'.)

Table 1 *Formulas and structures of some simple molecular substances*

Name and formula	Displayed formulae	Model of structure
Hydrogen, H_2	H — H	
Oxygen, O_2	O = O	
Water, H_2O	O / H H	
Methane, CH_4	H — C — H (with H above and below)	
Hydrogen chloride, HCl	H — Cl	
Chlorine, Cl_2	Cl — Cl	
Carbon dioxide, CO_2	O = C = O	

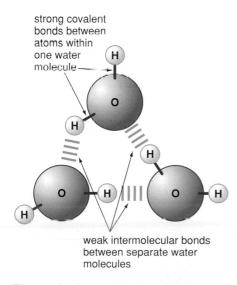

strong covalent bonds between atoms within one water molecule

weak intermolecular bonds between separate water molecules

Figure 1 *Covalent bonds and intermolecular bonds in water. Water is a simple molecular substance. In each water molecule, there are strong covalent bonds between the two hydrogen atoms and the oxygen atom. But the separate water molecules are only held together by relatively weak intermolecular bonds*

The properties of simple molecular substances

Simple molecular substances have similar properties. These properties are well illustrated by oxygen, water, methane and sugar.

The properties of simple molecular substances can be explained in terms of their structure and the weak forces between their molecules. In simple molecular substances, there are no ions (like ionic compounds) or freely moving electrons (like metals). So there are no electrical forces holding them together. Some simple molecular substances, like water and sugar, exist as liquids and solids so there must be some forces holding their molecules together.

● **Simple molecular substances are soft**. The separate molecules in simple molecular substances, like sugar, are usually further apart than atoms in metals and ions in ionic structures. The forces between the molecules are only weak and the molecules are easy to separate. Because of this, crystals of these substances are usually soft.

● **Simple molecular substances have low melting points and boiling points**. It takes less energy to separate the molecules in simple molecular substances than to separate ions in ionic compounds, or atoms in metals. So, simple molecular compounds have lower melting points and lower boiling points than ionic compounds and metals.

● **Simple molecular substances do not conduct electricity**. Simple molecular substances have no mobile electrons like metals. They have no ions either. This means that they cannot conduct electricity as solids, as liquids or in aqueous solution.

Molecular compounds

Metals can be mixed to form alloys, but they *never* react with each other to form compounds. For example, zinc and copper will form the alloy brass, but the two metals cannot react chemically because they both want to lose electrons and form positive ions.

Unlike metals, non-metals can react with each other and form a compound even though they both want to gain electrons. These *non-metal compounds* consist of both simple molecular compounds and giant molecular compounds, like silica (silicon dioxide, SiO_2) and polymers. They are sometimes called **molecular compounds**.

Forming molecular compounds – electron sharing

All atoms have a small positive centre called a **nucleus**, surrounded by a very large region in which negatively-charged electrons move. The negative charge on the electrons is balanced by positive charge in the nucleus, so that the whole atom is neutral. Almost all the mass of the atom is concentrated in the nucleus (Figure 2). Different atoms have different numbers of electrons. Hydrogen atoms are the smallest with only one electron, helium atoms have two electrons and oxygen atoms have eight electrons.

When two non-metals react to form a molecule, the regions of electrons in their atoms overlap so that each atom gains negative charge. The positive nuclei of both atoms attract the electrons in the region of overlap and this holds the atoms together (Figure 3). This type of bond formed by *electron sharing* between non-metals is a **covalent bond** (Unit K6). Notice that covalent bonding, like ionic bonding, involves attraction between opposite charges.

Did you know?

If the nucleus of an atom was magnified a million, million times, it would be as big as a pea. The total volume of the atom in which the electrons move would then be as large as Westminster Abbey. Compared to the nucleus, the electrons have a vast region in which to move.

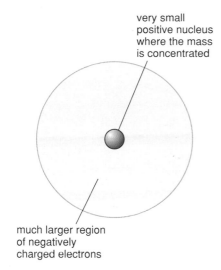

very small
positive nucleus
where the mass
is concentrated

much larger region
of negatively
charged electrons

Figure 2 *A simple picture of atomic structure*

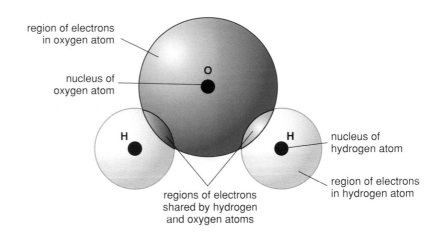

region of electrons
in oxygen atom

nucleus of
oxygen atom

O

H

H

nucleus of
hydrogen atom

region of electrons
in hydrogen atom

regions of electrons
shared by hydrogen
and oxygen atoms

Figure 3 *The simple structure of a molecule of water*

Covalent bonds hold atoms together *within* a molecule but there are also **intermolecular bonds** holding the separate molecules together in molecular liquids like water and molecular solids like sugar.

Formulas of molecular compounds

Table 1 includes the formulas and structures of some well-known molecular compounds. The structures are written so that the number of covalent bonds (drawn as a line —) to each atom can be seen. Notice that hydrogen can form one bond with other atoms (H —), so its **combining power** or **valency** is 1. The combining powers of chlorine and bromine are also 1. Oxygen forms two bonds with other atoms (— O — or O =). Its combining power is therefore 2. Nitrogen atoms form three bonds and carbon atoms form four bonds, so their valencies are 3 and 4 respectively.

Although we can predict the formulas of molecular compounds from the number of bonds which the atoms form, the only sure way of knowing a formula is by chemical analysis. For example, carbon forms four bonds and oxygen forms two bonds, so we would predict that carbon and oxygen will form a compound O = C = O. (Each bond is represented by a single line, so two lines show that there is a double bond between the atoms). This compound, carbon dioxide, does exist, but so does carbon monoxide, CO, which we could not predict.

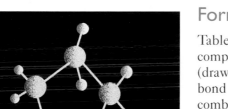

This model of a molecule was drawn using a computer to analyse the results obtained during the investigation of various organic substances

Study Questions

1 Explain the following:
covalent bond; *intermolecular bond*;
simple molecule; *non-metal compound*; *nucleus*.

2 Simple molecular substances often have a smell, but metals do not. Why is this?

3 A substance is a poor conductor of electricity in the solid state. It melts at 217°C and boils at 685°C. Could this substance be: (i) a metal, (ii) a non-metal, (iii) a giant molecule, (iv) an ionic solid, (v) a simple molecular solid?

4 What properties does butter have to show that it contains simple molecular substances?

5 Assuming the usual combining powers of the elements, draw the structures of the following compounds: (Show each bond as a line —)
dichlorine oxide (Cl_2O); *tetrabromomethane* (*carbon tetrabromide*, CBr_4); *nitrogen trichloride* (NCl_3); *hydrogen peroxide* (H_2O_2); *ethane* (C_2H_6); *ethene* (C_2H_4).

5 | Carbon Dioxide

Carbon dioxide is an important **simple molecular** compound. It links respiration and photosynthesis and is produced when carbon compounds burn. Carbon dioxide also has some important uses.

A fireman demonstrates in training the use of a small carbon dioxide fire extinguisher

- **Soda water and fizzy drinks**. Solutions of carbon dioxide in water have a pleasant taste – the taste of soda water. Soda water and other fizzy drinks are made by dissolving carbon dioxide in them at high pressure. When a bottle of the drink is opened, it fizzes because the pressure falls and carbon dioxide gas can escape from the liquid.

- **Fire extinguishers**. Liquid and gaseous carbon dioxide at high pressure are used in fire extinguishers. When the extinguisher is used, carbon dioxide pours out and smothers the fire. Carbon dioxide is heavier than air so it covers the fire and stops oxygen getting to it. The fire 'goes out' because carbon dioxide does not burn and substances will not burn in it.

- **Refrigeration**. Solid carbon dioxide is used for refrigerating ice-cream, soft fruit and meat. The solid carbon dioxide looks like ordinary ice, but it is colder and sublimes without going through a messy liquid stage. This is why it is called 'dry ice' or 'Dricold'.

Making carbon dioxide

Strong acids, like hydrochloric acid, sulphuric acid and nitric acid, react with carbonates to form carbon dioxide and water.

$$\text{acid} + \text{carbonate} \rightarrow \text{water} + \text{carbon dioxide}$$
$$2H^+(aq) + CO_3^{2-}(s) \rightarrow H_2O(l) + CO_2(g)$$

Small amounts of carbon dioxide are usually prepared from marble chips (calcium carbonate) and dilute hydrochloric acid (Figure 1).

$$\text{calcium carbonate} + \text{hydrochloric acid} \rightarrow \text{calcium chloride} + \text{water} + \text{carbon dioxide}$$
$$CaCO_3(s) + 2HCl(aq) \rightarrow CaCl_2(aq) + H_2O(l) + CO_2(g)$$

The carbon dioxide may be collected by downward delivery or over water.

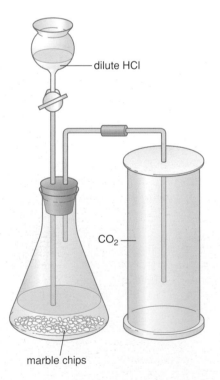

dilute HCl

CO₂

marble chips

Figure 1 *Making carbon dioxide in the laboratory. **Wear eye protection** if you are doing this*

The properties of carbon dioxide

Carbon dioxide is a typical non-metal oxide. It is acidic, gaseous and simple molecular. Figure 2 shows some other properties of carbon dioxide. Notice that it is slightly soluble in water. The dissolved gas provides water plants, like seaweed, with the carbon dioxide they need for photosynthesis. About 1% of the gas which dissolves in water reacts to form carbonic acid (H_2CO_3).

$$H_2O + CO_2 \rightarrow H_2CO_3$$

The solution of carbonic acid is a very weak acid. It turns blue litmus paper only a purplish-red.

Testing for carbon dioxide with limewater

The test for carbon dioxide uses its acidic property. Limewater is calcium hydroxide solution – a dilute alkali. When carbon dioxide is bubbled into limewater, the liquid goes milky as a white precipitate of calcium carbonate forms. Why does this precipitate form? First, the carbon dioxide reacts with OH^- ions in the alkali to form carbonate ions (CO_3^{2-}).

$$CO_2(g) + 2OH^-(aq) \rightarrow CO_3^{2-}(aq) + H_2O(l)$$

Then, CO_3^{2-} ions react with calcium ions in the limewater to form insoluble calcium carbonate.

$$Ca^{2+}(aq) + CO_3^{2-}(aq) \rightarrow CaCO_3(s)$$

PROPERTIES OF
CARBON DIOXIDE

• colourless

• no smell

• denser than air

• slightly soluble
  in water

• does not burn

• substances will
  not burn in it

Figure 2

Study Questions

1 List the important uses of carbon dioxide. For each use, explain why carbon dioxide is used.
2 How does carbon dioxide link respiration and photosynthesis?
3 Give two reasons why 'dry ice' is better than ordinary ice for refrigeration.
4 Carbon dioxide can be poured from a gas jar onto a lighted candle and the candle goes out. What does this simple experiment show about the properties of carbon dioxide?
5 a) How is carbon dioxide obtained from a carbonate?
   b) Write an equation for the reaction in part a).
   c) Why can the carbon dioxide be collected either by downward delivery or over water?
   d) How would you show that limestone is a carbonate?

'Dry ice' (solid carbon dioxide) being used to create a misty effect in the boat scene of 'Phantom of the Opera'

6 | Giant Ionic Structures

Forming ionic compounds – electron transfer

Ionic compounds form when metals react with non-metals. For example, when sodium burns in chlorine, sodium chloride is formed. This contains sodium ions (Na^+) and chloride ions (Cl^-).

$$Na \quad + \quad Cl \quad \rightarrow \quad Na^+ \quad \quad Cl^-$$

sodium atom   chlorine atom   →   sodium ion   chloride ion

These ions form by *transfer of electrons*. During the reaction, each sodium atom gives up one electron and forms a sodium ion.

$$Na \rightarrow Na^+ + e^-$$

The electron is taken by a chlorine atom to form a chloride ion.

$$Cl + e^- \rightarrow Cl^-$$

When ionic compounds form, metal atoms *lose* electrons and form *positive* ions, whilst non-metal atoms *gain* electrons and form *negative* ions. The metal has been oxidised by loss of electrons and the non-metal has been reduced by gaining electrons (Unit F3).

This transfer of electrons from metals to non-metals explains the formation of ionic compounds. Figure 1 shows what happens when calcium reacts with oxygen to form calcium oxide. In this case, two electrons are transferred from each calcium atom to each oxygen atom.

Chalk cliffs are composed of an ionic compound containing calcium ions (Ca^{2+}) and carbonate ions ($CO_3{}^{2-}$)

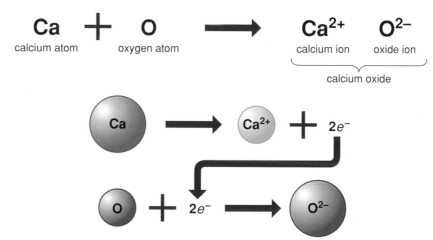

Figure 1

Bonding and properties of ionic compounds

In solid ionic compounds, the ions are held together by the attraction between positive ions and negative ions. Figure 2 shows how the ions are arranged in one layer of sodium chloride and Figure 3 is a 3-D model of its structure. Notice that Na^+ ions are surrounded by Cl^- ions and that Cl^- ions are surrounded by Na^+ ions.

This kind of arrangement in which large numbers of ions are packed together in a regular pattern is another example of a **giant structure**.

Figure 2 *The arrangement of ions in one layer of a sodium chloride crystal*

The force of attraction between oppositely charged ions is called an **ionic** or **electrovalent bond**.

Table 1 *The names and formulas of some salts*

Name of salt	Formula
Calcium nitrate	$Ca^{2+}(NO_3^-)_2$ or $Ca(NO_3)_2$
Zinc sulphate	$Zn^{2+}SO_4^{2-}$ or $ZnSO_4$
Iron(III) chloride	$Fe^{3+}(Cl^-)_3$ or $FeCl_3$
Copper(II) bromide	$Cu^{2+}(Br^-)_2$ or $CuBr_2$
Sodium carbonate	$(Na^+)_2CO_3^{2-}$ or Na_2CO_3
Potassium iodide	K^+I^- or KI

Strong ionic bonds (Unit K6) hold the ions together very firmly. This explains why ionic compounds:

- are **hard substances**,
- have **high melting points** and **high boiling points**,
- **do not conduct electricity when solid**, because the ions cannot move freely.
- **conduct electricity when molten or aqueous** as the charged ions can move freely in the liquid (see Units D3 and D4).

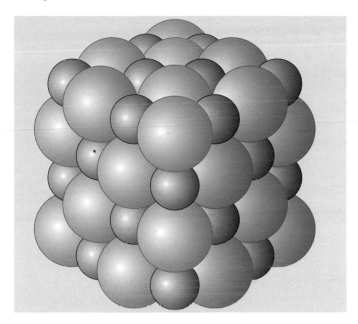

Figure 3 *A 3-D model of the structure of sodium chloride. The larger green balls represent Cl^- ions ($A_r = 35.5$). The smaller red balls represent Na^+ ions ($A_r = 23.0$)*

The formulas of ionic compounds

The formulas of ionic compounds, like sodium chloride (NaCl) and calcium oxide (CaO) can be obtained by balancing the charges on the positive and negative ions. For example, the formula of calcium chloride is $Ca^{2+}(Cl^-)_2$ or simply $CaCl_2$. Here, two Cl^- ions balance the charge on one Ca^{2+} ion. The formula $CaCl_2$ has a small 2 after the Cl to show that two Cl^- ions are needed for one Ca^{2+}. These formulas show the ratio of the numbers of ions present in the ionic compound.

Can you see that the number of charges on an ion is a measure of its **combining power** or **valency**? Na^+ has a combining power of 1, whereas Ca^{2+} has a combining power of 2. Na^+ can combine with only one Cl^- to form Na^+Cl^-, whereas Ca^{2+} can combine with two Cl^- ions to form $Ca^{2+}(Cl^-)_2$.

Elements such as iron, which have two different ions (Fe^{2+} and Fe^{3+}) have two valencies. Thus iron can form two different compounds with chlorine – iron(II) chloride, $FeCl_2$, and iron(III) chloride, $FeCl_3$.

Table 1 shows the names and formulas of some salts. Notice that the formula of calcium nitrate is $Ca(NO_3)_2$. The brackets around NO_3^- show that it is a single unit containing one nitrogen and three oxygen atoms with one negative charge. Thus, two NO_3^- ions balance one Ca^{2+} ion. Other ions like SO_4^{2-}, CO_3^{2-} and OH^- must also be regarded as single units and put in brackets when there are two or three of them in a formula.

Study Questions

1 Which of the following substances conduct electricity (i) when liquid; (ii) when solid: *diamond*; *potassium chloride*; *copper*; *carbon disulphide*; *sulphur*?

2 Look at Figures 2 and 3.
a) How many Cl^- ions surround one Na^+ ion in the 3-D crystal?
b) How many Na^+ ions surround one Cl^- ion in the 3-D crystal?

3 Write the symbols for the ions and the formulas of the following compounds: *potassium hydroxide*; *iron(III) nitrate*; *barium chloride*; *sodium carbonate*; *silver sulphate*; *calcium hydrogencarbonate*; *aluminium oxide*; *zinc bromide*; *copper(II) nitrate*; *magnesium sulphide*.

4 Sodium fluoride and magnesium oxide have the same crystal structure and similar distances between ions. The melting point of NaF is 992°C, but that of MgO is 2640°C. Why is there such a big difference in their melting points?

7

Salt – an Important Ionic Compound

Athletes and people who work in hot places usually take salt tablets to replace the salt they lose by sweating. Sweat is mainly salt solution

Large quantities of salt (sodium chloride) are found in seawater and in underground deposits as rock salt.

The sodium chloride is an important and valuable resource:

● in our diet,

● for treating icy roads,

● as a raw material for industry.

Sodium chloride is an essential mineral in our diet. Most foods contain salt but some foods are saltier than others. Our diet must contain the right amount of salt. Too much salt may cause high blood pressure. Too little salt causes sharp pains ('cramp') in our muscles.

Salt as a raw material for industry

Most of the salt that we sprinkle on our food and that is used in industry in this country comes from the underground deposits in Cheshire. The Cheshire salt mines produce millions of tonnes of salt every year. But, these are not mines like coal mines. Nobody needs to go underground.

The salt is obtained by **solution mining**. Water is pumped down into the deposits. The salt dissolves and is then pumped back to the surface as a concentrated solution called **brine**.

Large quantities of salt are used on the roads in winter, but the most important use of salt is as a raw material for industry. By far the biggest industrial use of salt is in the manufacture of chlorine, sodium hydroxide and hydrogen.

This is done by electrolysis of concentrated sodium chloride solution (brine). It is usually called the **chlor-alkali process**. Look at Figure 1 and notice how many important products come from the chlor-alkali process.

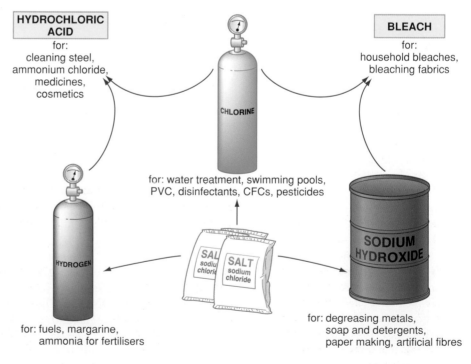

HYDROCHLORIC ACID
for:
cleaning steel,
ammonium chloride,
medicines,
cosmetics

CHLORINE

BLEACH
for:
household bleaches,
bleaching fabrics

for: water treatment, swimming pools,
PVC, disinfectants, CFCs, pesticides

HYDROGEN

SODIUM HYDROXIDE

for: fuels, margarine,
ammonia for fertilisers

for: degreasing metals,
soap and detergents,
paper making, artificial fibres

Figure 1 *Important products from the chlor-alkali process*

The chlor-alkali process

In Britain, the chlor-alkali process is carried out in Cheshire near the salt beds from which brine is obtained. The process is very expensive, needing enormous quantities of electricity for the electrolysis of the concentrated sodium chloride. Even so, the process is profitable because of the varied uses of the different products.

Modern chlor-alkali plants use a membrane cell (Figure 2) which causes less pollution and is cheaper than the older methods which used mercury as the cathode.

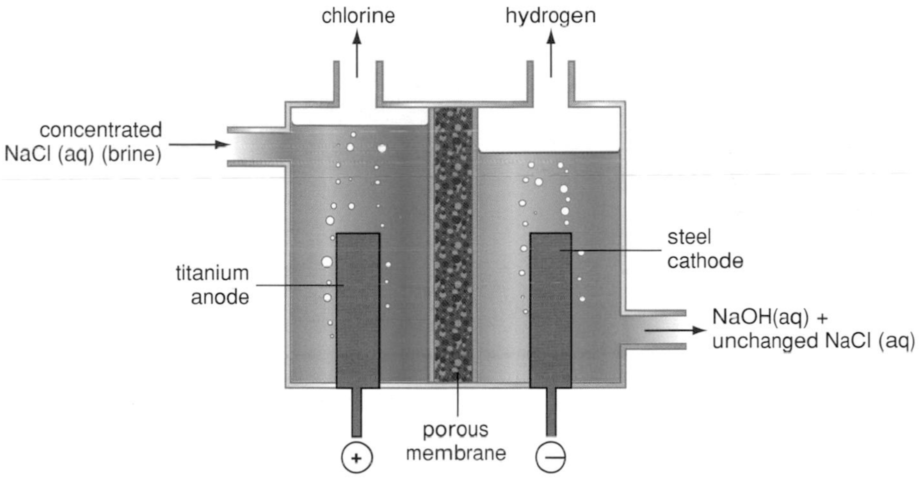

Study Questions

1 Draw a diagram or design a poster to illustrate the uses of sodium chloride (salt) and the materials which are obtained from it.
2 Solid sodium chloride does not conduct electricity, but liquid sodium chloride conducts well.
   a) Explain this statement.
   b) Write equations for the processes at the electrodes when liquid NaCl conducts.
3 Give three important uses of sodium chloride as pure salt, rock salt or brine. Explain why sodium chloride has these uses.
4 Substance X melts at a high temperature. Liquid X conducts electricity.
   a) Which of the following could be X:
   calcium chloride; *starch*; *copper*; *sulphur*; *polythene*; *bronze*; *carbon disulphide*; *zinc oxide*.
   b) Explain your answers to part a).
5 Explain the following points.
   a) Cattle require a salt lick during hot summer months.
   b) The use of crushed rock salt on icy roads does have a drawback for motorists.
   c) Salt is very unreactive, but sodium and chlorine, from which it is made, are both very reactive.

Figure 2 *Manufacturing chlorine, sodium hydroxide and hydrogen using a membrane cell*

The cell is called a membrane cell because a porous membrane separates the anode from the cathode. This prevents the products from mixing and reacting. Concentrated brine is slowly added to the anode compartment of the cell. This contains:

● $Na^+(aq)$ and $Cl^-(aq)$ ions from the sodium chloride, and

● $H^+(aq)$ and $OH^-(aq)$ ions in much lower concentration from the water.

As the solution passes through the anode compartment, chloride ions are attracted to the titanium anode. Here, they give up electrons to the anode and chlorine is produced.

$$\text{Anode } (+) \; 2Cl^-(aq) \rightarrow 2e^- + Cl_2(g)$$

Na^+ ions and water (containing H^+ and OH^- ions) pass through the porous membrane into the cathode compartment. As the solution moves past the cathode, H^+ ions take electrons from the steel cathode and hydrogen is produced.

$$\text{Cathode } (-) \; 2H^+(aq) + 2e^- \rightarrow H_2(g)$$

So, Cl^- ions are removed at the anode and H^+ ions are removed at the cathode, leaving Na^+ and OH^- ions in the solution. These flow out of the cathode compartment as a solution of sodium hydroxide.

The overall reaction of the chlor-alkali process is therefore:

$$\begin{matrix} \text{sodium} \\ \text{chloride} \end{matrix} + \text{water} \rightarrow \begin{matrix} \text{sodium} \\ \text{hydroxide} \end{matrix} + \text{chlorine} + \text{hydrogen}$$

$$2NaCl(aq) + 2H_2O(l) \rightarrow 2NaOH(aq) + Cl_2(g) + H_2(g)$$

8 From Sand to Glass

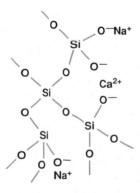

Bottles and windows are made from cheap soda glass

Different kinds of glass

We use different kinds of glass for different purposes. Three kinds of glass and their uses are illustrated in the photos below.

Glass dishes and ornaments use lead glass which is harder and shinier

Laboratory glassware and glass ovenware are made from borosilicate glass which is heat resistant

Making glass

Glass is usually made by heating a mixture of metal oxides or metal carbonates with pure sand (silicon dioxide, SiO_2) in a furnace. At the high temperatures involved, carbonates decompose to oxides and bubbles of carbon dioxide form in the mixture. For example,

$$CaCO_3(s) \rightarrow CaO(s) + CO_2(g)$$

The glass is heated further to make sure that all the bubbles escape and this produces a runny, molten liquid. The liquid is then cooled until it is thick enough to be moulded or blown into different shapes. On further cooling, the glass sets solid.

Figure 1 *The structure of pure silicon dioxide glass. (For simplicity, the structure is not drawn in three dimensions)*

The structure of glass

Different kinds of glass have different structures, varying from giant covalent to a mixture of giant covalent and giant ionic.

Pure hard glass can be made by simply heating silicon dioxide. The silicon dioxide melts at 1700°C to give a thick, viscous liquid. On cooling, the liquid forms a glassy, transparent solid. This glass has a giant covalent structure with every silicon atom covalently bonded to four oxygen atoms (Figure 1). The three-dimensional structure with strong covalent bonds between silicon and oxygen atoms makes the glass very hard.

Unfortunately, the high melting point of this glass makes it expensive to manufacture and difficult to mould. Because of this, most glasses are made from a mixture of silicon dioxide and metal oxides which lower the melting point. For example, soda glass is made from sand (silicon dioxide), limestone (calcium carbonate) and soda (sodium carbonate). The carbonates decompose to oxides on heating. So, the glass has a giant structure of atoms *and* ions (Figure 2). It has both ionic and covalent bonding.

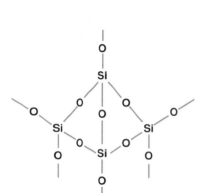

Figure 2 *The structure of soda glass. (For simplicity, the structure is not drawn in three dimensions)*

The properties of glass

Glass is:
- hard
- chemically unreactive
- easy to clean
- heat resistant
- an insulator
- transparent
- fairly cheap
- easily moulded.

Recycling glass

More than six thousand million glass bottles and jars are sold in Britain each year. Most of these are thrown away. A small proportion (perhaps one tenth) are recycled. This is disappointing for a number of reasons.

- Glass containers are relatively easy to clean, sterilise and refill.

- Glass can easily be crushed and added to furnaces to make new containers.

- Glass is made from materials such as sand, limestone and salt which have to be extracted from the Earth by processes which spoil the landscape and use up our energy supplies.

- Re-using and recycling glass could save huge amounts of energy.

For all these reasons, it is important to recycle more and more of our glass containers.

Study Questions

1 Get into a group with two or three others. Look at the properties and the structure of glass described in this unit.
   a) In your group, discuss how the structure of glass results in its properties.
   b) Why do you think glass cracks and breaks if it is dropped or if the temperature suddenly changes?
2 Glass insulators are often used on electricity pylons. Make a list of the properties of glass which make it particularly useful for this purpose.
3 Look at the energy costs involved in recycling glass in Table 1.
   a) What is the total energy cost of collecting, processing and delivering enough waste glass to the furnace to produce one kilogram of recycled glass?

Table 1

Recycling process	Energy cost per kg of recycled product/kJ
Collecting waste glass	350
Processing waste glass	100
Delivering waste glass to glass furnace	50

   b) The energy cost of extracting, processing and delivering enough raw materials to the furnace to produce one kilogram of new glass is 4500 kJ. How much energy is saved, per kilogram, if glass is recycled?
   c) How much energy is saved, per tonne, if glass is recycled? (1 tonne = 1000 kg)

   d) Suppose that all fuels used to provide this energy (petrol, diesel, fuel oil) produce 40 000 kJ per litre. How many litres of fuel are saved, per tonne, if glass is recycled?
   e) Suppose that all the fuels used in glass manufacture cost 50p per litre. How much money is saved, per tonne, if glass is recycled?
4 a) Why do you think so few glass containers are recycled at present?
   b) What proportion of glass containers do you think could be re-used or recycled? Explain your answer.
   c) How could we encourage people to re-use or recycle glass?

Section H Activities

Pole vaulting during the 1920s. What is the pole made from?

1 From bamboo to carbon fibre

The table below shows the changes in the world pole vault record since 1920.

Year	1920	1930	1940	1950	1960	1970	1980	1990
Height/m	4.2	4.3	4.5	4.6	4.8	5.3	5.7	6.1

1 Plot a graph of the world pole vault record against the year.

2 When did the record improve by the greatest amount?

The large increase in the pole vault record which you found in question 2 resulted from the use of glass fibre poles. Glass fibre is known as a **composite**. It is made up of two different materials – fibres of glass embedded in plastic. The resulting composite has the strength of one material and the flexibility of the other. Before 1960, poles were made of aluminium. Before aluminium, they were made of bamboo. During the 1980s, carbon fibre replaced glass fibre in poles and this has proved even better.

3 What is a 'composite'?

4 Which material in glass fibre gives it: (i) strength, (ii) flexibility?

5 Why do you think glass fibre was better than aluminium for poles?

6 Why do you think aluminium was better than bamboo?

7 Why is carbon fibre particularly good for poles?

2 Explaining the structure of rubber

Natural rubber is a hydrocarbon. It contains long chains of carbon atoms with hydrogen atoms attached to them (Figure 1). Each rubber molecule contains between 10 000 and 50 000 carbon atoms. Notice that every fourth bond between the carbon atoms is a double bond.

In natural rubber, millions of these long chains are tangled together like tangled pieces of wire.

Unfortunately, natural rubber is only partly elastic. When it is pulled or deformed, the molecules move over one another and do not return to their original position when the force is removed (Figure 2). Pulling a tangle of wires will have the same effect.

The structure of the natural rubber must be changed slightly to make it more elastic. If we use the wire model again, it is fairly obvious that the sliding and slipping can be prevented if pairs of wires are fixed together where they cross. But, how can this be done with natural rubber?

The answer lies in the carbon=carbon double bonds. If sulphur is heated with natural rubber, the carbon=carbon double bonds break open and sulphur atoms form links between the long carbon chains (Figure 3). This process is called **vulcanisation**.

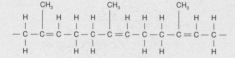

Figure 1 *Part of a molecule of natural rubber*

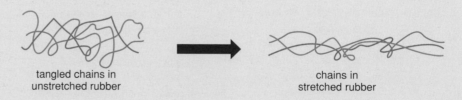

tangled chains in
unstretched rubber

chains in
stretched rubber

Figure 2 *Stretching natural rubber*

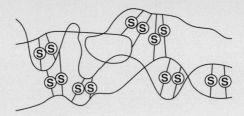

Figure 3 *Sulphur links between molecules of natural rubber*

The links between the rubber molecules stop the chains sliding over one another too much, yet the rubber stays elastic.

1 What kind of structure does natural rubber have?

2 How does the structure change after vulcanisation?

3 How many bonds does: (i) each carbon atom, (ii) each hydrogen atom form in natural rubber?

4 How do you think the elasticity of rubber will change as the amount of sulphur used for vulcanisation increases?

5 Use ball and spoke molecular models to build a model of part of a molecule of natural rubber like that shown in Figure 1. Does your model have any elastic properties? Describe how you checked this and say what the result was.

6 Build a second molecular model of part of a molecule of natural rubber. Now use your two models to explore how sulphur atoms can form cross links between the rubber molecules. (*Hint*: Look carefully at Figure 3 and note that each sulphur atom can form two bonds.)

Draw a structure for vulcanised rubber showing the bonds between atoms like those in Figure 1.

3 A site for ChlorChem

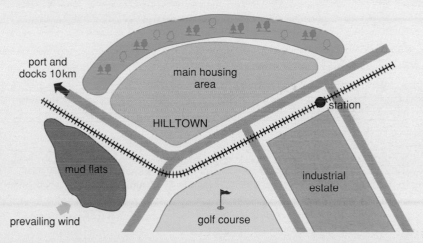

A map of Hilltown

A chemical company, ChlorChem, wants to build a new factory near Hilltown in order to manufacture chlorine and sodium hydroxide using brine.

1 What problems does this pose?

2 Where would you site this new factory?

3 What are the reasons for your choice of site?

4 The Council at Hilltown wants ChlorChem to build their factory on the mud flats. They have offered ChlorChem financial help if the factory is sited on the mud flats. What disadvantage will this site have for (i) ChlorChem, (ii) Hilltown?

4 Using *Word* to compare the four different types of structures

a) Choose a metal, an ionic substance, a simple molecular substance and a giant covalent (giant molecular) substance.

b) Using *Word* compare and contrast their properties and reactions.

c) Explain how the properties and reactions of each substance relate to its structure.

1 The structure of substances

The structures of materials can be studied using X-rays. The regular arrangement of particles in a crystal is called a **lattice**.

- The **structure and bonding** of a substance determine its **properties** and these properties determine its **uses**.
- All substances are made up from only three kinds of particle – **atoms, ions** and **molecules**.
- These three particles give rise to four different solid structures – **giant metallic**, **giant covalent**, **simple molecular** and **giant ionic**.

2 Particles, bonding and properties of the four different solid structures

Type of structure	Particles in the structure	Type of substance	Bonding	Properties	Structure
Giant metallic	**atoms** close-packed	metals e.g. Na, Fe, Cu and alloys such as steel	atoms are held in a close-packed giant structure by the attraction of positive ions for mobile electrons	<ul><li>high melting points and boiling points</li><li>conduct electricity</li><li>high density</li><li>hard but malleable</li></ul>	
Giant covalent (giant molecular)	**very large molecules** containing thousands of atoms (giant molecules)	a few non-metals (e.g. diamond, graphite) and some non-metal compounds (e.g. polythene, PVC, silicon dioxide (sand))	large numbers of atoms are joined together by strong covalent bonds to give a giant structure as a 3-D network or a very long, thin molecule	<ul><li>high melting points and boiling points</li><li>do not conduct electricity (except graphite)</li><li>hard but brittle (3-D networks) or flexible polymers</li></ul>	
Simple molecular	**small molecules** containing a few atoms	most non-metals and non-metal compounds e.g. O_2, S_8, H_2O, CO_2, sugar	atoms are held together in small molecules by strong covalent bonds The bonds between molecules are weak	<ul><li>low melting points and boiling points</li><li>do not conduct electricity</li><li>soft when solid</li></ul>	
Giant ionic	**ions**	metal/non-metal compounds e.g. Na^+Cl^-, $Ca^{2+}O^{2-}$, $Mg^{2+}(Cl^-)_2$	positive and negative ions are held together by the attraction between their opposite charges – ionic bonds	<ul><li>high melting points and boiling points</li><li>conduct electricity when molten and in aqueous solution</li><li>hard but brittle</li></ul>	

3 Useful substances from rocks and minerals

Salt (sodium chloride) has a giant ionic structure. It is an important raw material for the chlor-alkali industry. When concentrated salt solution is electrolysed, the products are chlorine, sodium hydroxide and hydrogen.

Sand (silicon dioxide) has a giant covalent structure. When silicon dioxide is heated, it forms pure hard glass. Ordinary glass for bottles is made by heating sand (silicon dioxide), limestone (calcium carbonate) and soda (sodium carbonate).

Section H Exam Questions

1 Look at the words in the box.

allotropes	carbohydrates	carbon
glucose	oils	soaps	sulphur

Copy and complete the sentences using words in the box.
Each word may be used only once or not at all.
(a) Diamond is made up of the non-metallic element .... which can exist in different physical forms. These are called ....
(b) Vegetable .... can be reacted with alkali to form ....

AQA 2000

2 Copy and complete the following table about calcium oxide and carbon dioxide.

	Calcium oxide	Carbon dioxide
Formula	CaO	
Appearance at room temperature		colourless gas
Solubility	slightly soluble in water	
Type of bonds		covalent
One use	to neutralise acidic soils	

AQA 2000

3 This question is about magnesium oxide and how it is formed from atoms of magnesium and oxygen.
(a) Copy and finish the sentences by choosing the **best** words from this list.
atoms, covalent, giant, high, ionic, ions, low, molecular.
Magnesium oxide is an example of a substance with _____ bonding. It has a _____ structure made up of _____
Strong forces between the particles in the structure cause magnesium oxide to have a _____ melting point.
(b) The table gives information about the electron arrangement in a magnesium atom and an oxygen atom.

atom	electron arrangement
Mg	2,8,2
O	2,6

Describe the changes in electron arrangement that take place when magnesium oxide is formed from magnesium and oxygen.
(c) Calculate the formula mass of magnesium oxide, MgO.

Use the Periodic Table to help you.
You **must** show how you work out your answer.

OCR 1999

4 The table shows some properties of diamond and graphite.

Diamond	Graphite
colourless, transparent crystals	black shiny solid
hardest natural substance known	flakes easily
non-conductor of electricity	conductor of electricity

(a) Why might you expect diamond and graphite to have the same properties?
(b) Explain why diamond and graphite do **not** have the same properties.
(c) Explain why diamond does **not** conduct electricity but graphite does.
(d) Write a balanced equation, including state symbols, for the reaction which occurs when graphite burns in excess air.

Edexcel 2000

5 The industrial *electrolysis* of an aqueous solution of sodium chloride is shown.

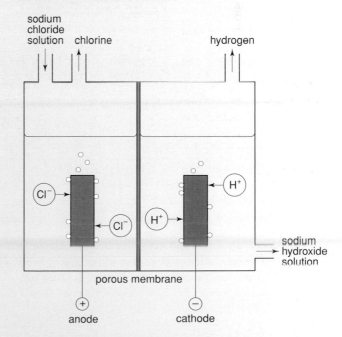

(a) What is meant by *electrolysis*?
(b) Explain how hydrogen and sodium hydroxide solution are produced.
(c) The equation for the anode reaction is:

$$2Cl^- \rightarrow Cl_2 + 2e^-$$

A current of 0.2 amps was passed through an aqueous solution of sodium chloride for 2 hours.

  (i) Calculate the number of coulombs of electricity passed.

  (ii) How many coulombs would be needed to form 71 g of chlorine?
  Relative atomic mass: Cl 35.5.
  96 500 coulombs is the amount of electricity carried by a mole of electrons.

  (iii) Using your answers in (i) and (ii) calculate the mass, in grams, of chlorine formed.

AQA 2000

6 (a) Sodium, atomic number 11, reacts with chlorine, atomic number 17, to form sodium chloride.

  (i) Give the electronic structures of the two elements.

  (ii) Explain, by means of a diagram or otherwise, the electronic changes that take place during the formation of sodium chloride. Include the charges on the ions.

  (iii) The table below shows some physical properties of sodium chloride.

Melting point (°C)	Boiling point (°C)	Solubility in water
801	1413	soluble

  Using the information in the table above, state the type of **structure** found in sodium chloride.

  (b) (i) Chlorine gas, Cl_2, consists of molecules. By means of a diagram, show the bonding in a chlorine molecule.

  (ii) Name this type of bonding.

WJEC 2000

7 (a) Use the periodic table to give the structure of a chlorine atom and a chloride ion.

  (b) Sodium chloride is an ionic compound containing sodium ions and chloride ions.

  Explain why ionic compounds have high melting points.

  (c) When aqueous sodium chloride is electrolysed, hydrogen and chlorine gases are produced.
  The diagram below shows the apparatus used to electrolyse aqueous sodium chloride. Write down the labels for A, B and C.

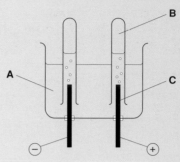

  (d) Describe a test for each of the gases formed.

  (i) Test for hydrogen,

  (ii) Test for chlorine.

  (e) In the industrial electrolysis of concentrated sodium chloride solution, three products are formed. Hydrogen and chlorine are two of the products.
  Name the other product.

Edexcel (specimen paper, 2003)

8 The diagrams below show the two allotropes of carbon.

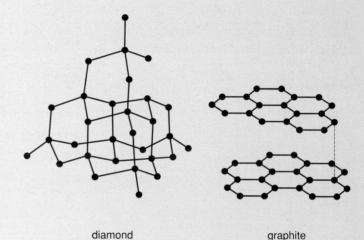

diamond   graphite

  (i) State **one** similarity and **one** difference in the type of **bonding** in diamond and graphite.

  (ii) State **one** physical property each of diamond and graphite, and give a use which depends upon the property given.

  I. Diamond – property, use

  II. Graphite – property, use

  (iii) Name the product formed when samples of each allotrope burn **completely** in air.

WJEC 2001

Useful Products from Oil

An aerial view of an oil refinery. Notice the fractionating towers, the storage tanks, the jetties where tankers can berth and the easy access to a motorway

By the end of this section you should:
- Know how crude oil can be separated by fractional distillation.
- Be able to recall the uses of products from crude oil.
- Know about the properties and reaction of alkanes (as saturated hydrocarbons) and alkenes (as unsaturated hydrocarbons).
- Understand how cracking produces additional amounts of petrol plus alkenes.
- Understand how polymers are formed from alkenes by polymerisation.
- Appreciate some uses of polymers (plastics).
- Know that temperature changes and energy changes often accompany reactions.
- Understand how bond making and breaking involves energy changes.
- Be able to recall the properties, reactions and uses of ethanol (alcohol) and ethanoic acid.

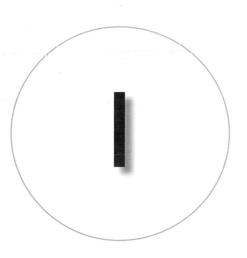

Energy from Fuels

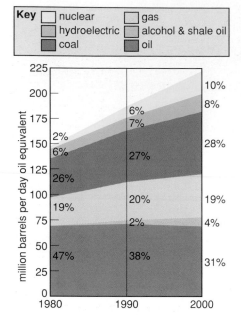

Figure 1 *The percentage contributions that different fuels have made to the world's energy requirements since 1980*

Everyday we use energy in our homes, schools and industries in thousands of different ways. We need energy to warm a room, cook a meal or light a torch. Although we use a lot of energy in our homes, industry uses far more. Energy is needed to turn raw materials like clay into useful things like bricks. It is also needed to mine coal and other minerals and to generate electricity. In fact, energy is essential to our society.

Most of the energy that we need is provided by fuels. When fuels, like natural gas, burn, they give out heat. In these reactions, chemical energy in the fuel is converted into heat.

$$CH_4 + 2O_2 \rightarrow CO_2 + 2H_2O + heat$$
(natural gas)

> Chemical reactions which *give out* heat are described as **exothermic**.

Other reactions such as the thermal decomposition of limestone to quicklime, need heat to make them happen. This heat is often provided by burning fuels.

$$CaCO_3 + heat \rightarrow CaO + CO_2$$
(limestone)   (quicklime)

> Chemical reactions which *take in* heat are described as **endothermic**.

Everyday, the world needs energy equivalent to about 200 million barrels of oil. This energy is provided by a range of fuels and other energy sources. Figure 1 shows how the world's energy requirements have been provided since 1980.

> Coal, oil and natural gas are the most commonly used fuels. They are called **fossil fuels** because they have formed from the remains of dead animals and plants.

How did fossil fuels form?

Three hundred million years ago, the Earth was covered in forests and the seas were teeming with tiny organisms. As these plants and animals died, huge amounts of decaying material piled up.

When the decaying material was in contact with air it was broken down by bacteria and it rotted away completely. During this process, compounds containing carbon and hydrogen in the rotting material reacted with oxygen in the air forming carbon dioxide and water.

In some places, however, the decaying material was covered by the sea, by sediment from rivers or by additional deposits of dead material. In these places, the material continued to decay, but in the absence of oxygen. It was still attacked by bacteria and also subjected to:

● high temperatures due to the heat produced as it rotted,

● high pressure from the water and sediment above.

Over millions of years, this led to the slow formation of oil and natural gas from sea creatures and coal from plants.

Mining for coal and metal ores provides fuel and important raw materials, but the effects of mining often ruin the countryside. These photos show an unsightly spoil heap near Shrewsbury (Shropshire, UK) and the same area after landscaping has started

Conserving fossil fuels

Fossil fuels are concentrated stores of chemical energy. When they burn, some of their chemical energy is released as heat. For 150 years, industrial countries have relied on fossil fuels for energy. Vast amounts of coal, oil and natural gas have been used for heating, for transport and to generate electricity. Large amounts of fossil fuels are still being used for these purposes, but they cannot last forever.

The Earth's resources of coal, oil and gas are limited. They are finite, non-renewable resources and, eventually, they will run out. Figure 2 shows how long these fuels will last if we continue to use them as we do now.

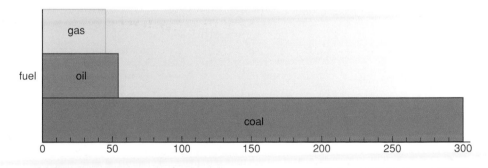

Figure 2 *How long will the world's reserves of fossil fuels last?*

Although coal is plentiful, oil and natural gas will probably start to run out in your lifetime. Because of this, it is important to conserve fossil fuels and avoid wasting energy. Our attempts to conserve fuels have led to:

● more economic and more efficient use of fuels,

● the manufacture of special fuels for some uses,

● research into alternative energy sources to fossil fuels,

● the use of better materials and better methods for insulation.

195

2 Crude Oil

This fossil of a prehistoric fish was left when the rest of it became crude oil. Crude oil has formed over millions of years from the effects of temperature, pressure and bacteria on dead sea creatures

Crude oil is the main source of fuels and organic chemicals in the UK. The crude oil comes from the North Sea and the Gulf area in the Middle East. It is a sticky, smelly, dark-brown liquid. Crude oil is a mixture containing hundreds of different compounds. These vary from simple substances like methane (CH_4) to complicated substances with long chains and rings of carbon atoms. Nearly all the substances in crude oil contain carbon. These carbon compounds are often called **organic compounds**. Coal, natural gas, wood and all living things also contain organic compounds.

A century ago oil was almost unknown. Now, our lifestyles depend on it. It is almost as important to modern day living as air and water. In this country, 70% of all organic chemicals come from oil. Antifreeze, brake fluid, lipstick, nylon, explosives and paint are all made from it. Without crude oil, there would be no petrol or diesel for cars, trains or aircraft. Transport would grind to a halt and any machine larger than a toy car would seize up from lack of lubricant.

We have enough oil to last another 60 years and new reserves are being discovered all the time. But, remember that crude oil is a finite, non-renewable resource. There is only a limited amount of it and it is not getting replaced. Once it has been used, it has gone forever. At present, we are using our oil reserves so fast that we need to ensure that crude oil is used more economically.

Separating crude oil into fractions

The carbon compounds in crude oil have different boiling points. This means that crude oil can be separated by boiling off portions over different temperature ranges.

> These portions are called **fractions** and the process of boiling off fractions is called **fractional distillation**.

Most of the fractions from crude oil are used as fuel. Figure 1 shows the small-scale fractional distillation of crude oil. The ceramic wool, soaked in crude oil is heated very gently at first and then more strongly so that distillate slowly drips into the collecting tube. Four fractions are collected, with the boiling ranges and properties shown in Table 1.

Table 1 also shows the industrial names of the fractions. Notice how the properties of the fractions gradually change in colour, viscosity and flammability.

Did you know?

Every stitch and article of your clothing could be made from textiles, including nylon and polyester, produced from crude oil?

Table 1 *The properties of fractions obtained by the small-scale fractional distillation of crude oil*

Boiling range (°C)	Name of fraction	Colour	Viscosity (runniness)	How does it burn? (flammability)
20–70	petrol (gasoline)	pale yellow	runny	easily with a clean yellow flame
70–120	naphtha	yellow	fairly runny	quite easily, yellow flame, some smoke
120–170	paraffin (kerosine)	dark yellow	fairly viscous	harder to burn, quite smoky flame
170–270	diesel oils	brown	viscous	hard to burn, very smoky flame

Figure I *The small scale fractional distillation of crude oil*

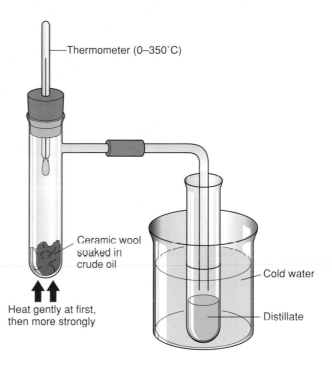

The fractions from crude oil contain mixtures of similar substances. These fractions contain compounds with roughly the same number of carbon atoms.

As the number of carbon atoms increases, the molecules get larger and they have a higher boiling point.

From Table 1 we can see that as the boiling range gets higher and the molecules get larger, the fractions are:

● less volatile,

● darker in colour,

● more viscous (less runny),

● less flammable and less easy to ignite.

The difficulty in igniting the higher fractions with larger molecules limits their use as fuels.

Separating crude oil for industry

Figure 2 shows the products and their boiling ranges at different heights in an industrial fractionating tower. Inside the tower there are horizontal trays at different levels.

The crude oil is heated in a furnace and the vapours pass into the lower part of the tower. As the vapours rise up the tower, the temperature falls. Different vapours condense at different heights in the tower, collect on the horizontal trays and are then tapped off.

Liquids like petrol, which boil at low temperatures, condense high up in the tower. Liquids like fuel oil, which boil at higher temperatures condense low down in the tower.

The fractions from crude oil contain mixtures of similar substances with roughly the same number of carbon atoms. Figure 2 also shows the number of carbon atoms in the constituents and the uses of each fraction. The uses of the various fractions depend on their properties.

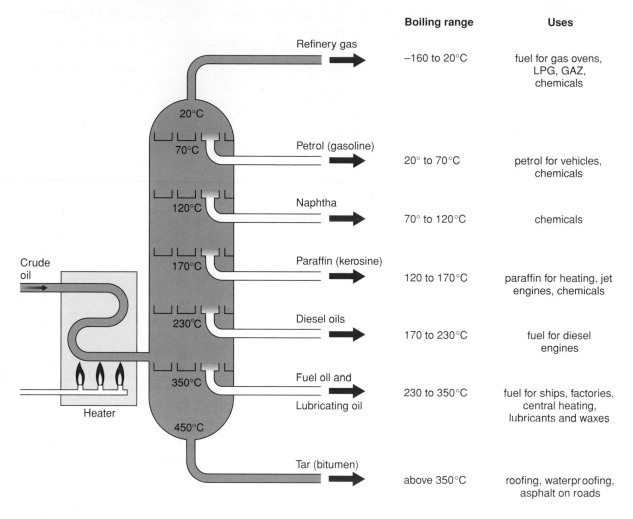

Boiling range	Uses
Refinery gas	−160 to 20°C	fuel for gas ovens, LPG, GAZ, chemicals
Petrol (gasoline)	20° to 70°C	petrol for vehicles, chemicals
Naphtha	70° to 120°C	chemicals
Paraffin (kerosine)	120 to 170°C	paraffin for heating, jet engines, chemicals
Diesel oils	170 to 230°C	fuel for diesel engines
Fuel oil and Lubricating oil	230 to 350°C	fuel for ships, factories, central heating, lubricants and waxes
Tar (bitumen)	above 350°C	roofing, waterproofing, asphalt on roads

Figure 2 *The fractions from crude oil and their uses*

- Petrol vaporises easily and is very flammable, so it is ideal for use in car engines.

- Fuel oil and lubricating oil are very viscous and do not ignite easily. They are used in lubricants and as fuel in central heating systems.

- Bitumen (tar) is solid, but easy to melt. It is used for waterproofing and mixed with stone chippings for road surfacing.

Study Questions

1 Look at the results in Table 1. How do the properties of the fractions change?
2 a) Why is crude oil important?
   b) Why should we try to conserve our reserves of crude oil?
   c) How is crude oil separated into various fractions at a refinery?
   d) What should we do to ensure that crude oil is used more economically?

3 a) List the main fractions obtained from crude oil.
   b) Give the main uses of each fraction.
4 a) What does the word 'organic' mean in everyday use?
   b) Why do you think the study of carbon compounds is called 'organic chemistry'?

   c) To a chemist, organic compounds are simple molecular compounds. What physical properties would you expect them to have?

Most of the substances in crude oil and in natural gas are **hydrocarbons**.

Hydrocarbons are substances containing only hydrogen and carbon.

Crude oil contains dozens of different hydrocarbons. These vary from methane (CH_4) with just one carbon atom per molecule to very complex hydrocarbons with more than 30 carbon atoms per molecule.

All these different hydrocarbons exist because carbon atoms can form strong covalent bonds with each other. Atoms of other elements cannot do this.

Because of these strong C—C bonds, carbon forms molecules containing straight chains, branched chains and even rings of carbon atoms. There are thousands of different hydrocarbons and millions of different carbon compounds.

Figure 1

Name	methane	ethane	propane	butane
Molecular formula	CH_4	C_2H_6	C_3H_6	C_4H_{10}
Displayed Formula	H—C—H with H above and H below	H—C—C—H with H above each and H below each	H—C—C—C—H with H above each and H below each	H—C—C—C—C—H with H above each and H below each
Molecular model (black balls for carbon, white for hydrogen)				

The four simplest hydrocarbons are methane, ethane, propane and butane. Figure 1 shows the molecular formulas, displayed formulas and molecular models for these four hydrocarbons. The displayed formulas show which atoms are attached to each other. But they cannot show the three-dimensional structures of the molecules which you should appreciate from the molecular models. There are four covalent bonds to each carbon atom. Each of these bonds consists of a pair of shared electrons (Unit K6). The four pairs of electrons around a carbon atom repel each other as far as possible. So, the bonds around each carbon atom spread out tetrahedrally, as in methane (Figure 2).

Methane, ethane, propane and butane are members of a series of compounds called **alkanes**. All other alkanes are named from the number of carbon atoms in one molecule. So C_5H_{12} is *pen*tane, C_6H_{14} is *hex*ane, C_7H_{16} is *hep*tane and so on. The names of all alkanes end in **–ane**.

Look at the formulas of methane, CH_4; ethane, C_2H_6; propane, C_3H_8 and butane C_4H_{10}. Notice that the difference in carbon and hydrogen atoms between methane and ethane is CH_2. The difference between ethane and propane is CH_2 and the difference between propane and butane is also CH_2. This is an example of a **homologous series**.

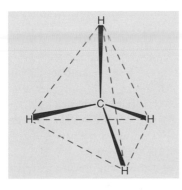

Figure 2 *The tetrahedral arrangement of bonds in methane*

A homologous series is a family of compounds with similar properties and in which the formulas differ by CH_2.

A small blue butane cylinder used to fuel a gas barbecue

Can you see from the displayed formulas in Figure 1 that if an alkane has n carbon atoms, it will have $2n + 2$ hydrogen atoms. (Every carbon atom in the chain has two hydrogen atoms, except the two C atoms at the ends of the chain, both of which have an extra H atom.)

This allows us to write a general formula for alkanes as C_nH_{2n+2}.

Isomerism

Earlier in this unit, we noted that carbon could form a large number of compounds. There are even more compounds than you might expect, because it is sometimes possible to join the same set of atoms in different ways. For example, take the formula C_4H_{10}. We know already that butane has the formula C_4H_{10}. But there is another compound which also has this formula. This other compound is called methylpropane (Figure 3). Notice that each carbon atom in butane and in methylpropane has four bonds and each H atom has one bond. Butane and methylpropane are two distinct compounds with different properties as shown in Figure 3.

Compounds like this with the same molecular formula, but different displayed formulas and different properties are called **isomers**.

Name	butane	methylpropane
Molecular formula	C_4H_{10}	C_4H_{10}
Displayed formula	H H H H | | | | H—C—C—C—C—H | | | | H H H H	H | H—C—H H | H | | | H—C—C—C—H | | | H H H
Melting point/°C	−138	−159
Boiling point/°C	0	−12
Density /g cm^{-3}	0.58	0.56

Figure 3 *Isomers with the formula C_4H_{10}*

The properties of alkanes

● **Low melting points and low boiling points**
Alkanes are typical molecular (non-metal) compounds. They have low melting points and low boiling points. Alkanes with one to four carbon atoms per molecule are gases at room temperature. Methane (CH_4) and ethane (C_2H_6) make up about 95% of natural gas. Propane (C_3H_8) and butane (C_4H_{10}) are the main constituents of 'liquefied petroleum gas' (LPG). The best known uses of LPG are 'Calor Gas' and 'GAZ' for camping, caravans and boats.

Alkanes with 5 to 17 carbon atoms are liquids at room temperature. Mixtures of these liquids are used in petrol, paraffin, lubricating oil and engine oil. Alkanes with 18 or more carbon atoms per molecule, such as bitumen (tar), are solids at room temperature. Even so, they begin to melt on very hot days.

Two red propane cylinders, stored outside

Notice that alkanes become less volatile and change from gases to liquids and then to solids as their molecules get larger.

● **Insoluble in water**
Alkanes are insoluble in water, but they dissolve in solvents like petrol.

● **Poor reactivity**
Alkanes do not contain ions and their C—C and C—H bonds are very strong. So they have very few reactions. They do not react with metals, acids or alkalis. It may surprise you, but petrol (which contains mainly alkanes) will not react with sodium, concentrated sulphuric acid or sodium hydroxide. You must **not** try any experiments with petrol. It is highly flammable.

Burning (combustion)

The most important reactions of alkanes involve burning. In a plentiful supply of air or oxygen, they are completely oxidised to carbon dioxide and water.

$$C_4H_{10} + 6\tfrac{1}{2}O_2 \rightarrow 4CO_2 + 5H_2O$$
(butane in GAZ)

Burning reactions are very exothermic. So, alkanes in natural gas and crude oil are used as fuels.

If there is too little air or oxygen, alkanes are only partially oxidised during burning. In this case, soot (carbon) and carbon monoxide are formed as well as carbon dioxide.

Carbon monoxide has no smell and it is very poisonous (toxic). It reacts with haemoglobin in the blood forming carboxyhaemoglobin and this reduces the capacity of the blood to carry oxygen. Because of this, it is dangerous to burn carbon compounds in a poor supply of air or in faulty gas appliances.

Study Questions

1 Explain the following:
 hydrocarbon; alkane; homologous series; isomerism.

2 a) Why is C_8H_{18} called octane?
 b) Draw a displayed formula for C_8H_{18}.
 c) How many H atoms will the alkane with ten carbon atoms have?

3 Why can a homologous series of compounds be compared to a group of elements in the periodic table?

4 Draw the displayed formulas for:
 (i) the three isomers with the formula C_5H_{12}; (ii) the two isomers with the formula C_3H_7Cl. (*Hint:* Cl atoms form one covalent bond in these isomers.)

5 a) Write an equation for the complete combustion of octane in petrol.
 b) What are the products when octane burns in a poor supply of oxygen?
 c) Why is it dangerous to allow a car engine to run in a garage with the door closed?

6 Why do alkanes change from gases to liquids and then to solids as their molecular size increases?

7 a) Use molecular models to build a molecule of hexane.
 b) Draw the displayed formula of hexane.
 c) Draw two other displayed formulas with the same molecular formula as hexane.
 d) Build molecular models of your structures in part c).

4 Cracking – more Petrol from Crude Oil

Fraction	Percentage in	
	crude oil	everyday demand
Fuel gas	2	4
Petrol	6	22
Naphtha	10	5
Kerosine	13	8
Diesel oil	19	23
Fuel oil and bitumen	50	38

Table 1 *Relative amounts of the different fractions in crude oil and in the everyday demand for each fraction*

During the 1930s, the demand for petrol increased much faster than the demand for heavier fractions which make up two-thirds of crude oil (Table 1). This meant that refineries were left with large unwanted amounts of the heavier fractions. Fortunately, chemists found ways of converting the heavier fractions into petrol and other useful products.

One method of converting the heavier fractions from crude oil into petrol is **catalytic cracking**.

Catalytic cracking involves the thermal decomposition of larger hydrocarbon molecules into simpler hydrocarbons using a catalyst at high temperature.

What are the products of cracking?

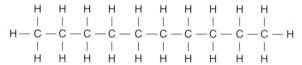

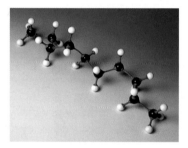

Figure 1 *A molecular model and the displayed formula of decane*

Look at the long molecule of decane ($C_{10}H_{22}$) in Figure 1. It has a chain of 10 carbon atoms with 22 hydrogen atoms. Now, suppose decane is cracked (split) between two carbon atoms. This cannot produce two smaller alkane molecules because there are not enough hydrogen atoms to go round. But suppose one product is the alkane, octane (C_8H_{18}). If C_8H_{18} is split off from $C_{10}H_{22}$, the molecular formula of the remainder is C_2H_4 (Figure 2). The chemical name for C_2H_4 is **ethene**. Notice in Figure 2 that ethene has a *double* bond between the two carbon atoms. This double bond allows all the carbon atoms in the products to have four bonds.

Hydrocarbons such as ethene, which contain a carbon—carbon double bond (C = C) are known as **alkenes**.

The names of alkenes come from the alkane with the same number of carbon atoms, using the ending –*ene* rather than –*ane*. Organic compounds, like alkanes, which have four single covalent bonds to all their carbon atoms, are described as **saturated compounds**. Alkenes, which have double bonds between some carbon atoms are described as **unsaturated compounds**.

Why do we now use unleaded petrol?

$$C_{10}H_{22} \longrightarrow C_8H_{18} + C_2H_4$$

H H H H H H H H H H
| | | | | | | | | |
H—C—C—C—C—C—C—C—C—C—C—H →
| | | | | | | | | |
H H H H H H H H H H

H H H H H H H H
| | | | | | | |
H—C—C—C—C—C—C—C—C—H +
| | | | | | | |
H H H H H H H H

H   H
 \   /
  C = C
 /   \
H   H

decane → octane + ethene

Figure 2 *When decane undergoes catalytic cracking, it forms an alkane, like octane, and an alkene, like ethene*

How are molecules cracked?

Unlike distillation, cracking is a chemical process. It involves breaking a strong covalent bond between two carbon atoms. This requires high temperatures and a catalyst of finely-powdered aluminium oxide and silicon(IV) oxide. The catalyst does not react with the crude oil fractions but it does provide a very hot surface that speeds up cracking. At high temperatures, the longer alkane molecules have more energy and they break apart forming two or more smaller molecules.

Cracking is important because it is used to produce more petrol. Larger alkanes in crude oil are cracked to produce alkanes with about eight carbon atoms like octane. These are the main constituents in petrol. The petrol obtained in this way is better quality than that obtained by the straightforward distillation of crude oil. Cracked petrol is therefore blended with other petrols to improve their quality.

Study Questions

1 Explain the words: *cracking; alkene; unsaturated.*
2 a) Why is cracking important?
  b) What conditions are used for cracking?
  c) Write an equation for the cracking of octane in which one of the products is pentane.
  d) Draw the displayed formulas of the products in part c).
  e) Cracking can produce hydrogen. Write an equation for the cracking of butane in which one of the products is hydrogen.
3 a) What is the name of the alkene of formula C_3H_6?
  b) Draw the displayed formula of C_3H_6.
  c) Why is there no alkene called methene?
4 a) Design a simple experiment in which you could attempt to crack some kerosine (paraffin) in order to obtain ethene. (Ethene is a gas at room temperature.)
  b) What safety precautions will you take in your experiment? Do not carry out your experiment until it has been checked by your teacher.
5 What changes do you think there will be in our lives when crude oil begins to run out?

The catalytic cracking plant at an oil refinery

Ethene is an important industrial chemical. It is manufactured by cracking the heavier fractions from crude oil. It can be made on a small scale by cracking paraffin oil using the apparatus in Figure 1.

In nature, ethene acts as a trigger for the ripening of fruit, particularly bananas

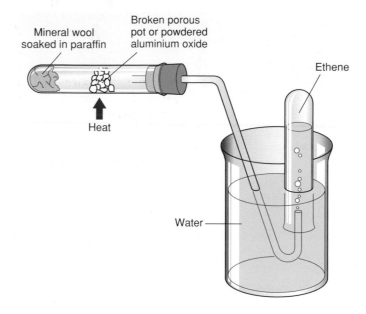

Figure 1 *Preparing ethene by cracking paraffin oil*

Wear eye protection if you are preparing ethene in this way. Remember that both paraffin and ethene are flammable. Beware of suck back and take care that the delivery tube does not get blocked.

Heat the middle of the tube below the porous pot or aluminium oxide. Heat will be conducted along the tube to vaporise the paraffin. The main gaseous product is ethene. Figure 2 shows some important properties of ethene.

Reactions of alkenes

Ethene, like ethane, is the first member of a homologous series. The second member of the series is propene, C_3H_6 (see question 1 at the end of this unit). The compounds in this homologous series are **alkenes**. Their structures are like alkanes but with a double bond in place of a carbon–carbon single bond. The general formula for alkenes is C_nH_{2n}.

Alkenes, such as ethene and propene, are much more reactive than alkanes. The most stable arrangement for the four bonds to a carbon atom is a tetrahedral one with four *single* bonds (Unit I3). This means that a $C = C$ bond is unstable. Some molecules can add across the double bond to make two single bonds. So, alkenes readily undergo **addition reactions**.

This explains why yellow-orange bromine water becomes colourless (decolorises) on shaking with an alkene, like ethene. The bromine molecules add across the double bond in ethene forming dibromoethane.

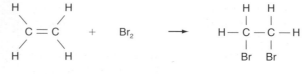

PROPERTIES OF
ETHENE

• colourless gas

• faint sweet smell

• about the same density as air

• insoluble in water

• burns with a yellow flame

• turns yellow / orange bromine water colourless

Figure 2 *Properties of ethene*

Ethene also has an addition reaction with hydrogen at 150°C using a nickel catalyst. The product of this reaction is ethane.

$$H_2C=CH_2 + H_2 \xrightarrow[150°C]{Ni\ catalyst} H_3C-CH_3$$

This process is known as **catalytic hydrogenation**. It is important in making margarine from vegetable oils in palm seeds and sunflower seeds. The vegetable oils are liquids containing carbon—carbon double bonds, like alkenes. During hydrogenation, some of these double bonds are converted to carbon—carbon single bonds by addition of hydrogen. This change in structure turns an oily liquid into a harder, fatty solid that can be used to make margarine.

Comparing alkanes with alkenes

Ethane and other alkanes are fairly unreactive. They react with oxygen (burning) and other reactive non-metals, like chlorine and bromine, but they do *not* react with bromine water.

In comparison, ethene and alkenes are very reactive because addition reactions can take place across their carbon—carbon double bonds ($C=C$).

Alkenes, like ethene, decolorise yellow-orange bromine water, but alkanes, like ethane, do not. This is used as a test for alkenes.

By controlling the amount of hydrogen added to vegetable oils like sunflower oil, margarine like Flora can be made as hard or as soft as required. Which of the two products in this photo is the most unsaturated?

Study Questions

1 The displayed formula of propene is shown below.

    a) Write equations for the reactions of propene with:
        (i) hydrogen; (ii) bromine.
    b) Draw the displayed formulas of the products in part a).
2 Three cylinders of gas are known to contain ethane, ethene and carbon dioxide but their labels are not clear. What simple tests would you make to show which gas is which?
3 Why are alkenes much more reactive than alkanes?
4 a) How is margarine made from vegetable oils?
    b) Explain what happens during the reaction in a).
    c) How can the melting point of the margarine be controlled?
5 Look at the structures of alkanes in Unit 13 and the structure of alkenes in this unit. Why is the general formula for alkenes C_nH_{2n}?

Polymers from Alkenes

Clingfilm is made from polythene

Ethene is a very valuable substance for the chemical industry. Ethene, propene and other alkenes are used to make important polymers because they are so reactive. These important polymers include polythene, polypropene, PVC, polystyrene and perspex.

Polythene (polyethene)

In the last unit, we learnt that ethene and other alkenes contain reactive carbon—carbon double bonds ($C = C$). These double bonds result in addition reactions with other substances such as hydrogen and bromine.

If the conditions are right, molecules of ethene will undergo addition reactions with each other to form polythene. Double bonds break leaving single bonds as the molecules join together (Figure 1).

Polythene is short for poly(ethene). 'Poly' means 'many'. So, polythene means 'many ethenes' joined together.

ethene molecules   part of the polythene molecule

Figure 1 *Molecules of ethene can undergo addition reactions with each other*

Polythene is manufactured by heating ethene at high pressure with special substances called **initiators**. Initiators help the double bonds in the ethene molecules to 'open up'. Carbon atoms in separate ethene molecules can then join together forming polythene.

When ethene forms polythene, very long chains are produced containing between 1000 and 5000 carbon atoms. The equation for this is usually summarised as:

In the structure of polythene, n is between 500 and 2500.

> Processes like this are called **addition polymerisations**.
> During addition polymerisation, small molecules, like ethene, add to each other to form a giant molecule.
> The giant molecule is called a **polymer**.
> The small molecules, like ethene, which add to each other are called **monomers**.

It is essential that the conditions used for polymerisation are just right. Figure 2 shows what happens (using paper clips) when unsuitable conditions are used.

Figure 3 lists the properties of polythene. These have led to many different uses. Polythene is the most important plastic at present. It is used as thin sheets for clingfilm and plastic bags. It is moulded into beakers, buckets and plastic bottles. It is used to insulate underwater cables.

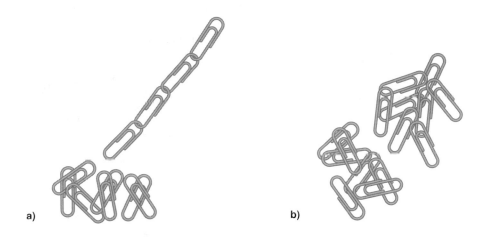

a)   b)

Figure 2 *a) Correct conditions for polymerisation b) Unsuitable conditions for polymerisation*

Other polymers

The two most useful and most commonly used polymers after polythene are **polypropene** and **PVC**. These are also manufactured by addition polymerisation. The structure and uses of these two polymers are shown in Table 1.

Table 1 *The structure and uses of polypropene and PVC*

Polymer	Polypropene poly (propene)	PVC polyvinylchloride poly (chloroethene)

Name and displayed formula of monomer	CH₃ H
	  \C = C/
	  / \
	H H
	
	Propene
		Cl H
		  \C = C/
		  / \
		H H
		
		Vinyl chloride
		(chloroethene)

Section of polymer structure	CH₃ H CH₃ H │ │ │ │ — C — C — C — C — │ │ │ │ H H H H	Cl H Cl H │ │ │ │ — C — C — C — C — │ │ │ │ H H H H
Major uses	Tough, easily moulded and easily coloured – used for crates and ropes	Tough, rigid, water resistant – used in rainwear, insulation on electric cables, guttering, drain pipes

Polythene, polypropene and PVC are soft, flexible and slightly elastic. They are often called **plastics**. Once a plastic has been produced, it is then turned into a useful article.

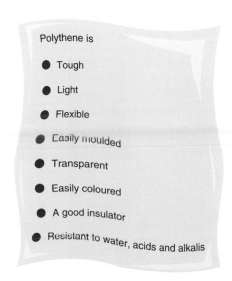

Polythene is

● Tough

● Light

● Flexible

● Easily moulded

● Transparent

● Easily coloured

● A good insulator

● Resistant to water, acids and alkalis

Figure 3 *The properties of polythene*

This is usually done by:

- **moulding** the warm, soft plastic under pressure, or
- **extruding** (pushing out) the warm, soft plastic into different shapes by forcing it through nozzles or between rollers.

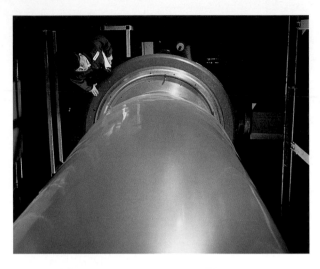

Polythene tubing emerging from an extrusion machine. The plastic is extruded from the container in which it is formed by hot pressursed air!

Most plastics consist of molecules with very long, thin chains. Sometimes, however, the long polymer molecules can form bonds with each other at points along the chain. This produces cross-linked three-dimensional structures which are harder and more rigid. Melamine, resins and superglues (epoxyglues) are examples of these cross-linked plastics.

The main raw material for all plastics is crude oil. Although these products have provided us with many new materials, they have one big disadvantage. They are **non-biodegradable**. This means that they are not decomposed by micro-organisms (bacteria), like wood and paper. So plastic rubbish lies around for years, littering the environment. In the last few years, biodegradable plastics have been developed. These are now used for bags, wrappings, bottles and other containers.

A biodegradable plastic bag

Study Questions

1 Explain the following:
polymer; addition polymerisation; non-biodegradable.

2 a) How is ethene manufactured?
  b) Why is ethene important in industry?

3 a) Give one use of plastic rubbish.
  b) Give one disadvantage of plastic rubbish.

4 a) Use molecular models to make three ethene molecules.
  b) Using these three ethene molecules, break the double bonds and produce a short portion of polythene chain. (Figure 1 will help you with this.)

5 Look at the displayed formulas of the monomers in Table 1.
  a) Which part of their displayed formulas do they have in common?
  b) What happens when these monomers polymerise to form polymers?
  c) Polystyrene is made from the following monomer.

$$C_6H_5 \quad \quad H$$
$$\diagdown \quad \quad \diagup$$
$$C = C$$
$$\diagup \quad \quad \diagdown$$
$$H \quad \quad \quad H$$

Draw a section of polystyrene showing six carbon atoms in the chain.

Polymers, like polythene, polypropene and PVC, together with man-made fibres, such as nylon and polyester, are called **plastics**.

Thermosoftening plastics

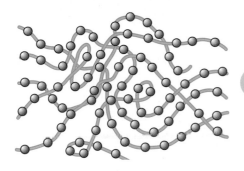

Figure 1 *Tangled chains of long, thin molecules in a thermosoftening plastic*

When polythene and nylon are warmed, they become soft and can be moulded. As they cool, they set hard again. Because of this, they are called **thermosoftening plastics**. Polypropene, PVC and polystyrene are also thermosoftening plastics.

Thermosoftening plastics contain long, thin molecules which form tangled chains (Figure 1). There are strong covalent bonds between the atoms along each chain, but weak forces between one chain and another. This means that the chains can move over each other easily on stretching, flexing or warming.

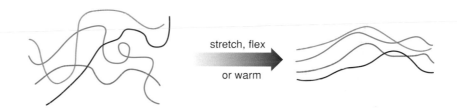

So, thermosoftening plastics:

- stretch easily,
- soften on warming,
- are flexible,
- can be shaped by warming and then moulding or extruding.

Thermosetting plastics

When melamine and resins are heated, they do *not* become soft. Once these plastics have been produced and moulded, they set hard and cannot be re-melted. Because of this, they are called **thermosetting plastics**. Polyester and most glues are also thermosetting plastics.

Thermosetting plastics contain a network of large cross-linked molecules (Figure 2). In these cross-linked plastics, there are strong covalent bonds between the atoms along each chain *and* also between one chain and another. This means that the chains cannot move over each other on stretching or warming.

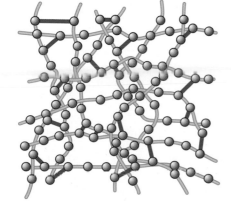

Figure 2 *Cross-links in a thermosetting plastic*

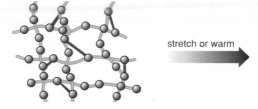

So, thermosetting plastics:

- are hard and rigid,
- burn or char on heating,
- cannot be re-moulded,
- do not soften or melt on heating.

Some thermosetting polymers form cross-links and harden at room temperature when a catalyst is added. One example of this is the polyester resin used in repair kits for car bodywork. The polyester molecules form cross-links and harden when mixed with the catalyst (hardener).

Plastic waste

In developed countries, plastic waste is a serious problem. Plastic bottles, polythene bags and other plastic articles litter our streets, our beaches and the countryside. Farmers have even complained of cows choking and dying after swallowing plastic bags that have been thrown away. We have to devise ways of alleviating this problem.

There are three ways in which we deal with plastic waste at present.

1 Landfill

Most plastic waste is dumped with other waste into rubbish tips.

'Chemical wood' is used to repair and fill holes in rotted wood. It contains a polyester resin which forms cross-links and sets hard when mixed with a catalyst

Did you know?

About 2 million tonnes of plastic waste are produced in the UK each year.

A landfill site for refuse. Notice the large proportion of plastic waste. What should we do to prevent plastic rubbish from littering our streets and the countryside?

2 Incineration

Plastics produce a lot of energy when they burn. So, plastics are burnt in incinerators with other combustible waste. The heat produced can be used to heat homes and factories or to generate electricity.

Unfortunately, some plastics produce very poisonous fumes when they are burnt. Plastics and other organic compounds containing chlorine and nitrogen produce hydrogen chloride (HCl) and hydrogen cyanide (HCN) respectively on combustion. These two gases are highly toxic and are more likely to form if there is a limited supply of air. These fumes must be removed before any waste gases are released into the air after incineration.

3 Recycling

At present, only a small amount of plastic waste is recycled. Thermosoftening plastics are fairly easy to recycle. They can be melted or softened and then remoulded. This is shown on the left-hand side of Figure 3.

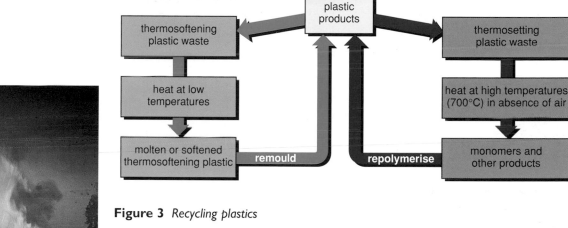

Figure 3 *Recycling plastics*

When foam-filled furniture burns, the fumes contain hydrogen chloride and hydrogen cyanide which are very poisonous

Thermosetting plastics are more difficult to recycle because they burn or char on heating. They are usually recycled by heating to about 700°C in the absence of air. This process is called **pyrolysis**. Under these conditions, the polymers cannot burn. Instead, they decompose to form their original monomers and other simple molecules. The original molecules can then be re-polymerised. This is shown on the right-hand side of Figure 3.

At present, it is uneconomical to recycle most plastic waste. This is largely because of the cost of collecting and separating it and the cost of energy in the recycling process. It is still cheaper to make new plastics from crude oil.

However, as oil becomes scarce and more expensive, recycling will become more economical. This is why research into pyrolysis and other recycling processes is being carried out.

Study Questions

1. a) Thermosoftening plastics can be compared to chocolate when it is warmed. Why is this?
   b) Thermosetting plastics can be compared to an egg when it is warmed. Why is this?
   c) What happens to the polythene molecules in clingfilm when it is stretched?

2. A small packaging company produces 50 kg of plastic waste each week. This could be used in an incinerator to provide heating for the factory. The incinerator would cost £1000.

Material	Heat produced by burning 1 kg
polythene	40 000 kJ
polystyrene	40 000 kJ
PVC	20 000 kJ
heating oil	40 000 kJ

   a) Use the table above to calculate how many kilograms of heating oil the plastic waste could save each week. Explain your calculation.
   b) What would this save in the cost of heating oil per week? (Assume heating oil costs £2 per kg.)
   c) How long would it take the company to save enough money to pay off the cost of the incinerator?

3. If plastics are not burnt completely, toxic carbon monoxide is produced. Some plastics burn to produce acidic gases containing hydrogen chloride. Design an incinerator in which plastics could be burnt completely. The incinerator must not expel any unburnt plastic or acidic gases.

4. Get into a small group with two or three others.
   List (i) the problems and (ii) the advantages of recycling plastic waste.

8

Alcohol – from Ethene or Sugar

Foam in copper brewery tanks. What causes the foam?

When people talk about alcohol, they really mean **ethanol**. Ethanol is the substance which makes alcoholic drinks intoxicating. It is also the major constituent in methylated spirits (meths). After water, this is the most widely used industrial solvent.

Producing ethanol

At one time, all ethanol, including methylated spirits, was produced by fermentation of sugars. Today, fermentation is still important in brewing and wine making, but industrial ethanol and methylated spirits are manufactured from ethene.

Fermentation – ethanol from sugar

The starting material for fermentation is a sugary solution of grape juice for making wine or malted barley for making beer. When yeast is added to these sugary solutions, enzymes (unit J5) break down the sugar to glucose and then to ethanol and carbon dioxide (Figure 1).

$$C_{12}H_{22}O_{11} \ + \ H_2O \ \rightarrow \ 2C_6H_{12}O_6$$
$$\text{sugar} \qquad\qquad\qquad\qquad \text{glucose}$$

$$C_6H_{12}O_6 \ \rightarrow \ 2CH_3CH_2OH \ + \ 2CO_2$$
$$\text{glucose} \qquad\quad \text{ethanol}$$

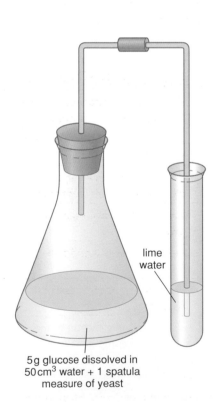

lime water

5 g glucose dissolved in 50 cm³ water + 1 spatula measure of yeast

Figure 1 *Making ethanol by fermentation on a small scale. Leave the apparatus in a warm place for five days. Then filter the solution in the conical flask and separate ethanol from the filtrate by fractional distillation. The first few drops of distillate will burn like ethanol. Why does the lime water go milky?*

Fermentation can only produce a weak solution of ethanol in water, but it is ideal for making wine (about 12% ethanol) and beer (about 3% ethanol). Fractional distillation is used to obtain higher concentrations of ethanol in spirits such as whisky, gin and vodka. These drinks contain about 40% ethanol.

Alcoholic drinks can be pleasant in small amounts. Their varied tastes are enjoyable and they have the effect of making people more relaxed. But alcoholic drinks taken in excess can be very dangerous. They have the effect of slowing down our reactions, they can cause permanent damage to the liver and they can be addictive like drugs.

Hydration – ethanol from ethene

Ethanol is manufactured by an addition reaction between ethene and steam (water). Ethene and steam are passed over a catalyst of phosphoric acid at 300°C and high pressure.

A reaction like this, which involves the addition of water is described as **hydration**.

Large quantities of ethanol are used in industry as solvents for paints, dyes, glues and soaps. Ethanol is miscible with both oils and water so it can be used with a wide range of solutes. It also evaporates quickly which makes it useful as a solvent for perfumes and aftershave lotions.

Most of the ethanol used in industry and in our homes is sold as methylated spirits (meths). This contains about 90% ethanol, 5% water and 5% methanol. The methanol gives the meths a bitter taste and makes it unfit to drink.

The two methods of producing ethanol are compared in Table 1.

Table 1 *Comparing the methods of producing ethanol*

	Fermentation	Hydration of ethene
Type of process	**Batch process** using fixed amounts of sugary solution	**Continuous process** – ethene and steam fed in continually
Raw material	Sugar (or starch) – a renewable resource	Ethene from cracking crude oil – a finite resource
Rate of reaction	Slow – process takes days if not weeks	Fast – process is catalysed at high temp and high pressure
Quality of product	% of ethanol is low, flavour is more important	100% ethanol can readily be produced
Use of product	Alcoholic drinks – beers, wines and spirits	Industrial solvent and fuel
Cost	Batch process and slow reaction – expensive	Continuous process and fast reaction – cheaper

Table 2 *The homologous series of alcohols*

CH_3OH methanol
CH_3CH_2OH ethanol
$CH_3CH_2CH_2OH$ propanol
$CH_3CH_2CH_2CH_2OH$ butanol

Ethanol and alcohols

Ethanol is a member of a large class of compounds called alcohols. All alcohols contain an –OH group attached to a carbon atom. The simplest alcohol is methanol, CH_3OH. The –OH group gives alcohols most of their characteristic properties and reactions. Because of this, it is sometimes described as the **functional group** in alcohols. In the same way, the functional group in alkenes is $C = C$.

Alcohols form a homologous series like alkanes and alkenes (see Table 2). They have similar properties which show a gradual change from one alcohol to the next and their molecular formulas increase by units of CH_2.

Notice from Table 2 that alcohols have names derived from the alkanes with the same number of carbon atoms (i.e. methanol from methane, ethanol from ethane, etc.).

The properties of ethanol

Figure 2 showing displayed formulas and molecular models for ethanol, ethane and water

ethanol   ethane   water

Figure 2 *The displayed formulas and molecular models for ethanol, ethane and water*

Methylated spirits is used in table polishes to spread the polish and obtain a smooth, shiny surface

Look at the structures of ethanol, ethane and water in Figure 2. Ethanol contains a CH_3CH_2- group like ethane and an $-OH$ group like water. So, we would expect ethanol to have some properties like ethane, and some like water.

- **Ethanol is a colourless liquid** (boiling point 78°C). It mixes with water in all proportions.

- **Ethanol is a very good solvent** for molecular substances and will also dissolve ionic substances like water.

- **Ethanol is highly flammable.** It burns very easily (like ethane) with a pale yellow flame forming carbon dioxide and water.

$$C_2H_6O + 3O_2 \rightarrow 2CO_2 + 3H_2O$$

Methylated spirits and ethanol are used as fuels in some countries.

- **Ethanol reacts with sodium** to produce hydrogen. This is very similar to the reaction of sodium with water.

| sodium | + | ethanol | → | sodium ethoxide | + | hydrogen |
| Na | + | CH_3CH_2OH | → | $CH_3CH_2O^-Na^+$ | + | H_2 |

| sodium | + | water | → | sodium hydroxide | + | hydrogen |
| Na | + | HOH | → | HO^-Na^+ | + | H_2 |

- **Ethanol is oxidised** to ethanoic acid (acetic acid) by oxygen in the air. Neither ethane, nor water have a reaction like this.

ethanol   ethanoic acid

Wine goes sour if the bottle is left open for a few days because the ethanol in it is oxidised to ethanoic acid by oxygen in the air. This is how wine vinegar is produced. Malt vinegar is made by a similar process using beer instead of wine.

Study Questions

1 Explain the words:
   fermentation; enzyme; alcohol.
2 a) Why is fermentation important?
   b) What are the main products of the fermentation of starch with yeast?
   c) What causes the fermentation process?
   d) Why are there two important and viable methods for the production of ethanol?
3 The adverts say, 'Don't drink and drive'. Why is this important?
4 a) If an alcohol has *n* carbon atoms, how many hydrogen atoms will it have?
   b) Write a general formula for the family of alcohols.
5 Look at the formula of propanol in Table 1.
   a) Draw another isomer for propanol which is also an alcohol.
   b) Use molecular models to construct propanol and its isomer from part a).

All these foods contain vinegar (ethanoic acid)

Ethanoic acid (acetic acid) is present in vinegar which is used as a flavouring and as a preservative in foods. It is also used to manufacture acetate rayon.

Ethanoic acid is a member of a large class of compounds called **carboxylic acids**. Carboxylic acids form a homologous series of compounds like alkanes and alcohols (Table 1).

Table 1 *The homologous series of carboxylic acids*

Name and formula	Displayed formula
methanoic acid HCOOH	H—C with =O and —OH
ethanoic acid CH_3COOH	H—C(H)(H)—C with =O and —OH
propanoic acid CH_3CH_2COOH	H—C(H)(H)—C(H)(H)—C with =O and —OH

Did you know?

Dogs can track people because they can detect differences in the carboxylic acids in our sweat.

All carboxylic acids contain a –COOH group. This is their functional group which gives them similar properties and reactions.

Notice from Table 1 that carboxylic acids, like alcohols, have names derived from alkanes with the same number of carbon atoms (i.e. methanoic acid from methane, ethanoic acid from ethane, etc.).

More complex carboxylic acids are present in oranges and lemons, in vitamin C and in aspirin tablets.

Oranges, lemons and other citrus fruits contain citric acid. Vitamin C is ascorbic acid which is found in fresh fruit and vegetables. Aspirin is another carboxylic acid which is taken to relieve pain and to prevent heart attacks in patients with circulatory problems.

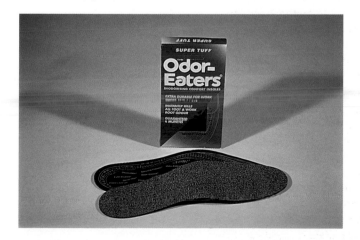

The unpleasant odours from sweaty feet are carboxylic acids including butanoic acid ($CH_3CH_2CH_2COOH$). Odor-eaters are soles that can be placed in footwear to absorb the smelly chemicals which are present in sweat

The properties of ethanoic acid

Ethanoic acid and other carboxylic acids are weak acids.

Ethanoic acid reacts as a typical acid with:

- indicators
- metals
- bases
- carbonates.

e.g.

sodium + ethanoic acid → sodium ethanoate + hydrogen

$$2Na + 2CH_3COOH \rightarrow 2CH_3COO^-Na^+ + H_2$$

sodium hydroxide + ethanoic acid → sodium ethanoate + water

$$NaOH + CH_3COOH \rightarrow CH_3COO^-Na^+ + H_2O$$

The salts from ethanoic acid are called **ethanoates**. They are ionic compounds like the salts from all acids. There is more about ethanoic acid as a weak acid and the typical reactions of acids in Unit G3.

Esterification

Although ethanoic acid and other carboxylic acids have similar reactions to other acids with indicators, metals and bases, they have one reaction which is very different.

Carboxylic acids react with alcohols to produce **esters**.

This reaction:

alcohol + carboxylic acid → ester + water

is called **esterification.**

The reaction is carried out by warming the alcohol and acid with a little concentrated sulphuric acid, which acts as a catalyst for the reaction.

e.g.

ethanol + ethanoic acid → ethyl ethanoate + water

$$CH_3CH_2OH + CH_3COOH \rightarrow CH_3CH_2OCOCH_3 + H_2O$$

Esters are sweet smelling substances used in perfumes and flavourings. For example, ethyl ethanoate and propyl ethanoate give a synthetic pear flavour and ethyl butanoate gives a pineapple flavour.

Study Questions

1. The general formula for carboxylic acids is $C_nH_{2n+1}COOH$. Explain this.

2. Carboxylic acids form a homologous series of compounds in which properties change gradually from one member to the next. The boiling points of methanoic, ethanoic, propanoic and butanoic acids are 101°C, 118°C, 141°C and 166°C respectively.
   a) Plot these boiling points (y-axis) against relative molecular mass (x-axis).
   b) Use the graph to estimate the boiling point of pentanoic acid.

3. Write word equations and balanced chemical equations for the reactions of ethanoic acid with: (i) magnesium; (ii) copper oxide; (iii) sodium carbonate; (iv) methanol.

4. Esters form a homologous series of compounds.
   a) What is the general formula for esters?
   b) What is the functional group in all esters?

Figure 1 *Exothermic and endothermic reactions*

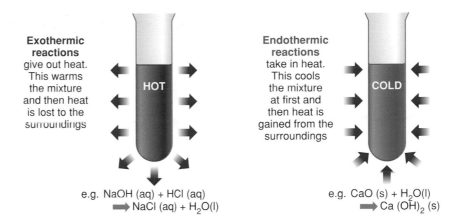

Exothermic reactions give out heat. This warms the mixture and then heat is lost to the surroundings

HOT

e.g. NaOH (aq) + HCl (aq) ➡ NaCl (aq) + $H_2O(l)$

Endothermic reactions take in heat. This cools the mixture at first and then heat is gained from the surroundings

COLD

e.g. CaO (s) + $H_2O(l)$ ➡ Ca $(OH)_2$ (s)

When chemical reactions occur, there is often a temperature change. The temperature change occurs because heat is either given out or taken in as the substances react.

Most chemical reactions are **exothermic**, *giving out heat* as the substances react (Unit I1). Burning fuels are an obvious example of exothermic reactions. Fuels provide most of the heat and energy we use in our homes and industries.

A smaller number of reactions *take in heat* and these are described as **endothermic** reactions (Figure 1).

Measuring energy changes

The amount of energy *given out* or *taken in* during a chemical reaction can be measured. Normally, we measure the heat given out or taken in when one mole of a substance reacts. This energy (heat) change for a reaction is given the symbol ΔH.

For an exothermic reaction, the sign of ΔH is *negative*. This is because the chemicals have *lost* energy to the surroundings. For an endothermic reaction, ΔH is *positive* because the chemicals *gain* energy from the surroundings.

For example, when 1 mole (12 g) of carbon burns, 394 kJ of heat is given out. So we can write:

$$C(s) + O_2(g) \rightarrow CO_2(g) \qquad \Delta H = -394 \text{ kJ}$$

The energy changes in chemical reactions can be summarised in **energy level diagrams**. Figure 2 shows the energy level diagram for burning carbon. In this case, the reaction is exothermic. Energy is lost as the reactants form the product, so the product is at a lower energy level.

It is useful to know how much energy is produced when different fuels burn. This can help us to decide the best fuel for a particular use.

Figure 3 shows a simple apparatus that we could use to measure the heat given out when a liquid fuel like meths burns. **Wear eye protection** if you try this experiment and remember that liquid fuels are highly flammable.

The heat produced from the burning meths warms the water in the metal can.

1 We can work out the heat produced by measuring the temperature rise of the water.

2 We can find the mass of meths which is burnt from the loss in weight of the liquid burner.

3 We can then calculate the heat produced when 1 g of the fuel burns.

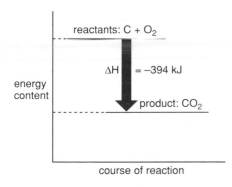

reactants: C + O_2

ΔH = −394 kJ

energy content

product: CO_2

course of reaction

Figure 2 *An energy level diagram for the reaction when carbon burns*

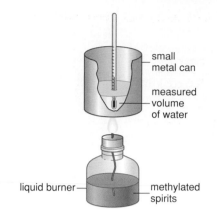

Figure 3

Table 1 *The results of an experiment to measure the heat produced when meths is burnt*

Mass of burner + meths at start of experiment	= 271.8 g
Mass of burner + meths at end of experiment	= 271.3 g
∴ Mass of meths burnt	= 0.5 g
Volume of water in can	= 250 cm³
∴ Mass of water in can	= 250 g
Rise in temp. of water	= 10°C

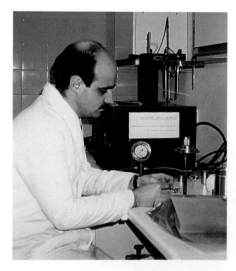

Food scientists use bomb calorimeters like the one in this photo to measure the energy produced by different fuels and food

The results from one experiment are shown in Table 1.

In the experiment, 250 g of water are warmed up by 10°C.

We know that 4.2 joules of heat warm up 1 g of water by 1°C.

So, 250×4.2 J   warm up 250 g of water by 1°C
∴ $250 \times 4.2 \times 10$ J   warm up 250 g of water by 10°C.

This amount of heat is produced by 0.5 g of meths.

$$0.5 \text{ g meths produce } 250 \times 4.2 \times 10 \text{ J} = 10\,500 \text{ J}$$
$$= 10.5 \text{ kJ}$$

∴ 1 g of meths produces 21 kJ

Meths is mainly ethanol (alcohol), CH_3CH_2OH. If we assume that meths is pure ethanol ($M_r = 46$), then:
the heat produced when 1 mole of ethanol burns = 46×21 kJ = 966 kJ
So we can write:
$$C_2H_6O(l) + 3O_2(g) \rightarrow 2CO_2(g) + 3H_2O(l) \quad \Delta H = -966 \text{ kJ}$$

Where does the energy come from?

When a chemical reaction occurs, bonds in the reactants must *break* so that new bonds can be *made* in the products.

Breaking bonds involves pulling atoms apart and this requires energy. On the other hand, making bonds helps to make atoms more stable and this gives out energy.

> Bond *breaking* is endothermic.
> Bond *making* is exothermic.

Figure 4 shows the bond breaking and bond making when hydrogen reacts with chlorine to form hydrogen chloride. The bonds between hydrogen atoms in H_2 molecules and those between chlorine atoms in Cl_2 molecules must first break. These bond breaking processes require energy. New bonds are then made between H and Cl atoms as they form hydrogen chloride. This process gives out energy.

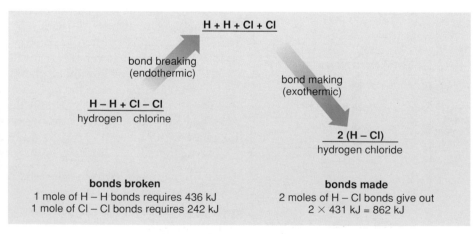

Figure 4 *Bond breaking and bond making when hydrogen and chlorine react*

Table 2 *Bond energies for some different bonds*

Bond	Bond energy /kJ per mole
H–H	436
Cl–Cl	242
H–Cl	431
C–H	413
C–C	347
O=O	498
C=O	805
H–O	464

We can work out the energy changes in these processes using **bond energies** (Table 2).

> Bond energies tell us the average amount of energy taken in or given out when one mole of bonds are broken or made.

From Figure 4:

total energy required for bond breaking = $436 + 242 = 678$ kJ

total energy given out on bond making = 862 kJ

$$\therefore \text{ overall energy change} = 184 \text{ kJ given out}$$
$$\therefore \qquad \Delta H = -184 \text{ kJ}$$

An energy level diagram for this reaction is shown in Figure 5. In an exothermic reaction such as this, the energy released in forming new bonds in the product is greater than the energy needed to break original bonds in the reactants.

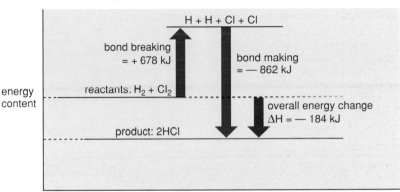

Figure 5 *An energy level diagram for the reaction between hydrogen and chlorine*

In endothermic reactions, it is the opposite. The energy needed to break existing bonds is greater than the energy released in forming new bonds and ΔH will have a positive value.

Study Questions

1 The simple apparatus in Figure 3 does not give very accurate results. An accurate value for the heat produced when meths burns is about 30 kJ per gram.

   a) Why do you think the apparatus in Figure 3 gives inaccurate results?

   b) How would you modify the apparatus in Figure 3 to obtain more accurate results?

2 Draw a diagram of the apparatus you would use to find the heat produced when 1 g of a firelighter burns.

3 When 100 cm³ of 1.0 mol dm⁻³ hydrochloric acid is added to 100 cm³ of 1.0 mol dm⁻³ sodium hydroxide, the temperature of the mixture rises by 6.5°C.

   a) What mass of solution is warmed up? (Assume 1 cm³ of solution has a mass of 1 g.)

   b) How many joules warm up the mixture? (Assume 4.2 J warm up 1 g of solution by 1°C.)

   c) How many moles of hydrochloric acid react?

   d) How much heat is produced when 1 mole of hydrochloric acid reacts? This is called the **heat of neutralisation** of hydrochloric acid.

   e) Write a balanced equation for the reaction involved in d).

4 The energy change for the manufacture of lime (CaO) from limestone (CaCO₃) can be written as:

$$CaCO_3(s) \rightarrow CaO(s) + CO_2(g)$$
$$\Delta H = +178 \text{ kJ}$$

   a) Is the reaction exothermic or endothermic?

   b) Do the products contain more or less energy than the reactants?

   c) Draw an energy level diagram for the reaction.

5 Use the data in Table 2 to find the overall energy change for the reaction when methane burns.
$$CH_4 + 2O_2 \rightarrow CO_2 + 2H_2O$$
(Hint: the bonding in O₂ is O = O and in CO₂ it is O = C = O.)

Section 1   Activities

1 Choosing the right plastic

The properties of six important plastics are shown in the table below. Use the data in the table to suggest which plastic is best to manufacture:

a) containers for lemon juice,
b) laboratory safety screens,
c) wrapping material for cheese,
d) the handles for screwdrivers,
e) the inside surface of frying pans,
f) tea mugs.

In each case, explain why you chose the particular plastic.

Plastic	Relative strength	Flexibility	Maximum temperature for use/°C	Resistance to dilute acids	Resistance to oils	Clarity	Cost /£ per kg
High density polythene	4	fairly stiff	150	excellent	good	poor	0.8
Low density polythene	1	very floppy	70	good	good	poor	0.7
Perspex	9	stiff	90	good	good	excellent	1.6
Polycarbonate	9	stiff	140	excellent	poor	good	3.0
PTFE	30	fairly flexible	250	excellent	excellent	poor	20.0
Urea-formaldehyde resin	9	very stiff	75	poor	good	poor	0.9

2 Chemicals from crude oil – crossword

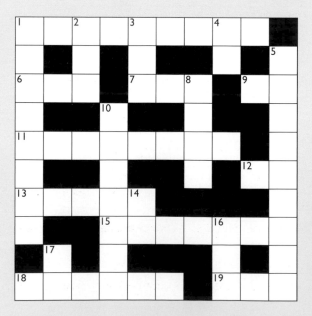

Across

1. (and 1 down) This method is used to split large molecules in the heavier fractions of crude oil (9, 8)
6. Electric currents are measured using this unit (3)
7. Liquid petroleum gas is sold for camping and caravanning under this trade name (3)
9. The formula of a compound produced when fuels do not burn fully (2)
11. Another name for the paraffin fraction from crude oil (8)
12. Symbol for a valuable metal used for jewellery (2)
13. This polymer was named after New York and London because it was first synthesized in both cities at the same time (5)
15. The simplest alkane (7)
18. Probably the most important fraction from crude oil (6)
19. All alkenes have names ending in this (3)

Down

1. (see 1 across)
2. Trichlorophenol is usually shortened to this (3)
3. An abbreviated name for liquid petroleum gas (3)
4. The formula of iodine monofluoride (2)
5. The common name for the most important synthetic plastic (9)
8. The metal used for galvanizing (4)
10. A small molecule which can add to itself (7)
14. The symbol for a noble gas used in advertising (2)
16. All alkanes have names ending in this (3)
17. The symbol of a gas used in weather balloons (2)

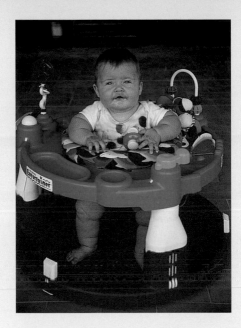

What were toys made of before we had plastics?

3 Pros and cons of the oil industry

Fuels and plastics are probably the most useful and most beneficial products of the oil industry but they also create some problems.

Get into small groups of three or four to discuss the following four questions. Prepare a short report on each question for the whole class.

I What benefits do we get from the range of: (i) fuels; (ii) plastics from crude oil?

2 What problems have resulted from the extraction and transport of crude oil?

3 What problems have resulted from the use of fuels from crude oil?

4 What problems have resulted from the disposal and recycling of plastic waste?

4 Margarine from vegetable oil

The apparatus below can be used to add hydrogen to vegetable oils and make margarine.

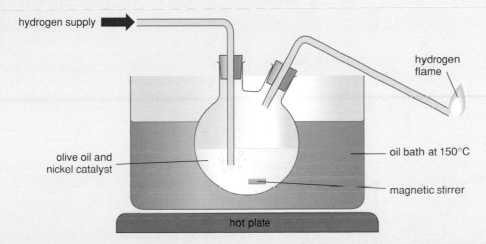

Fraction	Boiling range in °C
Gas	below 40
Petrol	40–160
Kerosine	160–250
Diesel oil	250–300
Lubricating oil	300–350

I At the start of the experiment, hydrogen is passed through the apparatus for a few minutes before the flame is lit. Why is this done?

2 Choose a crude oil fraction from the table on the left for use in the oil bath. Explain your choice.

3 Give one reason for using a hotplate rather than a Bunsen for heating.

4 Each molecule in olive oil contains three carbon—carbon double bonds. How many hydrogen atoms will have been added to one molecule when the reaction is complete?

5 What simple test would you use to show that the reaction had completely saturated the carbon-carbon double bonds in olive oil?

6 What has been done in the experiment to speed up the reaction?

7 Some brands of margarine are described as **polyunsaturated**. What does this mean?

5 Searching the web – fuel cells

Use a search engine to find out what **fuel cells** are, how they work and what use they may be in the future.

Section 1 Summary

1 Crude oil and its products

- Crude oil is a finite, non-renewable **fossil fuel** like coal and natural gas.

- Crude oil contains hundreds of different carbon compounds. These and other carbon compounds are often called **organic compounds**.

- Most of the compounds in crude oil are **hydrocarbons** – compounds containing only hydrogen and carbon. Hydrocarbons are typical simple molecular compounds. They have low melting points and boiling points. They do not conduct electricity and are insoluble in water.

- Crude oil is separated into different fractions by **fractional distillation**. More petrol is required than can be provided by fractional distillation. Additional petrol can be obtained by **cracking** the heavier fractions of diesel and fuel oil using a catalyst at high temperature.

2 Alkanes

- Alkanes form a homologous series of hydrocarbons with similar properties in which the formulas differ by CH_2 e.g. methane, CH_4; ethane, C_2H_6; propane, C_3H_8; etc.

- Alkanes have strong C—C and C—H bonds so they have few reactions. They do, however, burn on reaction with oxygen.

3 Alkenes

- Alkenes contain a carbon—carbon double bond (C = C).
  They are described as **unsaturated**. Compounds with entirely single bonds like alkanes are described as **saturated**.

- Alkenes are much more reactive than alkanes.
  Their reactive double bond allows them to undergo **addition reactions** with bromine water, with hydrogen and with water (forming ethanol).

4 Polymers/plastics

- Alkenes are so reactive they can be made to undergo addition reactions with themselves (as monomers) to form **polymers**. e.g. ethene polymerises to polythene (polyethene).

- These polymers, including polythene, polypropene, PVC and melamine are important **plastics**.

- There are two types of plastic:
  thermosoftening plastics, like polythene, polypropene and PVC, which soften on warming and set hard again on cooling;
  thermosetting plastics, like melamine and glues, which cannot be softened once they have set hard.

5 Ethanol and alcohols

- Ethanol is produced by two processes. They are:
  Fermentation of sugars for the production of alcoholic drinks,
  Hydration of ethene from cracking for the production of industrial alcohol and methylated spirits.

- Alcohols form a homologous series of compounds with the general formula $C_nH_{2n+2}O$. Their functional group is –OH.

- Ethanol is a solvent for both molecular and ionic substances. It burns in air (oxygen), reacts with sodium producing hydrogen and is oxidised to ethanoic acid.

6 Ethanoic acid and carboxylic acids

- Carboxylic acids form a homologous series of compounds with the general formula $C_nH_{2n}O_2$. Their functional group is –COOH.

- Carboxylic acids are **weak acids**.

- Ethanoic acid reacts as a **typical acid** with indicators, metals, bases and carbonates.

- Carboxylic acids react with alcohols to form **esters**. The reaction: alcohol + carboxylic acid $\rightarrow$ ester + water is known as **esterification**.

7 Energy changes

- Chemical reactions are often accompanied by temperature changes.

- **Exothermic reactions** *give out heat*. **Endothermic reactions** *take in heat*.

- The energy (heat) change in a reaction is given the symbol **ΔH**. This can be shown alongside the equation or in an energy level diagram.
  ΔH relates to the number of moles shown in the equation or on the energy level diagram.
  ΔH is *negative* for exothermic reactions.
  ΔH is *positive* for endothermic reactions.

- **Bond energies** tell us the average amount of energy taken in or given out when one mole of bonds are broken or made.

- **Bond breaking** is endothermic. **Bond making** is exothermic.

- Using bond energies, it is possible to calculate the energy change in a reaction by considering the bonds broken and made.

1   Crude oil is an important resource.
    It was formed over millions of years from the remains of dead plants and animals that were buried in sediments.
    (a) Describe the conditions necessary for these remains to form crude oil.
    (b) (i)   The oil industry uses fractionating towers to split crude oil into more useful substances. The table shows some information about the fractions.
          Write out statements to fill the **two** spaces in the table.

boiling point range	number of carbon atoms in molecules	name	main use
up to 40°C	1–4	refinery gas	bottled gas
40–160°C	5–10	gasoline	petrol for cars
160–250°C	11–12	kerosene	....
250–340°C	13–25	diesel oil	diesel engine fuel
above 340°C	above 25	bitumen	....

    (ii) How does the boiling point change as the number of carbon atoms, in the above molecules, increases?
    (iii) Explain how the process of fractional distillation separates crude oil into more useful substances.
    (iv) Octadecane, $C_{18}H_{38}$, is found in the diesel oil fraction.
          Suggest the boiling point of octadecane. Use the table to help you.
    (c) (i)   Octadecane can be **cracked** into smaller molecules.
          One way is shown in the equation.

    $C_{18}H_{38} \rightarrow C_8H_{16} + C_8H_{18} + C_2H_4$
    octadecane → octene + ... + ...

          Copy and finish the word equation for this reaction.
    (ii) Explain why cracking long chain compounds such as octadecane enables oil companies to make more profit.
          Use the equation in **(c)(i)** to help you with your answer.
    (d) The refinery gases fraction contains propene and propane.

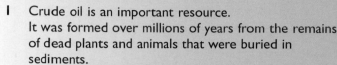

propene   propane

    (i)   Describe a chemical test which can be used to distinguish between propene and propane.
    (ii) Propene can be polymerised, but propane cannot. Explain why this is so.
    (iii) Write an equation to represent the polymerisation of propene.

OCR 2001

2   Ethanol is manufactured in two ways.
    (a) Ethanol is produced by the fermentation of a carbohydrate.
    (i)   What must be added to a solution of the carbohydrate to make fermentation occur?
    (ii) Name the process used to separate ethanol from the fermentation mixture.
    (b) Ethanol is produced by the hydration of ethene.
    (i)   Write a balanced chemical equation, including state symbols, for the hydration of ethene.
    (ii) State the conditions for this reaction.
    (c) Country **A** is a large country where the climate allows crops to grow easily. It is a relatively poor country with no oil reserves.
    Country **B** is densely populated. It is a relatively rich country and has its own oil reserves.
    Explain, with reasons in each case, which method of ethanol production (fermentation or hydration) is likely to be used in each country.
    (d) Ethane can be formed by dehydrating ethanol using concentrated sulphuric acid.
    (i)   Copy and complete the equation for this process.

    $C_2H_5OH \rightarrow C_2H_4 + $ ....

    (ii) Calculate the maximum volume of ethene, measured at room temperature and atmospheric pressure, that can be produced from 2.30 kg of ethanol.
    (Relative atomic masses: C = 12; H = 1.0; O = 16)
    (1 mol of gas occupies 24.0 dm³ at room temperature and atmospheric pressure.)
    (iii) The concentrated sulphuric acid used in the process is manufactured using the Contact process. Describe and explain how sulphur trioxide, produced in the Contact process, is converted into sulphuric acid. Include a balanced equation in your answer.

Edexcel 2001

3 (a) Describe briefly how crude oil was formed.

(b) Propene and propane can be produced from crude oil.

   (i) A propene molecule (C_3H_6) can be represented by the structure shown below.

$$
\begin{array}{c}
H \qquad\quad H \quad H \\
\diagdown \qquad\quad | \qquad | \\
C = C - C - H \\
\diagup \qquad\qquad\quad | \\
H \qquad\qquad\quad H
\end{array}
$$

      Draw a similar diagram to show the structure of a propane molecule (C_3H_8).

   (ii) Which molecule, propene or propane, is unsaturated?

      Give a reason for your answer.

(c) The equation below represents the polymerisation of propene.

$$
n \left(\begin{array}{c} H \quad H \\ | \quad\ | \\ C = C \\ | \quad\ | \\ H \quad CH_3 \end{array} \right) \longrightarrow \left(\begin{array}{c} H \quad H \\ | \quad\ | \\ -C - C - \\ | \quad\ | \\ H \quad CH_3 \end{array} \right)_n
$$

   (i) Name the polymer produced by this reaction.

   (ii) Explain the meaning of the term polymerisation.

                     AQA 2000

4 Ethanol can be made from sugar solution by the process of fermentation.

Fermentation is the method used to make alcoholic drinks.

(a) State why distillation can be used to separate the ethanol from the fermented mixture

(b) (i) Give **one** health problem associated with alcoholic abuse.

   (ii) Give **one** social problem associated with alcoholic abuse.

(c) Ethanol in wine is easily changed to ethanoic acid (vinegar).

   (i) What causes this change?

   (ii) Give the name for the chemical process taking place.

                   WJEC 2000

5 Glucose can be fermented with yeast to produce ethanol and carbon dioxide.

The equation which represents this reaction is shown below.

$$C_6H_{12}O_6(aq) \quad \rightarrow \quad 2C_2H_5OH(aq) \quad + \quad 2CO_2(g)$$

(a) (i) Yeast is needed for the fermentation. Why is yeast not written in the equation?

   (ii) Suggest why temperatures above 45°C are not used for fermentation.

(b) Use the equation above to help you with the following calculations.

0.10 mole of glucose was completely fermented. Calculate:

   (i) the number of moles of ethanol produced.

   (ii) the mass in grams of ethanol produced. (Relative atomic masses: $H = 1$, $C = 12$, $O = 16$)

   (iii) the volume, at room temperature and pressure, of carbon dioxide gas produced. (1 mole of any gas occupies 24 litres at room temperature and pressure)

(c) Most of the pure ethanol made in the United Kingdom is made from ethene. Ethene is reacted with steam in the presence of a catalyst. The equation which represents the reaction is:

$$C_2H_4(g) \quad + \quad H_2O(g) \quad \rightarrow \quad C_2H_5OH(g)$$

Explain why **this** process is preferred to fermentation by the chemical industry.

Your answer should include:
- information about the raw materials,
- the type of process,
- the rate of reaction,
- the quality of the product.

(d) Ethanol can be converted to ethanoic acid, CH_3COOH.

   (i) What type of reaction takes place when ethanol is converted to ethanoic acid?

   (ii) Ethanol and ethanoic acid can react in the presence of an acid catalyst to produce ethyl ethanoate. What type of substance is ethyl ethanoate?

(e) Ethanol and ethanoic acid are both colourless liquids at room temperature.

Describe what you would **see** if sodium carbonate solution was added to each liquid in separate test tubes.

                   AQA 2000

6 The alcohols are an example of an homologous series.

(a) (i) The structures of the first two alcohols in the series are shown.

      Copy and complete the table to show the names and the structures of all the alcohols.

Name	Structure
....	H | H—C—O—H | H
Ethanol	H H | | H—C—C—O—H | | H H
Propanol	
Butanol	

(ii) Why are these alcohols members of the same homologous series?

(iii) Describe a trend in a physical property of these alcohols.

(b) Compounds in the same homologous series undergo similar chemical reactions.
Describe one such reaction of the alcohols.
Write a balanced equation to show this reaction for one of the alcohols.

Edexcel (specimen paper, 2003)

7   Cars in Brazil use ethanol as a fuel instead of petrol (octane). The ethanol is produced by the fermentation of sugar solution from sugar cane.

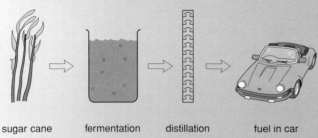

sugar cane   fermentation   distillation   fuel in car

(a) What must be added to sugar solution to make it ferment?

(b) Choose the most suitable temperature for a fermentation.

0°C   10°C   30°C   70°C   100°C

(c) (i) What compounds are formed by the complete combustion of ethanol?

(ii) Why are these compounds **not** harmful to the environment?

(d) Suggest why pollution from cars is less when using ethanol instead of petrol.

(e) Give **one** reason why ethanol is **not** used as a fuel for cars in Britain.

(f) Some information about octane and ethanol is shown.

Property	Octane	Ethanol
Melting point in °C	−57	−113
Boiling point in °C	125	78.5
Density in g/cm^3	0.70	0.79
Heat produced in kJ/mol	5512	1367

Explain a similarity between octane and ethanol that allows ethanol to be used as a fuel in cars.

AQA 2000

8   Octane is a saturated hydrocarbon.
Its graphical (displayed) formula is

H   H   H   H   H   H   H   H
\| \| \| \| \| \| \| \|
H—C —C —C —C —C —C —C —C —H
\| \| \| \| \| \| \| \|
H   H   H   H   H   H   H   H

(a) Choose from the following words the family to which octane belongs.

alkanes   alkenes   carbohydrates   carbonates

(b) The products formed when octane burns in air depend upon the amount of air.
Explain this statement.

(c) When octane vapour is passed over a heated catalyst a reaction takes place.
Ethene and hydrogen are the only products.

(i) What type of reaction is taking place?

(ii) Copy, finish and balance the symbol equation for this reaction.

octane   →   ethene   +   hydrogen
C_8H_{18} → ......C_2H_4 + ...

(iii) Excess ethene is bubbled through bromine water.
What colour change would you see?

(d) Ethene is used as the raw material for making poly(ethene).

(i) Draw the graphical (displayed) formula of ethene and of poly(ethene).

(ii) Poly(ethene) has replaced paper and cardboard for many packaging uses.
Suggest one advantage and one disadvantage of poly(ethene) compared to paper and cardboard. Do not consider the relative costs of the materials.

OCR 2000

Reaction Rates

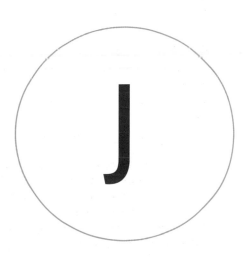

Explosives are used in mining to break up rock. Explosions with dynamite are so fast that they occur in less than a millisecond

By the end of this section you should be able to:

- Recall the great variation in the rates at which different reactions take place.
- Understand how temperature, concentration, surface area and catalysts affect reaction rates.
- Explain how reaction rates depend on the collisions between particles, how often particles collide and the energy with which particles collide.
- Understand the effect of temperature and pH on the rates of enzyme-catalysed reactions.
- Describe the use of enzymes in baking, brewing and other industries.
- Understand the importance of converting nitrogen to ammonia.
- Recall how nitrogenous fertilisers are manufactured, their effect on plant growth and the problems caused by their over-use.
- Understand that temperature and pressure can affect the yield in reversible reactions.

J

How Fast?

Limestone is weathered so slowly that it takes centuries before the effect is noticed. The face on this statue has been reacting with the carbonic acid in rainwater for more than 300 years

Everyday we are concerned about how fast things happen. We want to know how quickly we can get to school, how fast a car is travelling or how soon the post will arrive. We are also interested in how fast some chemical reactions occur, how long we need to boil an egg or bake a cake and how quickly the rust appears on bikes and cars.

Most kitchens have a cooker to speed up chemical reactions during the cooking of food and a fridge to slow down reactions and prevent food going bad.

Different chemical reactions go at different rates.

Some reactions, like explosions, are incredibly fast. A small explosion takes place during the 'pop' test for hydrogen. When a burning splint is put into a test tube of hydrogen, there is a 'pop'. Heat from the flame causes hydrogen to react instantly with oxygen in the air forming water vapour.

$$\text{hydrogen} + \text{oxygen} \rightarrow \text{water}$$
$$2H_2(g) + O_2(g) \rightarrow 2H_2O(g)$$

Other reactions, like the rusting of steel and the weathering of limestone on buildings, happen so slowly that it may be years or even centuries before we notice their effects.

Most reactions take place at speeds somewhere between these extremes. The reactions which take place when coal is burnt and when food is cooked are good examples of reactions which occur at steady rates.

Why are reaction rates important?

Bio-yoghurt is made using bacteria. Enzymes in the bacteria react with the sugar in milk to form lactic acid. This makes the milk curdle to produce yoghurt

Reaction rates are very important in living things.

Most of the reactions in our bodies and in other living things would never happen if the reacting substances were just mixed together. Fortunately every reaction in our bodies is helped along by its own special **catalyst**. Catalysts allow the chemicals to react more easily. The catalysts in living things are called **enzymes**. Without enzymes the reactions in your body would stop and you would die.

One of these enzymes is amylase. Amylase is present in saliva. It speeds up the first stage in the breakdown of starch in foods such as bread, potatoes and rice.

Reaction rates are also important in industry.

Industrial chemists are not usually satisfied with just turning one substance into another. They want to carry out reactions faster and more cheaply. In industry, speeding up slow reactions makes them more economical because saving time usually saves money.

The key reaction in the manufacture of sulphuric acid is the contact process (Unit G1). This involves converting sulphur dioxide and oxygen to sulphur trioxide.

$$\text{sulphur dioxide} + \text{oxygen} \rightarrow \text{sulphur trioxide}$$
$$2SO_2 + O_2 \rightarrow 2SO_3$$

At room temperature, this reaction will not happen. But chemical engineers have found that the reaction takes place quickly at 450°C if a catalyst of vanadium(V) oxide or platinum is used. By using a catalyst, sulphuric acid can be made faster and more cheaply. This is important because sulphuric acid is a major industrial chemical. Many industrial processes also use enzymes. These processes include brewing, baking, yoghurt-making and cheese-making (Unit J5).

Study Questions

1 Make a list of the various ways in which gardeners speed up the growth rate of their plants.

2 Find out about the process of fermentation in the manufacture of beer and wine. What part do catalysts play in the process? Prepare a short report of your findings.

3 a) State three ways in which food can be preserved and stored without 'going bad'.

   b) What conditions slow down the rate at which foods deteriorate (go bad)?

4 a) How do you think a pressure cooker speeds up the rate at which food is cooked?

   b) Why do you think a microwave oven can speed up the rate at which food is cooked?

A workman fitting a special catalyst section to the exhaust system of a car. The catalyst removes carbon monoxide and nitrogen oxide from the car's exhaust fumes

229

A chemical reaction cannot happen unless particles in the reacting substances collide with each other.

This statement explains why reactions between gases and liquids usually happen faster than reactions involving solids. Particles in gases and liquids can mix and collide much more easily than particles in solids. In a solid, only the particles on the surface can react.

During a reaction, reactants are being used up and products are forming. The amounts of the reactants fall as the amounts of the products rise. So, we can measure reaction rates by measuring how much of a reactant is used up or how much of a product forms in a given time.

$$\text{Reaction rate} = \frac{\text{change in amount of a substance}}{\text{time taken}}$$

For example, when 0.1 g of magnesium was added to dilute hydrochloric acid, the magnesium reacted and disappeared in 10 seconds.

$$\therefore \quad \text{Reaction rate} = \frac{\text{change in mass of magnesium}}{\text{time taken}}$$
$$= \frac{0.1 \text{ g}}{10} \text{ magnesium used up per second}$$
$$= 0.01 \text{ g s}^{-1}$$

Strictly speaking, this is the *average* reaction rate over the 10 seconds for all the magnesium to react. Although reaction rates are usually measured as changes in mass or volume with time, we can also use changes in concentration, pressure and colour with time.

Calculating reaction rates

When marble chips (calcium carbonate) react with dilute hydrochloric acid, carbon dioxide is produced.

$$\begin{array}{ccccccc} \text{calcium} & + & \text{hydrochloric} & \rightarrow & \text{calcium} & + & \text{water} + \text{carbon} \\ \text{carbonate} & & \text{acid} & & \text{chloride} & & \text{dioxide} \end{array}$$

$$CaCO_3(s) + 2HCl(aq) \rightarrow CaCl_2(aq) + H_2O(l) + CO_2(g)$$

The carbon dioxide escapes from the flask and so the mass of the flask and its contents decrease.

The rate of the reaction can be studied using the apparatus in Figure 1. Figure 2 shows how you could follow the reaction using data logging equipment.

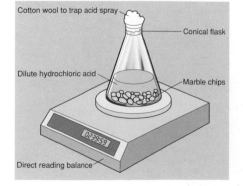

Figure 1 *Measuring the rate of reaction between marble chips and hydrochloric acid*

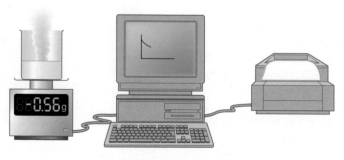

Figure 2 *Data logging equipment to follow the experiment*

The results of one experiment are given in Table 1. These results have been plotted on a graph in Figure 3. During the first minute there is a decrease in mass of 1.5 g as carbon dioxide escapes.

$\therefore$ Average rate of reaction in the first minute

$$= \frac{\text{change in mass}}{\text{time taken}} = \frac{1.5}{1} = 1.5 \text{ g of carbon dioxide per minute}$$

During the second minute (from time = 1 minute to time = 2 minutes), 1.0 g of carbon dioxide escapes.
$\therefore$ Average rate of reaction in the second minute

$$= \frac{1.0}{1} = 1.0 \text{ g of } CO_2 \text{ per minute.}$$

Notice that the reaction is fastest at the start of the reaction when the slope of the graph in Figure 3 is steepest. During the reaction, the rate falls and the slope begins to level off. Eventually the reaction rate becomes zero and the graph becomes flat with a slope (gradient) of zero.

Study Questions

1 Look at the results in Table 1 and the graph in Figure 3.
  a) What mass of carbon dioxide is lost from the flask in:
   (i) the third minute (time 2 to 3 minutes); (ii) the fourth minute (time 3 to 4 minutes); (iii) the fifth minute (time 4 to 5 minutes)?
  b) What is happening to the reaction rate as time passes?
  c) Explain the change in reaction rate with time.
  d) Why does the graph become horizontal after a while?
2 a) When magnesium reacts with dilute hydrochloric acid, does the magnesium react faster at the start of the reaction or at the finish?
  b) Give two reasons for your answer in part a).
3 a) Weedkillers can be added to a lawn either as solid pellets or as aqueous. solutions. Which method will affect the weeds faster? Explain your answer.
  b) The selective weedkiller 2,4D kills dandelions in a lawn, but not the grass. How do you think it works?

Table 1 *The results of one experiment to measure the rate of reaction between marble chips and dilute hydrochloric acid*

Time /minutes	Mass of flask and contents (g)	Decrease in mass (g)	Decrease in mass for each minute interval (g)
0	78.00	0	
			1.50
1	76.50	1.50	
			1.00
2	75.50	2.50	
			0.55
3	74.95	3.05	
			0.35
4	74.60	3.40	
			0.19
5	74.41	3.59	
			0.08
6	74.33	3.67	
			0.03
7	74.30	3.70	
			0
8	74.30	3.70	

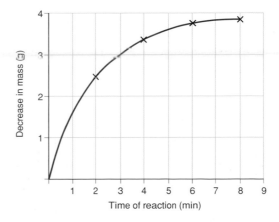

Figure 3

Making Reactions go Faster

Anyone who has tried to light a fire knows that it is easier to burn sticks than logs. The main reason for this is that sticks have a greater surface area. There is a larger area of contact with the air and so sticks burn more easily.

In general, reactions go faster when there is more surface area to react.

It's easier to get a fire started with sticks rather than logs

Surface area and reaction rates

Joanne and Sunil used the reaction between marble chips (calcium carbonate) and dilute hydrochloric acid to study the effect of surface area on reaction rate.

$$CaCO_3(s) + 2HCl(aq) \rightarrow CaCl_2(aq) + H_2O(l) + CO_2(g)$$

Figure 1 shows their apparatus. During the reaction, carbon dioxide escapes from the reacting mixture and collects in the syringe. Their results are shown in Figure 2.

In experiment I, they used five small marble chips (total mass = 2 g) and 50 cm³ of dilute hydrochloric acid.

In experiment II, they used one large marble chip (mass = 2 g) and 50 cm³ of the same acid.

There is more than enough marble in both experiments, so the acid will be used up first.

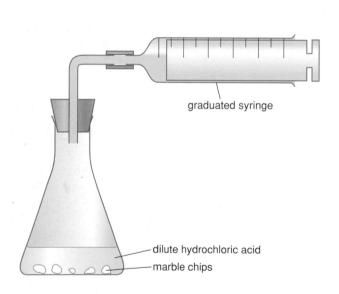

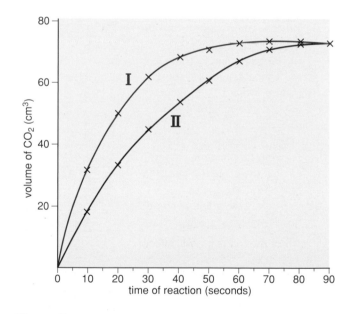

Figure 1 *Investigating the effect of surface area on reaction rate*   **Figure 2**

Look at the results of the experiments in Figure 2.

1 Why is the final volume of carbon dioxide the same in both experiments?

2 Why do graphs become flat?

3 Which graph shows the larger volume of CO_2 produced per minute at the start of the experiment?

4 Which experiment begins at the faster rate?

5 Why is the reaction rate different in the two experiments?

Concentration and reaction rates

Substances that burn in air burn much more rapidly in oxygen. Charcoal in a barbecue normally burns very slowly with a red glow. But, if you blow onto it so that it gets more air and more oxygen, it glows much brighter and may burst into flames. In oxy-acetylene torches, acetylene burns in pure oxygen. These torches produce temperatures up to 2800°C and the flame can be used to cut through sheets of metal.

$$\text{acetylene} + \text{oxygen} \rightarrow \text{carbon dioxide} + \text{water}$$
$$C_2H_2 + 2\tfrac{1}{2}O_2 \rightarrow 2CO_2 + H_2O$$

Chemical reactions occur when particles of the reacting substances collide with each other.

When oxygen is used instead of air, the concentration of oxygen is greater. So, collisions between acetylene molecules and oxygen molecules occur more often. The reaction happens faster and gives off more heat. Pure oxygen is also used to speed up chemical changes in the body. This can help the recovery of hospital patients suffering from extensive burns.

In general, reactions go faster when the concentration of reactants is increased.

In reactions between gases, the concentration of each gas can be increased by increasing its pressure. Some industrial processes will only occur at very high pressures. For example, in the Haber process, (Unit J7), nitrogen and hydrogen can be made to react at a reasonable rate by increasing the pressure to 250 times atmospheric pressure.

Study Questions

1 It takes about 10 minutes to fry chips, but about 20 minutes to boil potatoes. Larger potatoes take even longer to boil.
   a) Why do larger potatoes take longer to cook than small ones?
   b) Why can chips be cooked faster than boiled potatoes?
   c) Why can boiled potatoes be cooked faster in a pressure cooker?
2 Why do gaseous reactions go faster if the pressure of the reacting gases is increased?
3 Which of the following will affect the rate at which a candle burns: *the temperature of the air; the shape of the candle; the air pressure; the length of the wick?* Explain your answer.
   State two other factors that will affect the rate at which a candle burns.
4 Design an experiment to investigate the effect of acid concentration on the weathering of limestone.
   Do not carry out your experiment unless it has been checked by your teacher.

Oxy-acetylene flames being used to cut through a large sheet of steel. In oxy-acetylene torches, acetylene burns very rapidly in pure oxygen

Temperature and Reaction Rates

Fish, meat and soft fruit can be kept for long periods in a freezer where the temperature is about −18°C. (The temperature in a fridge is about 5°C)

Milk will keep for days in a cool refrigerator, but it turns sour very quickly if it is left in the sun. Other perishable foods, like strawberries and cream also go bad more quickly at higher temperatures.

This is because:

> Chemical reactions go faster at higher temperatures.

Chemical reactions can be speeded up by increasing the temperature, or slowed down by reducing the temperature. The chemical reactions which occur when food is cooked would never happen unless the food was heated.

The effect of temperature on reaction rates can be studied using the reaction between sodium thiosulphate solution ($Na_2S_2O_3(aq)$) and dilute hydrochloric acid.

sodium thiosulphate	+	hydrochloric acid	→	sodium chloride	+	water	+	sulphur dioxide	+	sulphur

$$Na_2S_2O_3(aq) + 2HCl(aq) \rightarrow 2NaCl(aq) + H_2O(l) + SO_2(g) + S(s)$$

When the reactants are mixed, a fine precipitate of sulphur starts to form. The solution turns cloudy and then more yellow (Figure 1).

Figure 1 *Investigating the effect of temperature on reaction rate*

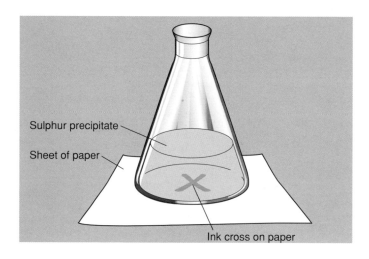

Sulphur precipitate

Sheet of paper

Ink cross on paper

As the precipitate forms, the ink cross on white paper slowly disappears. We can study the reaction rate by mixing 5 cm³ of dilute hydrochloric acid with 50 cm³ of sodium thiosulphate solution and then measure the time it takes for the cross to disappear.

Table 1 shows the results obtained when the reaction was carried out at different temperatures.

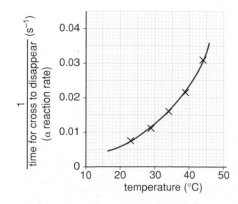

Figure 2 *A graph of the reciprocal of the time for the cross to disappear (∝ reaction rate) against temperature*

Table 1 *Studying the reaction between sodium thiosulphate solution and dilute hydrochloric acid at different temperatures*

Temperature (°C)	Time for cross to disappear (s)	$\dfrac{1}{\text{time for cross to disappear}}$ (s^{-1})
23	132	0.0076
29	90	0.0111
34	65	0.0154
39	46	0.0217
44	33	0.0313

Study Questions

1 The curves in the graph in Figure 4 show the volume of hydrogen produced during different experiments to investigate the reaction between magnesium and hydrochloric acid. Curve X is obtained when 1 g of magnesium ribbon reacts with 100 cm³ (excess) hydrochloric acid at 30°C. Which of the curves A, B, C or D would you expect to obtain when:

a) 1g of magnesium ribbon reacts with 100 cm³ of the same acid at 50°C?

b) 1g of magnesium ribbon reacts with 100 cm³ of the same acid at 15°C?

c) 0.5g of magnesium ribbon reacts with 100 cm³ of the same acid at 30°C?

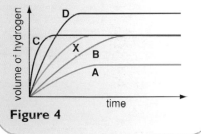

Figure 4

Notice from the results in Table 1 that:

- The cross disappears more quickly at higher temperatures. This means that the reaction goes faster at higher temperatures.

- If the temperature rises by 10°C, the reaction rate is about twice as fast. For example, at 29°C the cross disappears in 90 seconds, whilst at 39°C it disappears in about half that time (46 seconds).

Using the equation for reaction rate in Unit J2, we can say,

$$\text{reaction rate} = \frac{\text{change in amount of sulphur}}{\text{time taken}}$$

$$= \frac{\text{amount of sulphur precipitated}}{\text{time taken}}$$

The cross disappears at the same thickness of precipitate each time. So, the amount of sulphur precipitated is the same at each temperature.

$$\therefore \text{ reaction rate} \propto \frac{1}{\text{time for cross to disappear}}$$

Figure 2 shows a graph of this reciprocal against temperature. The graph shows clearly that the reaction rate increases as temperature increases.

Why do chemical reactions go faster at higher temperatures?

At higher temperatures, particles move about faster. So they collide more often and this causes the reactions to go faster. But particles do not always react when they collide. Particles must collide with enough energy to react. Sometimes the particles collide but do not have enough energy for bonds to stretch and break. Higher temperatures give particles more energy, so that if they collide, they are more likely to react.

So there are two reasons why reactions go faster at higher temperatures:
- The particles move faster at higher temperatures and collide more often;
- The particles collide with more energy at higher temperatures, so more collisions result in a reaction.

Figure 3 *If cars collide at slow speeds (with low energy), they hardly dent each other. But if cars collide at high speeds (with high energy), they get smashed to pieces*

The collisions between reacting particles can be compared to collisions between cars (Figure 3). If particles collide with little energy, bonds cannot break to form new substances. If cars collide at slow speeds (with low energy), they hardly dent each other. But, if cars collide at high speeds (with high energy), they bend and break.

Hydrogen peroxide solution, $H_2O_2(aq)$, decomposes very slowly into water and oxygen at room temperature.

$$2H_2O_2(aq) \rightarrow 2H_2O(l) + O_2(g)$$

When manganese(IV) oxide (MnO_2) is added, the hydrogen peroxide decomposes very rapidly. The manganese(IV) oxide helps the hydrogen peroxide to decompose, but it is not used up in the reaction.

The manganese(IV) oxide left at the end of the reaction weighs exactly the same as that at the start. This means that the manganese dioxide has acted as a **catalyst**.

> Catalysts are substances which change the rate of chemical reactions without being used up during the reaction.

How do catalysts work?

Different catalysts work in different ways. Solid catalysts, like manganese dioxide and platinum alloys in catalytic converters, work by adsorption (Figure 1).

Did you know?

Catalytic converters remove 90% of the polluting gases from car exhaust fumes.

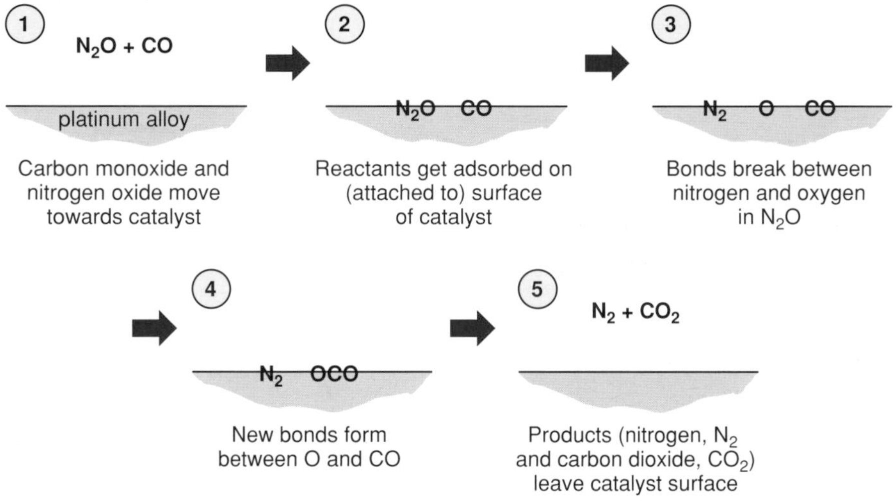

(1) N₂O + CO

platinum alloy

Carbon monoxide and nitrogen oxide move towards catalyst

(2) N₂O   CO

Reactants get adsorbed on (attached to) surface of catalyst

(3) N₂   O   CO

Bonds break between nitrogen and oxygen in N₂O

(4) N₂   OCO

New bonds form between O and CO

(5) N₂ + CO₂

Products (nitrogen, N₂ and carbon dioxide, CO₂) leave catalyst surface

Figure 1 *Platinum alloy in a catalytic converter allows poisonous carbon monoxide and nitrogen oxide to react more easily forming harmless nitrogen and carbon dioxide*

The molecules of reacting substances get adsorbed on (attached to) the surface of the catalyst. This brings the reacting molecules close together. Their bonds can now stretch and break more easily. New bonds can also form more easily to give the products.

Finally, the products leave the surface of the catalyst so that it can be used again.

Catalysts can be compared to motorways. Catalysts (motorways) provide a faster, easier path (route) for the reaction (journey). This needs less energy (petrol) than the uncatalysed reaction (winding and narrow roads).

Catalysts play an important part in the chemical industry. They are used in the production of petrol (Unit I4), margarine (Unit I5), sulphuric acid (Unit G1) and ammonia (Unit J7). Catalysts speed up these industrial processes and the products are obtained faster. They also allow the processes to occur at lower temperatures with a saving on energy costs.

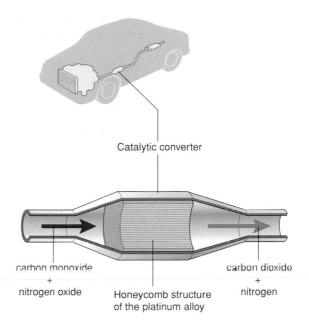

Catalytic converter

carbon monoxide
+
nitrogen oxide

Honeycomb structure
of the platinum alloy

carbon dioxide
+
nitrogen

The catalysts in many of these important industrial processes are transition metals or their compounds. Iron is the catalyst for the manufacture of ammonia in the Haber process. Nickel is the catalyst in the production of margarine. Platinum or vanadium(V) oxide is the catalyst for the manufacture of sulphuric acid.

Enzymes – biological catalysts

> Enzymes are biological catalysts.

Enzymes catalyse the production of sugars by photosynthesis and the breakdown of our food. They also catalyse the synthesis of important chemicals like proteins in our muscles and DNA in our genes.

Enzymes are crucial to life. Without enzymes, the reactions in our bodies and in all living things would go so slowly that we would die.

Enzymes are proteins. They are synthesised in living things using other enzymes as catalysts.

Figure 2 *Liver and some plant tissues contain an enzyme called catalase. The enzyme is produced by organisms in order to break down hydrogen peroxide. As the photos show, liver can decompose hydrogen peroxide very rapidly. The catalase in liver is thousands of times better than manganese(IV) oxide in catalysing the decomposition of hydrogen peroxide*

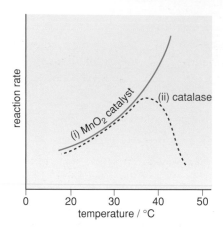

Figure 3 *Comparing the rate of decomposition of H_2O_2 at different temperatures with (i) MnO_2 as catalyst, (ii) the enzyme catalase*

Enzymes are very *specific* in the reactions they catalyse. So, catalase, the enzyme which breaks down hydrogen peroxide (Figure 2) does not catalyse the breakdown of any other molecules similar to hydrogen peroxide, like water.

The effect of temperature on enzymes

Figure 3 shows how the rate of decomposition of hydrogen peroxide changes with temperature:

(i) using manganese(IV) oxide as a catalyst, and

(ii) using the enzyme catalase.

Most catalysed reactions go faster as the temperature rises like the graph for MnO_2 in Figure 3. The reaction rates of enzyme-catalysed reactions also increase at fairly low temperatures like catalase in Figure 3. But, above about 40°C their reaction rate decreases rapidly as temperature rises.

This is because enzymes are proteins and their complicated structure is disrupted as the temperature rises. This disruption to the protein structure is called **denaturation**. As the enzyme's structure is disrupted, it becomes less and less effective as a catalyst. As the temperature rises further, the structure of the enzyme changes even more. The enzyme is said to be denatured and the reaction eventually stops.

The effect of temperature on enzyme catalysed reactions leads to a temperature at which the enzyme works best. This is called the **optimum temperature** for the enzyme. Look carefully at Figure 3. What is the optimum temperature for catalase?

Denaturation occurs when an egg is fried. The white of an egg contains mainly protein (albumen). As the egg is fried, the albumen is denatured and it changes from clear and runny to white and solid

The effect of pH changes on enzymes

Most enzymes work best when the pH is close to neutral (i.e. pH = 7). If the pH is changed by adding acid or alkali, enzymes work less well.

Figure 4 shows the effect of pH changes on the enzyme, amylase. Amylase is present in our saliva. It breaks down starch to form maltose.

$$\text{starch} + \text{water} \xrightarrow{\text{amylase}} \text{maltose}$$

H^+ ions from an acid or OH^- ions from an alkali react with enzymes. This changes the composition and structure of an enzyme and it works less effectively.

Different enzymes work best at different pH values. Look at Figure 4. At what pH does amylase work best?

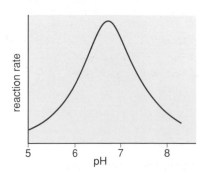

Figure 4 *The effect of pH on the reaction rate of amylase*

Using enzymes

Processes like brewing, bread-making and cheese-making have used enzymes for thousands of years. Brewing and bread-making involve fermentation. During this process, enzymes in yeast cells break down sugars to form ethanol and carbon dioxide.

$$sugar \xrightarrow{yeast} ethanol + carbon\ dioxide$$
$$C_6H_{12}O_6 \xrightarrow{yeast} 2C_2H_5OH + 2CO_2$$

Beer and wine are made by allowing yeast to metabolise a sugary liquid. In beer, the sugary liquid is obtained from barley. In wine-making, the sugary liquid is obtained from grape juice.

Bread-makers are more interested in the carbon dioxide produced by fermentation rather than the alcohol (ethanol). When yeast is added to dough, fermentation takes place. Bubbles of carbon dioxide are produced causing the dough to rise. This process results in the baked bread being light and palatable.

In the last two or three decades, enzymes have added new dimensions to the chemical industry. They are used to bring about reactions at normal temperatures and pressures which would otherwise require high temperatures and pressures. Enzymes have been trapped in gels and attached to inert solids for new processes. These 'immobilised' enzymes are:

● easier to separate from a reacting mixture,

● more stable for a longer period and

● less sensitive to changes in temperature and pH.

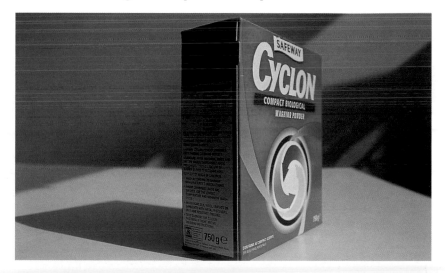

Biological washing powders contain protein-digesting and fat-digesting enzymes (proteases and lipases). These break down stains from food and blood. They can work at relatively low temperatures up to about 40°C. This saves energy, but they cannot work above 50°C. Some people can develop a skin allergy to them.

In industry:

● 'immobilised' enzymes are used to produce insulin and vitamins,

● protease enzymes are used to 'pre-digest' the proteins in baby foods,

● isomerase is used to convert glucose in syrup to its isomer fructose. This is sweeter than glucose, so it can be used in smaller quantities in slimming foods.

Study Questions

1 The catalysts in many reactions are transition metals or their compounds. Make a list of six reactions catalysed by transition metals or their compounds.

2 Discuss the following questions in groups of two or three.
   a) Why do plants grow faster in warm, wet weather than in cold, dry weather?
   b) Why do some gardeners add fertiliser to the soil?
   c) Are fertilisers catalysts?

3 Describe an experiment that you could carry out to show that manganese(IV) oxide is not used up when it catalyses the decomposition of hydrogen peroxide.

4 The sketch graph below shows how the rates of decomposition of hydrogen peroxide: (i) with a manganese (IV) oxide catalyst and (ii) with an enzyme (catalase) catalyst, are affected by changes in temperature. Explain the change in reaction rate with temperature in each case.

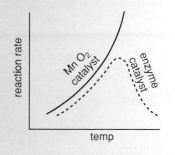

Baking a cake is an irreversible reaction

When you bake a cake, chemical reactions take place in the cake mixture. Once the cake is baked, it is impossible to turn it back into flour, margarine, eggs and sugar.

The same applies when you burn charcoal in a barbecue. The charcoal, which is mainly carbon, reacts with oxygen in the air forming carbon dioxide.

$$\text{carbon} + \text{oxygen} \rightarrow \text{carbon dioxide}$$
$$\text{(charcoal)}$$
$$C(s) + O_2(g) \rightarrow CO_2(g)$$

No matter what you do, carbon dioxide cannot be turned back into charcoal and oxygen.

Reactions like this which cannot be reversed are called **irreversible reactions**.

Most of the chemical reactions that we have studied so far are also irreversible. But there are some processes which can be reversed. For example, ice turns into water on heating.

$$\text{ice} \xrightarrow{\text{heat}} \text{water}$$
$$H_2O(s) \xrightarrow{\text{heat}} H_2O(l)$$

If the water is now cooled, ice reforms.

$$\text{water} \xrightarrow{\text{cool}} \text{ice}$$
$$H_2O(l) \xrightarrow{\text{cool}} H_2O(s)$$

These two parts of this reversible process can be combined in one equation as:

$$H_2O(s) \underset{\text{cool}}{\overset{\text{heat}}{\rightleftharpoons}} H_2O(l)$$

When blue hydrated copper sulphate is heated, it decomposes to white anhydrous copper sulphate and water vapour.

$$\text{hydrated copper sulphate} \xrightarrow{\text{heat}} \text{anhydrous copper sulphate} + \text{water}$$
$$CuSO_4.5H_2O(s) \xrightarrow{\text{heat}} CuSO_4(s) + 5H_2O(g)$$
$$\text{(blue)} \qquad \text{(white)}$$

Ice melts as it warms up in a drink. If the drink is cooled, ice will reform. This is a reversible process

If water is now added, the change can be reversed and blue hydrated copper sulphate reforms.

$$CuSO_4(s) + 5H_2O(l) \rightarrow CuSO_4.5H_2O(s)$$
$$\text{(white)} \qquad \text{(blue)}$$

These two processes can be combined in one equation as

$$CuSO_4.5H_2O(s) \underset{\text{mix reactants}}{\overset{\text{heat}}{\rightleftharpoons}} CuSO_4(s) + 5H_2O(l)$$

Reactions like this which can be reversed are called **reversible reactions**.

The reaction between nitrogen and hydrogen to form ammonia is also reversible. This can be demonstrated using the apparatus in Figure 1. You should **not** attempt the experiment yourself. It should only be demonstrated by your teacher.

Using the syringes, the mixture of hydrogen and nitrogen is pushed to and fro over the heated iron wool. The gases in the syringes are then ejected onto damp red litmus paper. The litmus paper turns blue showing that ammonia has been produced. Ammonia is the only common alkaline gas.

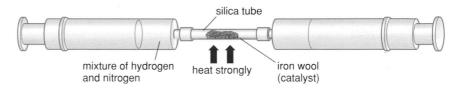

Figure 1 *The reaction between nitrogen and hydrogen to form ammonia*

$$\text{nitrogen} + \text{hydrogen} \rightarrow \text{ammonia}$$
$$N_2(g) + 3H_2(g) \rightarrow 2NH_3(g)$$

The experiment can be repeated, starting with ammonia in the syringes. This time, nitrogen and hydrogen are produced when the gas is pushed to and fro over the heated iron wool.

$$2NH_3(g) \rightarrow N_2(g) + 3H_2(g)$$

These experiments show that the reaction between nitrogen and hydrogen to form ammonia is reversible. In fact, this reaction is the basis of the Haber process to manufacture ammonia (Unit J7 of this section).

Coming to equilibrium

During a reversible reaction, the reactants are sometimes *completely* changed to the products. But, in other cases, the reactants are *only partly* converted to the products. For example, if ice and water are kept at 0°C, neither the ice nor the water seems to change. We say the two substances are in **equilibrium**. When two substances are in equilibrium like this, we replace the reversible arrows sign ($\leftrightarrows$) in the equation with the equilibrium arrows sign ($\rightleftharpoons$).

So, at 0°C,

$$\text{ice} \rightleftharpoons \text{water}$$
$$H_2O(s) \rightleftharpoons H_2O(l)$$

In the same way, nitrogen and hydrogen will come to equilibrium with ammonia in the apparatus shown in Figure 1.

$$N_2(g) + 3H_2(g) \rightleftharpoons 2NH_3(g)$$

When equilibrium is reached, the amounts and concentrations of the reactants and products do not change any more. However, reactions are still going on both forwards and backwards.

Nitrogen and hydrogen are still reacting to form ammonia whilst ammonia is decomposing to re-form nitrogen and hydrogen. These two processes, the forward reaction and the backward reaction, are taking place at the same speed. So, there is no change in the overall amounts of any substance.

This is described as a **dynamic equilibrium** to indicate that substances are 'moving' (reacting) in both directions at equilibrium.

Study Questions

1   Explain the following terms: *irreversible reaction*; *reversible reaction*; *dynamic equilibrium*.

2   Look closely at Figure 1 and the accompanying text.
   a)   What conditions are chosen to speed up the reaction?
   b)   How could you show that hydrogen is still present in the mixture of gases at the end of the reaction?
   c)   Why should the Bunsen heating the silica tube be turned off before testing for any gases?

3   When purple hydrated cobalt chloride ($CoCl_2.6H_2O$) is heated, it changes to blue anhydrous cobalt chloride.
   a)   Write an equation for this reaction.
   b)   How is the reaction reversed?
   c)   How is this reaction used as a test for water?

Manufacturing Ammonia – The Haber Process

7

Fritz Haber (1868–1934). In 1904, Haber began to study the reaction between nitrogen and hydrogen. By 1908, he had found the most economic conditions to make ammonia (NH₃). The ammonia could then be used to make ammonium salts and nitrates for fertilisers

During the last century, populations in Europe and America increased very rapidly. More crops and more food were needed to feed more and more people. This led farmers and gardeners to use nitrogen compounds as fertilisers (Unit J8). Initially, the main source of nitrogen compounds for fertilisers was sodium nitrate from Chile, but this was also being used to manufacture explosives such as nitroglycerine and trinitrotoluene (TNT). By 1900, supplies of sodium nitrate in Chile were running out.

Another supply of nitrogen had to be found or many people would starve. The obvious source of nitrogen was the air. But how could this unreactive gas be converted into ammonia (NH_3) and then ammonium salts and nitrates for use as fertilisers?

Several chemists began to research the problem at the beginning of the 20th century. The German chemist, Fritz Haber was clearly the most successful. Haber began studying the reaction between nitrogen and hydrogen in 1904. By 1908, he had found the most economic conditions to make ammonia from nitrogen and hydrogen on a large scale. By 1913, the Haber process had become the most important method of manufacturing ammonia.

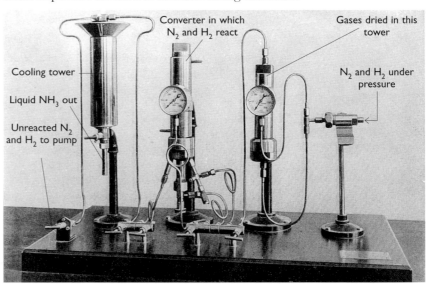

The original apparatus used by Fritz Haber to make ammonia

A flow scheme for the modern Haber process is shown in Figure 1. Notice that the raw materials for the process are:

- **air** which is liquefied and then fractionally distilled to provide nitrogen and
- either **natural gas** or **naphtha** to provide hydrogen.

The key reaction of the Haber process then involves the reaction of nitrogen with hydrogen to produce ammonia. The reaction is carried out under extreme conditions:

- a pressure of 200 atmospheres,
- a temperature of 450°C,
- with a catalyst of iron.

The reaction can be summarised as:

$$N_2(g) \ + \ 3H_2(g) \xrightarrow[\text{+ iron catalyst}]{\text{200 atm, 450°C}} 2NH_3(g)$$

Under these conditions, about 25% of the nitrogen and hydrogen are converted to ammonia. The hot gases from the converter are then cooled to liquefy the ammonia. The unreacted nitrogen and hydrogen are recycled.

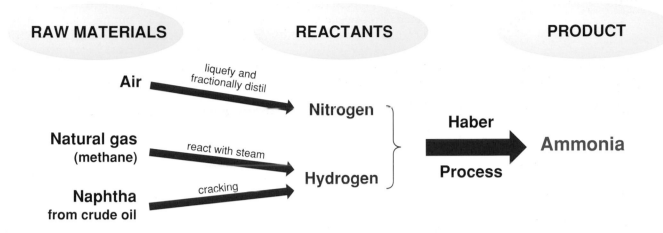

Figure 1 *A flow scheme for the Haber process*

Getting the most for your money

Industrial chemists want to produce materials as fast and as cheaply as possible. They want to produce as much product as possible for the money they spend. In order to do this, they choose raw materials and conditions which:

> 1 use the cheapest materials (reactants) and equipment,
>
> 2 keep the reaction rate as fast as possible,
>
> 3 give the highest yield of product at equilibrium.

The importance of these three points is well illustrated by the Haber process

1 Cost of Materials

The raw materials for the Haber process (Figure 1) are chosen so that ammonia is produced as economically as possible.

● Air, which provides nitrogen is plentiful and costs nothing.

● Natural gas or naphtha, which provide hydrogen, are plentiful and relatively cheap.

● Iron, the cheapest metal, is used as the catalyst.

Electricity is also needed and this is the most costly item. Electricity maintains the high temperatures for the Haber process itself and for the production of hydrogen from either natural gas or naphtha. Electricity is also needed for the operation of distillation and pumping equipment.

2 Fast reaction rate

Three conditions ensure a high reaction rate in the Haber process.

1 A pressure of 200 atm which concentrates the nitrogen and hydrogen.

2 A temperature of 450°C.

3 A catalyst of iron.

Catalysts are essential for many industrial processes. By using a suitable catalyst, it is possible to carry out difficult reactions like the Haber process. Other processes can be carried out at lower temperatures and lower pressures when a catalyst is used. This makes them more economical.

Another way to ensure the most efficient conversion of the reactants to products is to remove the products as fast as they form. This prevents the reverse reaction.

In the Haber process, this is done by condensing and removing the ammonia. The unreacted nitrogen and hydrogen can then be recycled. Continually removing the product in this way will, of course, prevent the process from coming to equilibrium.

3 High yield

Look carefully at Figure 2. This shows the percentages of ammonia at equilibrium when nitrogen and hydrogen react under different conditions of temperature and pressure. The graphs in Figure 2 show that the yield (percentage) of ammonia *increases* when:

- **The pressure is increased.**
  At 450°C, the percentage yield of ammonia is 20% at 100 atm, 33% at 200 atm and 41% at 300 atm.

- **The temperature is reduced.**
  At 200 atm, the percentage yield of ammonia is 16% at 550°C, 33% at 450°C and 53% at 350°C.

Figure 2 *The percentage (yield) of ammonia at equilibrium under different temperatures and pressures*

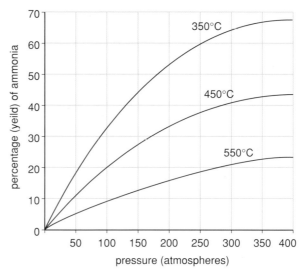

These two conclusions suggest that the best conditions for the manufacture of ammonia would be:

(i) high pressure and

(ii) low temperature.

But these conditions only relate to obtaining the highest possible yield. There are two other important points to consider – the costs and the reaction rate.

High pressures require special pumps and very costly equipment to withstand the high pressures.

Low temperatures may produce a high yield of ammonia at equilibrium, but if the temperature is too low, the reaction rate becomes very slow.

So, chemical engineers have to weigh up different factors in choosing the best conditions for the Haber process.

Very high pressures would give a high yield and a fast reaction rate, but the cost of equipment would be excessive. Low temperatures would give a high yield, but a very slow reaction rate.

In practice, they have chosen a compromise:

- a medium pressure of 200 atmospheres and

- a medium temperature of 450°C.

Study Questions

1　What are the main factors that affect the rate of a chemical reaction?

2　a)　Name three industrial processes that use a catalyst. Say what the catalyst is in each case.

　　b)　Why are catalysts important in industry?

3　At the beginning of the 20th century, Haber synthesised ammonia from nitrogen and hydrogen. Why was this so important?

4　What conditions in the Haber process increase the rate of reaction between nitrogen and hydrogen?

Table 1 *The main uses of ammonia*

Use	Approx. %
Fertilisers	75
Nitric acid	10
Nylon	5
Wood pulp and organic chemicals	10

Ammonia is an important chemical in industry and agriculture. Most of it is used to make fertilisers and nitric acid (Table 1). The uses of ammonia depend on its properties. These are listed in Figure 1.

Ammonia is a pungent, poisonous (toxic) gas. You can smell it in household and lavatory cleaners. Ammonia is very soluble in water because it can form strong bonds with water molecules. Some of it reacts with water to form a solution containing ammonium ions (NH_4^+) and hydroxide ions (OH^-).

$$NH_3(g) + H_2O(l) \rightleftharpoons NH_4^+(aq) + OH^-(aq)$$

The ammonia solution is a weak alkali because only a small proportion of it forms NH_4^+ and OH^- ions. The OH^- ions make the solution alkaline.

Testing for ammonia

> Ammonia is the only common gas which is alkaline. So, we can test for it using damp red litmus paper. Ammonia turns damp red litmus paper blue.

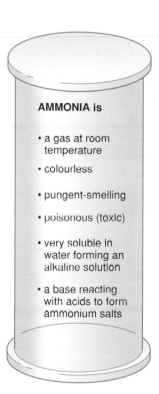

AMMONIA is

- a gas at room temperature
- colourless
- pungent-smelling
- poisonous (toxic)
- very soluble in water forming an alkaline solution
- a base reacting with acids to form ammonium salts

Figure 1 *Properties of ammonia*

Ammonia as a base – neutralisation reactions

Ammonia is a base. It reacts with acids to form ammonium salts. This is how important fertilisers are made. For example, ammonium nitrate ('Nitram') is made by reacting ammonia with nitric acid.

> This is an example of **neutralisation**. The base (ammonia) neutralises the acid (nitric acid) to produce a salt (ammonium nitrate).

$$\text{base} + \text{acid} \rightarrow \text{salt}$$
$$\text{ammonia} + \text{nitric acid} \rightarrow \text{ammonium nitrate}$$
$$NH_3 + HNO_3 \rightarrow NH_4NO_3$$

Ammonia also has a neutralisation reaction with sulphuric acid.

$$\text{ammonia} + \text{sulphuric acid} \rightarrow \text{ammonium sulphate}$$
$$2NH_3 + H_2SO_4 \rightarrow (NH_4)_2SO_4$$

This reaction is used to make ammonium sulphate for use as a fertiliser.

Ammonia to nitric acid – base to acid

About 10% of ammonia is used to manufacture nitric acid. Nitric acid is used to produce fertilisers such as ammonium nitrate and explosives like TNT (trinitrotoluene) and dynamite.

There are three stages in the manufacture of nitric acid from ammonia.

1 Oxidising the ammonia to nitrogen oxide (NO) using a platinum alloy catalyst at 900°C.

$$\text{ammonia} + \text{oxygen} \rightarrow \text{nitrogen oxide} + \text{water}$$
$$4NH_3 + 5O_2 \rightarrow 4NO + 6H_2O$$

2 Oxidising the nitrogen oxide to nitrogen dioxide (NO_2) by mixing with air.

$$\text{nitrogen oxide} + \text{oxygen} \rightarrow \text{nitrogen dioxide}$$
$$2NO + O_2 \rightarrow 2NO_2$$

3 Reacting the nitrogen dioxide and oxygen with water to form nitric acid (HNO_3).

$$\text{nitrogen dioxide} + \text{oxygen} + \text{water} \rightarrow \text{nitric acid}$$
$$4NO_2 + O_2 + 2H_2O \rightarrow 4HNO_3$$

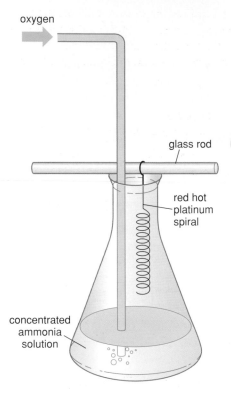

oxygen

glass rod

red hot platinum spiral

concentrated ammonia solution

Figure 2

The first two stages in this process can be carried out in a fume cupboard using the apparatus in Figure 2. Ammonia evaporates from the solution and reacts with oxygen on the platinum spiral (catalyst). Nitrogen oxide (NO) is produced which reacts with oxygen in the air to form brown fumes of nitrogen dioxide.

Nitric acid is a typical strong acid, like hydrochloric acid and sulphuric acid. The dilute acid shows typical acid reactions with indicators, metals, bases and carbonates (see Unit G3).

Fertilisers

Nitrogen fertiliser has been added to the soil on the left of this field. This has produced greener, taller and bushier wheat plants

Plants need certain essential elements to grow well. These essential elements are called **nutrients**.

If crops are grown every year on the same land, these nutrients get used up. The soil becomes infertile and plants are stunted. Their leaves become yellow and seeds and fruits are small.

Carbon dioxide and water provide the carbon, oxygen and hydrogen which plants need. After these three elements, the most important nutrient for plant growth is nitrogen. Nitrogen is essential for the synthesis of proteins and chlorophyll in plants. Shortages of nitrogen in the soil are soon noticed. Plants become stunted and their leaves turn yellow due to a lack of chlorophyll.

For plants to grow well, any shortages of nitrogen must be replaced. This is done by adding fertilisers to the soil.

Nitrogen fertilisers

A bag of NPK fertiliser. What do the letters N, P, and K stand for?

Nitrogen fertilisers are usually nitrates or ammonium salts. Ammonium nitrate ('Nitram'), NH_4NO_3, is the most widely used fertiliser because:

- it is soluble in water,
- it can be stored and transported as a solid,
- it contains a high percentage of nitrogen (Table 1).

Study Questions

1 Ammonia was passed over a black oxide powder (A). The black oxide turned to a pinky-brown solid (B) which conducted electricity. At the same time, drops of a colourless liquid (C) collected on the cooler parts of the apparatus and an unreactive, odourless and colourless gas (D) was produced. Liquid C boiled at 373 K.

a) Name the substances A, B and C.

b) Write a word equation for the reaction between ammonia and the black oxide (A).

c) What is gas D?

2 Write equations for the reactions of nitric acid with: (i) zinc; (ii) copper(II) oxide; (iii) potassium hydroxide; (iv) sodium carbonate.

3 a) Why should a fertiliser be soluble?

b) What are the problems in storing, transporting and using fertilisers?

c) Make a list of the important properties of an ideal fertiliser.

4 a) Why are fertilisers important?

b) What problems are caused by their over-use?

5 a) Describe how you would make a sample of ammonium sulphate.

b) Design an experiment to see if ammonium sulphate acts as a fertiliser for peas or beans.

6 a) Many farmers use NPK fertiliser. What do N, P and K stand for?

b) Nitrochalk can act as a fertiliser *and* cure soil acidity. Explain why it can do both of these jobs.

The higher the percentage of nitrogen in a fertiliser the better. This means that less useless material needs to be stored and transported. Other nitrogen fertilisers are ammonium sulphate, urea and nitrochalk. Nitrochalk is a mixture of ammonium nitrate and chalk (calcium carbonate). This provides nitrogen for the soil and it also reduces soil acidity.

Table 1 *The percentage of nitrogen in different fertilisers*

Fertiliser	Formula	Mass of one mole	Mass of nitrogen in one mole	% of nitrogen
Ammonium nitrate	NH_4NO_3	80 g	28 g	$\frac{28}{80} \times 100 = 35$
Ammonia	NH_3	17 g	14 g	$\frac{14}{17} \times 100 = 82$
Ammonium sulphate	$(NH_4)_2SO_4$	132 g	28 g	$\frac{28}{132} \times 100 = 21$
Urea	N_2H_4CO	60 g	28 g	$\frac{28}{60} \times 100 = 47$

Fertilisers are substances which increase the yield from crops.

Fertilisers are now essential. We cannot feed everyone in the world at present. Every year, we hear about people starving somewhere in the world. These problems would be ten times worse without fertilisers. But, there are problems if fertilisers are over-used.

● Fertilisers can change the soil pH and harm plants and animals in the soil.

● Fertilisers can be washed into the ground and pollute our drinking water.

● Fertilisers allow elements in the fertilisers that are not required by plants to accumulate in the soil.

● Fertilisers are washed off the land into streams and rivers. This allows algae to grow rapidly using up all the dissolved oxygen in the water. Fish, water plants and algae themselves which need oxygen begin to die. As the dead animals and plants decay, the river becomes a stinking mess. This process is called **eutrophication**.

Blue-green algae grow rapidly in water polluted with nitrate fertiliser

9

The Nitrogen Cycle

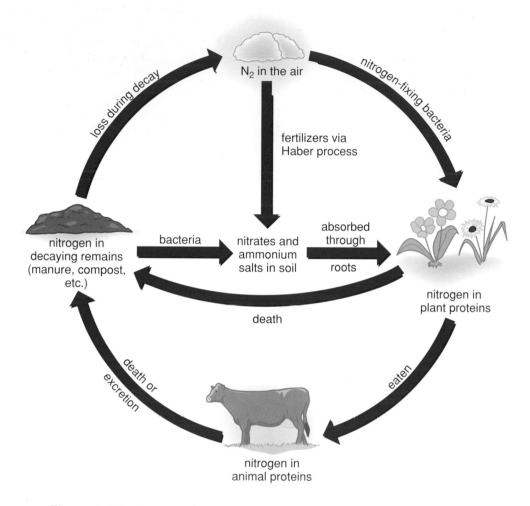

Figure I *The nitrogen cycle*

Some plants, called legumes, have nodules on their roots like these in the photo. These nodules contain bacteria which convert nitrogen from the air into compounds the plant can use for growth

In the last unit, we looked at man-made inorganic fertilisers like ammonium nitrate, ammonium sulphate and nitrochalk. Large quantities of natural organic fertilisers are also used by farmers and gardeners. The most widely used organic fertilisers are manure and compost which contain decaying matter from animals and plants (see the lower half of Figure 1). The nitrogen compounds in manure and compost are decomposed by bacteria to nitrates and ammonium salts. These substances dissolve in rainwater and are absorbed through the roots of plants (centre of Figure 1). The nitrates and ammonium salts are then used by plants to synthesize the chlorophyll and proteins that they need for growth. Animals have to eat plants and other animals in order to get the nitrogen and the proteins which they need.

Manure and compost are excellent fertilisers, but they take time to break down and there are not enough of them for all the crops we grow. Because of this we need large amounts of inorganic fertilisers. Small quantities of the nitrogen that crops need are provided by nitrogen-fixing bacteria in the soil. These bacteria can convert nitrogen from the air into nitrogen compounds that can be used by plants. Some of these nitrogen-fixing bacteria live in nodules on the roots of plants such as peas, beans and clover (top right, Figure 1).

This conversion of atmospheric nitrogen to nitrogen compounds in plants is sometimes called *natural* nitrogen fixation. The conversion of atmospheric nitrogen to ammonia using the Haber process is described as *industrial* nitrogen fixation.

Although nitrogen is returned to the soil when living matter decays, some of the nitrogen compounds in the manure and compost are decomposed to nitrogen gas which escapes into the air (top left, Figure 1). This is another reason why fertilisers are added to the soil in heavily cultivated areas.

> The continual transfer of nitrogen from the air, into plants and animals, through decaying remains and back to the air (as shown in Figure 1) is called the **nitrogen cycle**.

Part of the European 'grain mountain'. Is it right that huge amounts of food are kept in store whilst thousands of people are starving?

The world food problem

500 million people in the world are starving. This alarming figure suggests that we must increase food production, but the problem is not so simple.

- In Europe and North America there are 'mountains' of surplus food but most poor countries cannot afford to buy it.

- In some poor countries, the rich have plenty to eat.

- Some countries need to export food to earn foreign currency even though some of their own people are starving.

Three possible ways of reducing the world food problem are:

1 Increasing birth control

It is estimated that the world population will be 7000 million by the year 2005. Some people think that the population problem is more serious than the food problem.

2 Improving farming methods

This includes watering the deserts, preventing soil erosion, developing better varieties of crops, breeding healthier, more productive cattle and using improved pesticides.

3 Finding new food supplies

These might involve farming the sea and growing bacteria on vegetable oils and cellulose to produce food.

During a lightning flash, nitrogen reacts with oxygen in the air to form nitrogen oxides. These react with rain water to produce nitric acid, which increases the nitrogen content of the soil.

Study Questions

1 What is meant by: (i) natural nitrogen fixation; (ii) industrial nitrogen fixation; (iii) the nitrogen cycle?

2 a) What is the difference between man-made and natural fertilisers?
   b) What happens to the nitrogen compounds in compost as it decays?
   c) Why do plants require nitrogen?
   d) Why do farmers and gardeners use man-made fertilisers as well as natural fertilisers?

3 What should the more developed nations do to solve the world food problem?

4 a) What problems are caused by the over-use of fertilisers?
   b) Explain why these problems arise.

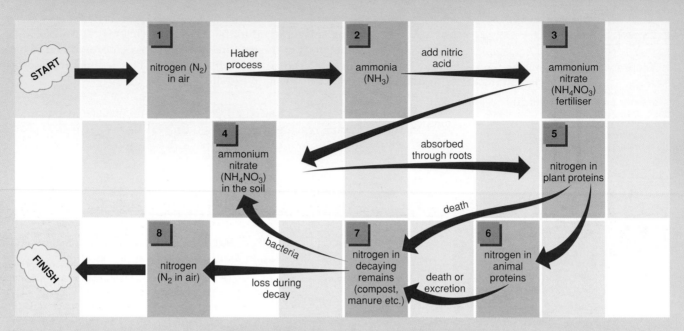

1 The Nitrogen Cycle Game

The Nitrogen Cycle Game is a mixture of 'Monopoly' and 'Trivial Pursuits'. It is based on fertilisers and the nitrogen cycle.

Chance cards

First, make 10 CHANCE cards by writing the letters A to J on 10 pieces of card. Shuffle these cards and place the pile face downwards on the table.

Rules

(i)   Any number of people can play the game.

(ii)   You can play as an individual or in teams.

(iii) Each person (or team) starts at number 1 in the diagram and moves to the next number if they give the correct answer to a question from the other team.

(iv)   If you answer the question incorrectly, you do *not* move.

(v)   When a team are asking questions, they should make up questions using pages 242 to 249.

(vi)   Questions are put to each person (team) in turn.

(vii) At number 4, each person (team) takes a CHANCE card. The letter on the CHANCE card tells you how you must move according to the instructions below.

(viii) The winning person (team) is the first to reach number 8.

Instructions

A Fertiliser washed out of soil. Go back to 1.

B Fertiliser gets mixed with compost. Go to 7.

C Fertiliser taken up by plants. Move to 5.

D Fertiliser returned to factory by farmer. Go back to 3.

E Fertiliser decomposes to ammonia. Go back to 2.

F Fertiliser accidentally eaten by cattle. Go on to 6.

G Soil is frozen by cold weather. Stay at 4.

H Important nutrients missing from soil. Stay at 4.

I Fertiliser changes the soil pH and plants cannot grow. Stay on 4 and miss a turn.

J Ideal conditions of pH and temperature for plant growth. Move to 7.

2 AMMChem plant proposed for Oakbridge

AMMChem plant for Oakbridge

Yesterday, Sandra Bigg, Mayor of Oakbridge, admitted that Council officials had met representatives of AMMChem. AMMChem are the world's largest manufacturer of fertilisers. Mayor Bigg said. "The firm are seeking permission to build a chemical plant on the North side of Oakbridge."

AMMChem produces ammonia and nitric acid and uses them for the manufacture of ammonium nitrate (Nitram). It also sells large quantities of ammonia and nitric acid to other companies.

Mrs. Bigg welcomed the plant. She said, "It will help the town's economy. The plant will employ 150 local people. It is also estimated that each person employed by AMMChem will create jobs for another 3 or 4 people in local businesses. This will reduce unemployment in the town." At present, about 2000 people in Oakbridge are unemployed. This is 10% of the workforce.

Mayor Bigg also pointed to two other benefits from the plant AMMChem would pay business rates to Oakbridge Council at the commercial level. This would make a large increase in revenue and hold down the increases in council tax to home owners. Farmers near Oakbridge would save about £10 per tonne on Nitram fertiliser because they would be paying lower transport costs. A representative for the National Farmers's Union has estimated that about 500 tonnes of Nitram fertiliser are used each year on farms near Oakbridge.

Herb Green, Secretary of the Oakbridge Environmental Group, was asked for his views. He said, 'we are concerned about emissions of ammonia and nitrogen oxides from the plant and possible accidents when chemicals are being transported. How will these affect the beautiful countryside around Oakbridge? Just image what would happen if the plant was not working properly and excessive amounts of ammonia or nitric acid got into the River Soak? Why can't the Mayor persuade cleaner industries to move into the area? Anyway, farmers are using less artificial fertilisers these days and growing more organic food."

Earlier today, Dr. Ken Bond, Managing Director of AMMChem issued the following statement:

"Some chemical companies have caused environmental problems but AMMChem have an excellent record. Our Safety Division checks processes and equipment continuously and ensures that all our operations are safe and pollution free.

No industry is without risks. Ammonia is very toxic and it is manufactured at high pressure and high temperature. An accident at the plant or during transportation would create a serious health hazard. But, accidents are very rare, AMMChem have been involved in only one death from such accidents in the last ten years. In recent years, industry and society have begun to realise their joint responsibility for the production of chemicals which will benefit society."

Suppose you live in Oakbridge.

1 Make a list of the possible problems from the AMMChem plant.

2 Make a list of the possible benefits from the AMMChem plant.

3 Write a letter to the Oakbridge Chronicle expressing your views about the proposed plant. (You may want to support the proposal or to be very critical of it.)

4 Suppose you are a town councillor in Oakbridge. Make a list of other points you would want to consider or other information which you would need before deciding whether AMMChem should build the proposed plant.

1 Reaction rates

- Different chemical reactions happen at very different rates.
- Reaction rates are very important in living things and in industry
- A chemical reaction cannot happen unless particles in the reacting substances collide with each other.
- Reaction rate $= \dfrac{\text{change in amount of substance}}{\text{time taken}}$

2 What affects reaction rates?

In general, reactions go faster when:

- there is more surface area to react,
- the temperature is increased,
- the concentration of reactants is increased,
- a catalyst can be used.

There are two reasons why reactions go faster at higher temperatures:

- The particles move faster and collide more often.
- The particles collide with more energy, so more collisions result in a reaction.

3 Catalysts and enzymes

- Catalysts are substances which change the rate of chemical reactions without being used up during the reaction.
- Enzymes are biological catalysts.
- Enzymes are very sensitive to changes in temperature and pH.
- Enzymes are proteins and their complex structure is disrupted as the temperature rises. This disruption of the protein structure is called **denaturation.**

4 Reversible reactions and equilibria

- **Reversible reactions** can go in both directions (from reactants to products and from products to reactants) depending on the conditions.
- When a reaction reaches **equilibrium**, both the forward reaction and the backward reaction are going on at the same rate.
- Conditions of temperature and pressure influence the position of an equilibrium. The conditions chosen for an industrial process must take into consideration:
  - the cost of materials and equipment,
  - the reaction rate,
  - the yield of product at equilibrium.

5 The Haber process can be summarised as:

$$N_2(g) + 3H_2(g) \xrightarrow[\text{+ iron catalyst}]{200 \text{ atm, } 450°C} 2NH_3(g)$$

6 Ammonia

- The test for ammonia is to turn damp red litmus paper blue.
- Ammonia is a base. It neutralises acids to form ammonium salts.

7 Fertilisers

- Fertilisers are substances which increase the yield of crops.
- Fertilisers are essential if we are to provide sufficient food for the world population. If fertilisers are over-used, they can cause the pollution of drinking water and eutrophication in rivers and lakes.
- The continual transfer of nitrogen from the air, into plants and animals, through decaying remains and back to the air is called the nitrogen cycle.

Section J   Exam Questions

1   Calcium carbonate reacts with dilute hydrochloric acid. During the reaction carbon dioxide and water are formed.
   a)   (i)   Write the word equation for this reaction.
        (ii)   Describe the test for carbon dioxide.
   b)   Some students investigated the rate of reaction of lumps of calcium carbonate with hydrochloric acid.
        They carried out the reaction in a flask on a top pan balance as shown below.

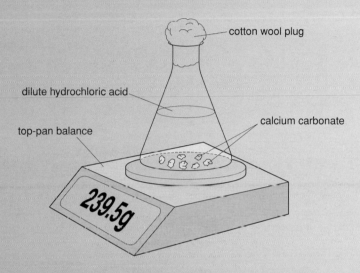

cotton wool plug

dilute hydrochloric acid

top-pan balance

calcium carbonate

239.5g

The students recorded the mass at known times after the start. Their results are shown on the graph.

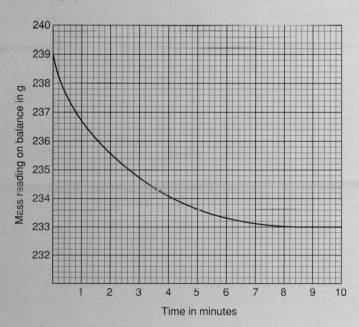

(i)   How does the mass of the reaction mixture change during the reaction?
        (ii)   Explain why this change in mass takes place.
        (iii)   Use the graph to find the reading on the balance at the end of this reaction.
   c)   The experiment was repeated using the same masses of acid and calcium carbonate as in the first experiment but using powdered calcium carbonate instead of lumps.
        How did the rate of reaction change when powder was used instead of lumps?
   d)   Suggest THREE ways of increasing the rate of reaction of a finely powdered solid with an acid.

Edexcel 2000

2   A student studied the effect of temperature on the rate of reaction between hydrochloric acid and sodium thiosulphate.

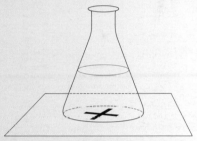

   ●   The student mixed 50 cm^3 of a sodium thiosulphate solution and 5 cm^3 of hydrochloric acid in a flask.
   ●   The flask was placed over a cross.
   ●   The student timed how long after mixing the cross could no longer be seen.
   a)   (i)   Copy out and balance the chemical equation for this reaction.

$Na_2S_2O_3(aq) + HCl(aq) \rightarrow NaCl(aq) + H_2O(l) + SO_2(g) + S(s)$

        (ii)   What causes the cross to be seen no longer?
   b)   A graph of the results is shown.

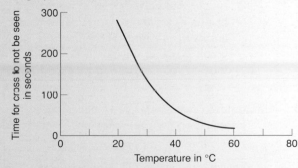

   (i)   What effect does temperature have on the rate of this reaction?
   (ii)   Explain why temperature has this effect on the rate of reaction.

AQA 2000

3 The graph (**A**) below shows the volume of carbon dioxide formed during a reaction between *excess* marble chips (calcium carbonate) and dilute hydrochloric acid.

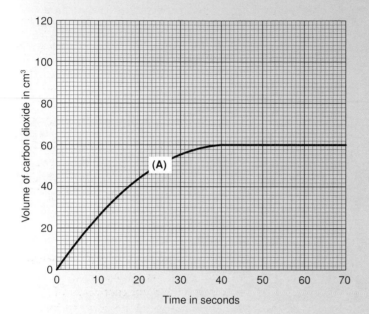

(i) Copy out the grid above and draw on it graph A. On the same grid sketch carefully the graph that would be obtained if the acid had been replaced by
  I. an equal volume and concentration of hydrochloric acid at a *lower* temperature with the marble chips still in excess. Label this graph **B**.
  II. an equal volume of hydrochloric acid of *double* the concentration with the marble chips still in excess. Label this graph **C**.

(ii) I. On the came grid sketch carefully the graph that would be obtained if the marble chips had been ground to a powder with the volume and concentration of the acid the same as for graph **A**. Label this graph **D**.
  II. Explain your answer to part (ii) I.

WJEC 2000

4 Ammonia is made using the Haber process
  a) The equation for the reversible reaction is:

$$N_2(g) + 3H_2(g) \rightarrow 2NH_3(g)$$

  What is the source of the nitrogen used in the Haber process?

  b) The hydrogen used in the Harber process is obtained by heating methane with steam:

$$CH_4(g) + H_2O(g) \rightarrow 3H_2(g) + CO(g)$$

What is the source of the methane gas for this reaction?

  c) (i) Most of the ammonia produced is reacted with acids to form fertilisers.
    Write a balanced equation for the reaction of ammonia with nitric acid.
    (ii) Why do most farmers add fertilisers to their crops?
    (iii) Excess fertiliser is washed off fields into rivers. State **two** consequences of this.

Edexcel (specimen paper, 2003)

5 a) The Haber process manufactures ammonia:

$$N_2(g) + 3H_2(g) \rightleftharpoons 2NH_3 (g).$$

  (i) State what is meant by the symbol $\rightleftharpoons$.
  (ii) The graph below shows the yield of ammonia at different pressure and temperature conditions.

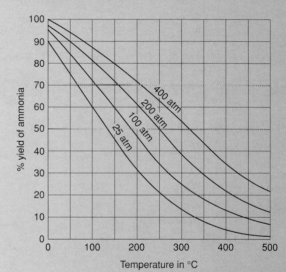

Use the graph to find the
  I. pressure needed to obtain 30% yield of ammonia at 350°C,
  II. temperature needed to obtain 60% yield of ammonia at a pressure of 25 atmospheres,
  III. % yield of ammonia at 450°C and 100 atmospheres.

  (iii) State the purpose of the iron catalyst in the production of ammonia.

  b) Ammonia is used to make the nitrogenous fertiliser, ammonium sulphate.
  (i) Do the advantages of the use of fertilisers outweigh the disadvantages?
    Give **two** reasons to support your answer.
  (ii) Calculate the relative molecular mass (M_r) of ammonium sulphate, $(NH_4)_2SO_4$.

$A_r(H) = 1;$ $A_r(N) = 14;$ $A_r(O) = 16;$ $A_r(S) = 32.$

WJEC 2001

6 Hydrogen peroxide, H_2O_2, is often used as a bleach. It decomposes forming water and oxygen.

a) (i) Write the balanced chemical equation for the decomposition of hydrogen peroxide.

   (ii) Give a test for oxygen and the result of the test.

b) The rate of decomposition of hydrogen peroxide at room temperature is very slow. Manganese oxide is a catalyst which can be used to speed up the decomposition. Copy and complete the sentence.

A catalyst is a substance which speeds up a chemical reaction. At the end of the reaction, the catalyst is ....

c) Two experiments were carried out to test if the amount of manganese oxide, MnO_2 affected the rate at which the hydrogen peroxide decomposed.

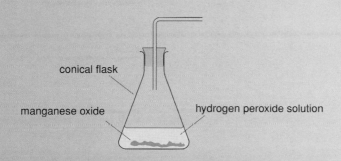

conical flask

manganese oxide

hydrogen peroxide solution

(i) Copy and complete the diagram to show how you could measure the volume of oxygen formed during the decomposition.

(ii) The results are shown in the table.

Time in minutes	0	0.5	1	1.5	2	2.5	3	3.5
Volume of gas in cm³ using 0.25 g MnO_2	0	29	55	77	98	116	132	144
Volume of gas in cm³ using 0.25 g MnO_2	0	45	84	118	145	162	174	182

Copy the grid below and draw a graph of these results. The graph for 0.25 g MnO_2 has been drawn for you.

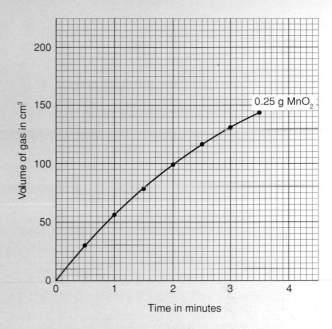

(iii) Explain why the slopes of the graphs become less steep during the reaction.

(iv) The same volume and concentration of hydrogen peroxide solution was used for both experiments. What **two** other factors must be kept the same to make it a fair test?

AQA 1999

7 Read the following poem about the manufacture of ammonia, NH_3, and answer the questions that follow.

The Haber Process
by Martin Perry

Dry nitrogen and hydrogen gas,
Over a finely divided iron catalyst are passed.
The gases in ratio one to three,
At a pressure of 200 and a temperature of 450 degrees C.

Ammonia gas is produced,
From its choking smell this is deduced.
From the ammonia is made ammonium sulphate,
And also the fertiliser, ammonium nitrate.

[Taken from *Chemistry Poems*, *Education Today*, Volume 38 no. 2]

a) This word equation represents the reaction between nitrogen and hydrogen.

nitrogen + hydrogen $\rightleftharpoons$ ammonia

(i) Write the balanced symbol equation for this reaction.

(ii) The symbol "$\rightleftharpoons$" means that the reaction is reversible. Explain what is meant by a reversible reaction.

(iii) The reaction producing ammonia is exothermic. In industry, the conditions used are a pressure of 200 atmospheres and a temperature of 450°C.
Explain fully why **both** of these conditions are chosen.

b) (i) Calculate the relative formula mass (M_r) of ammonia, NH_3.
(Relative atomic masses: H = 1, N = 14)

(ii) Calculate the percentage of nitrogen in ammonia.

c) (i) Ammonium nitrate is a fertiliser. What is a fertiliser?

(ii) Ammonium nitrate is formed when ammonia reacts with nitric acid. Nitric acid is manufactured from ammonia.
Describe how nitric acid is made from ammonia.
Your answer should include:
● the types of reaction which occur;
● the conditions used;
● the energy changes involved.

AQA 2000

8   This question is about catalase, an **enzyme** in vegetables.
Catalase acts as a catalyst for the splitting up of hydrogen peroxide.

hydrogen peroxide → water + oxygen

a) Sam does an experiment at 20°C.
She uses 25 cm³ of hydrogen peroxide solution and 1 cm³ of catalase solution.
She measures the volume of gas given off each minute for five minutes.
The table shows her results.

time in minutes	0	1	2	3	4	5
volume of gas in cm³	0	25	40	53	50	50

Plot a graph of Sam's results. Put volume of gas in cm³ along the vertical axis and time in minutes along the horizontal.
(i) Label and choose the best scale for the vertical axis and the horizontal axis.
(ii) Plot the points on the grid.
(iii) Finish the graph by drawing the curve of best fit.
(iv) Sam does the experiment again but this time at 30°C.
Draw, on your grid, the graph she would expect to get.

b) The strength of a hydrogen peroxide solution is sometimes given as 'volume strength'.
A 10-volume solution produces 10 cm³ of oxygen for each 1 cm³ of solution used.
What is the 'volume strength' of the hydrogen peroxide Sam used?

OCR 1999

9   The Haber process is used to make ammonia NH_3. The table shows the percentage yield of ammonia at different temperatures and pressures.

a) (i) Use the data in the table to draw two graphs. Draw one graph for a temperature of 350°C and the second graph for a temperature of 500°C.
Plot 'percentage (%) yield of ammonia' vertically and 'pressure (atmospheres)' horizontally. Label each graph with its temperature.

(ii) Use your graphs to find the conditions of temperature in °C and pressure in atmospheres needed to give a yield of 30% ammonia.

(iii) On your grid sketch the graph you would expect for a temperature of 450°C.

b) (i) This equation represents the reaction in which ammonia is formed.

$$N_{2(g)} + 3H_{2(g)} \rightleftharpoons 2NH_{3(g)} + heat$$

What does the symbol $\rightleftharpoons$ in this equation tell you about the reaction?

(ii) Use your graphs and your knowledge of the Haber process to explain why a temperature of 450°C and a pressure of 200 atmospheres are used in industry.

c) (i) Ammonium nitrate is one type of artificial fertiliser.
Calculate the relative formula mass of ammonium nitrate NH_4NO_3.
(Relative atomic masses: H = 1, N = 14, O = 16.)

(ii) Use your answer to part (c)(i) to help you calculate the percentage by mass of nitrogen present in ammonium nitrate NH_4NO_3.

Pressure (atmospheres)	Percentage (%) yield of ammonia at 350°C	Percentage (%) yield of ammonia at 500°C
50	25	5
100	37	9
200	52	15
300	63	20
400	70	23
500	74	25

AQA 1999

Atomic Structure and Chemical Bonding

Scientists working in radiation laboratories must handle radioactive isotopes by remote control from the other side of very thick glass windows

By the end of this section, you should be able to:

- Recall that atoms consist of nuclei containing protons and neutrons surrounded by orbiting electrons.
- Describe the charges and relative masses of protons, neutrons and electrons.
- Explain the terms *atomic number*, *mass number* and *isotopes*.
- Understand the way electrons are arranged in atoms.
- Appreciate how the reactions of elements depend on the arrangement of electrons in their atoms.
- Explain chemical bonding in terms of the transfer or sharing of electrons.
- Understand how ions are formed when atoms gain or lose electrons.
- Understand how covalent bonds are formed when atoms share electrons.

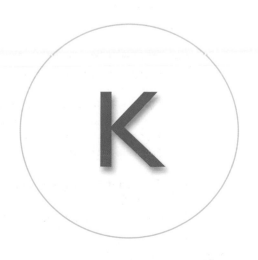

Inside Atoms

J.J. Thomson, Professor of Experimental Physics at Cambridge University and winner of the Nobel Prize for Physics in 1906

Just over a century ago, scientists thought that atoms were solid particles like tiny snooker balls. Then, between 1897 and 1932, experiments showed that atoms are made of three types of particles – protons, neutrons and electrons. In this unit we shall study some of the evidence for these particles.

1897 – Thomson discovers electrons

In 1897, J.J. Thomson was investigating the way that gases conduct electricity. When he connected 15 000 volts across the terminals of a tube containing a gas, the glass walls glowed a bright-green colour. Rays travelling in straight lines from the negative terminal hit the glass and made it glow. Thomson called these rays **cathode rays** because they came from the negative terminal or cathode. Experiments with a narrow beam of cathode rays (Figure 1) showed that they could be deflected by an electric field. When cathode rays passed between charged plates, they always bent towards the positive plate. This showed that the rays were negatively charged.

Further study showed that cathode rays consisted of negative particles which were 1840 times lighter than hydrogen atoms. Thomson called these tiny negative particles **electrons**.

Cathode rays were always the same even when the gas in the tube was different or the terminals were made of different substances. This suggested that *all* substances contained electrons.

Did you know?

Seven of J.J. Thomson's students won Nobel prizes for Chemistry or Physics. He was a brilliant teacher.

1909 – Geiger and Marsden explore the nucleus

As atoms are neutral, they must contain positive charge to balance the negative charge on their electrons. Geiger and Marsden found a method of probing inside atoms using alpha-particles from radioactive substances as 'bullets'. Alpha-particles are positive helium ions, He^{2+}. When alpha particles were fired at very thin sheets of metal foil, most of the alpha particles passed straight through the foil. But, some of the alpha particles were deflected by the foil and a few of them even appeared to bounce back from it (Figure 2).

Figure 1 *Deflection of cathode rays by an electric field*

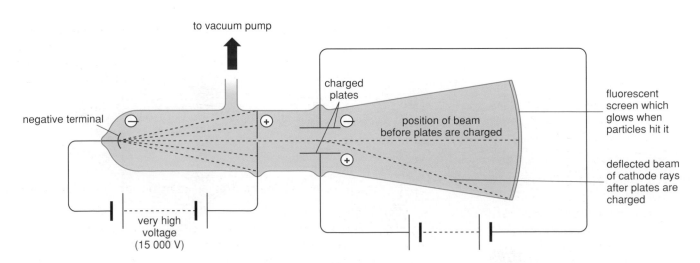

to vacuum pump

negative terminal

very high voltage (15 000 V)

charged plates

position of beam before plates are charged

fluorescent screen which glows when particles hit it

deflected beam of cathode rays after plates are charged

Ernest Rutherford who succeeded J.J.Thomson as Professor of Experimental Physics at Cambridge University in 1919. Rutherford received the Nobel Prize for Chemistry in 1908 while he was working at Manchester University

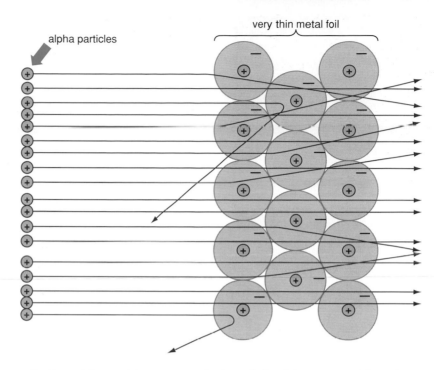

Figure 2 *Most alpha-particles pass straight through the foil, some are deflected and a few even rebound from the foil*

Study Questions

1 What are: (i) cathode rays; (ii) electrons; (iii) protons?

2 What evidence is there that electrons are: (i) negatively charged; (ii) the same in all substances?

3 Why did Geiger and Marsden's experiment suggest that atoms have a small positive nucleus surrounded by a much larger region of empty space?

4 Using Rutherford's ideas, how is the position of an element in the periodic table related to the number of electrons in its atoms?

5 When electrons pass between charged plates they are deflected towards the positive plate. What will happen when alpha-particles pass between charged plates?

1911 – Rutherford explains the structure of atoms

Rutherford explained Geiger and Marsden's results by suggesting that:

> atoms have a very small positive **nucleus** surrounded by a much larger region of empty space in which there are **electrons**.

During Geiger and Marsden's experiments, most of the positive alpha-particles pass straight through the large empty space. A few alpha particles pass close to a positive nucleus and get deflected. Occasionally an alpha-particle approaches a nucleus head-on. When this happens, the positive alpha-particle is repelled by the positive nucleus and bounces back.

Rutherford compared the structure of an atom to the Solar System. He suggested that:

- each atom had a positive nucleus, orbited by tiny negative electrons like planets orbiting the Sun.

- the positive charge of the nucleus was provided by positive particles, which he called **protons**.

- the smallest atoms were those of hydrogen with one proton balanced by one orbiting electron. Atoms of helium, the next smallest, contain two protons and two electrons; lithium atoms have three protons and three electrons, and so on.

2 The Structure of Atoms

James Chadwick discovered neutrons in 1932 when he was working with Rutherford in Cambridge. In 1935, he won a Nobel Prize for this achievement

Rutherford was very successful in explaining atomic structure, but one big problem remained. Hydrogen atoms contain one proton and helium atoms contain two protons. So the relative atomic mass of helium should be two, since the relative atomic mass of hydrogen is one. But the relative atomic mass of helium is four and *not* two.

James Chadwick, one of Rutherford's students, discovered where the extra mass in helium came from. Chadwick showed that the nuclei of atoms contained *uncharged* particles as well as positively charged protons. Chadwick called these uncharged particles **neutrons**. Experiments showed that neutrons have the same mass as protons. This helped Chadwick to explain the problem concerning the relative atomic masses of hydrogen and helium (Table 1).

Table 1 *The relative atomic masses of hydrogen and helium*

	Hydrogen atom	Helium atom
Number of protons	1	2
Number of neutrons	0	2
Relative mass	1	4
Relative atomic mass	1	4

Hydrogen atoms have one proton, no neutrons and one electron. Since the mass of the electron is almost zero compared to the proton and neutron, a hydrogen atom has a relative mass of one unit. Helium atoms have two protons, two neutrons and two electrons. The two protons and two neutrons give a helium atom a relative mass of four units. Thus, a helium atom is four times as heavy as a hydrogen atom and the relative atomic mass of helium is four.

Did you know?

James Chadwick started his research under Rutherford in 1911. In 1913, he moved to Germany to work with Geiger. This was bad timing because the first World War started in 1914 and Chadwick was locked in Germany. As soon as the war ended, he returned to work with Rutherford in Cambridge.

Protons, neutrons and electrons

We now know that:

- all atoms are made up from three basic particles – protons, neutrons and electrons.
- the nuclei of atoms contain protons and neutrons.
- the masses of a proton and a neutron are almost the same.
- protons have a positive charge, but neutrons have no charge.
- electrons move in space around the nucleus.
- the mass of an electron is negligible compared to a proton or neutron.
- electrons have a negative charge.
- in any atom, the number of electrons is equal to the number of protons.
- all atoms of a particular element have the same number of protons.
- atoms of different elements have different numbers of protons.

The positions, masses and charges of protons, neutrons and electrons are summarised in Table 2.

Table 2 *Properties of the three sub-atomic particles*

Particle	Position	Mass (relative to a proton)	Charge (relative to that on a proton)
Proton	Nucleus	1	+1
Neutron	Nucleus	1	0
Electron	Shells	$\frac{1}{1840}$	1

Different atoms have different numbers of protons, neutrons and electrons. The hydrogen atom is the simplest of all atoms. It has one proton in the nucleus, no neutrons and one electron (Figure 1). The next simplest atom is that of helium, with two protons, two neutrons and two electrons. The next, lithium, has three protons, four neutrons and three electrons. Heavier atoms can have large numbers of protons, neutrons and electrons. For example, atoms of uranium have 92 protons, 92 electrons and 143 neutrons.

Notice that hydrogen with the simplest atoms and the first element in the periodic table, has one proton. Helium, the second element in the periodic table, has two protons. Lithium, the third element in the periodic table has three protons and so on. So, the position of an element in the periodic table tells us how many protons it has.

Notice also that atoms have equal numbers of protons and electrons, so that the positive charges (on the protons) balance the negative charges (on the electrons).

If the nucleus of an atom was enlarged to the size of a pea and put on top of Nelson's Column, the electrons furthest away would be on the pavement

Study Questions

1 What are the charges, relative masses and positions in an atom of protons, neutrons and electrons?
2 How many protons, neutrons and electrons are there in one:
   (i) H atom; (ii) H$^+$ ion;
   (iii) Li atom; (iv) Li$^+$ ion?
3 Oxygen is the eighth element in the periodic table. How many protons and electrons are there in one: (i) O atom, (ii) O^{2-} ion, (iii) O$_2$ molecule, (iv) H$_2$O molecule?
4 Lithium atoms have three protons, four neutrons and three electrons. Why is the relative atomic mass of lithium about seven?
5 Make a list of important dates, scientists, and facts in the development of our ideas about atomic structure.

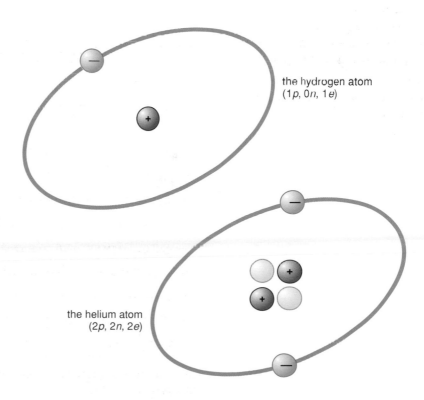

the hydrogen atom
(1*p*, 0*n*, 1*e*)

the helium atom
(2*p*, 2*n*, 2*e*)

Figure 1 *Protons, neutrons and electrons in a hydrogen atom and a helium atom*
($\oplus$ ≡ *proton*, ○ ≡ *neutron*, $\ominus$ ≡ *electron*)

Atomic Number and Mass Number

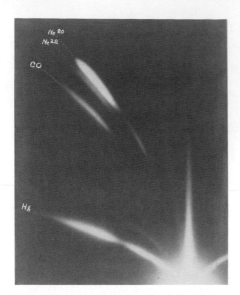

This photograph shows evidence for the two isotopes in neon, neon-20 and neon-22. Notice that the trace from neon-20 is much stronger than that from neon-22. What does this tell you about the two isotopes? What does CO represent?

Only hydrogen atoms have one proton. Only helium atoms have two protons. Only lithium atoms have three protons, and so on. This means that the number of protons in an atom decides which element it is. Because of this, scientists have a special name for the number of protons in the nucleus of an atom. They call it the **atomic number** and use the symbol Z to represent atomic number. So, hydrogen has an atomic number of one (Z = 1), helium has an atomic number of two (Z = 2) and so on.

Aluminium is the thirteenth element in the periodic table with 13 protons. Its atomic number is therefore 13 (Z = 13).

Protons do not account for all the mass of an atom. Neutrons in the nucleus also contribute to the mass. Therefore, the *mass* of an atom depends on the number of protons plus the number of neutrons. This number is called the **mass number** of the atom (symbol A). So,

> Atomic number, Z = number of protons.
> Mass number, A = number of protons + number of neutrons

Hydrogen atoms (with one proton and no neutrons) have a mass number of one (A = 1). Helium atoms (two protons and two neutrons) have a mass number of four (A = 4) and lithium atoms (three protons and four neutrons) have a mass number of seven (A = 7). We can write the symbol $^{7}_{3}\text{Li}$ (Figure 1) to show the mass number and the atomic number of a lithium atom. The mass number is written at the *top* and to the left of the symbol. The atomic number is written at the *bottom* and to the left. A lithium ion is written as $^{7}_{3}\text{Li}^{+}$. A sodium atom (11 protons and 12 neutrons) is written as $^{23}_{11}\text{Na}$.

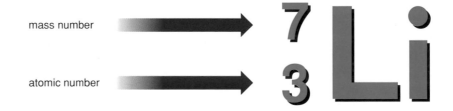

Figure 1

Using the periodic table (Unit E3), we can calculate the atomic number of an element, because the elements are arranged in order of atomic number. Therefore, the sixth element in the periodic table has an atomic number of six; the twentieth element an atomic number of 20 and so on.

Isotopes

A lot of elements have relative atomic masses which are nearly whole numbers. For example, the relative atomic mass of nitrogen is 14.01 and that of sodium is 22.99. This is not surprising. The mass of an atom depends on the mass of protons and neutrons in its nucleus and the relative mass of both these particles is 1.00.

But, some elements have relative atomic masses that are nowhere near whole numbers. For example, the relative atomic mass of chlorine is 35.5 and that of copper is 63.5. At one time, chemists could not understand why the relative atomic masses of these elements were not close to whole numbers. F.W. Aston discovered the answer in 1919 when he built the first mass spectrometer.

Using his mass spectrometer, Aston could compare the masses of atoms. He discovered that some elements had atoms with different masses. When atoms of these elements were ionised and passed through a mass spectrometer, the beam of ions separated into two or more paths (Figure 2). This suggested that one element could have atoms with different masses.

Atoms of the same element with different masses are called **isotopes**.

Each isotope has a relative mass close to a whole number, but the average atomic mass for the mixture of isotopes is not always close to a whole number. This is studied further in the next unit.

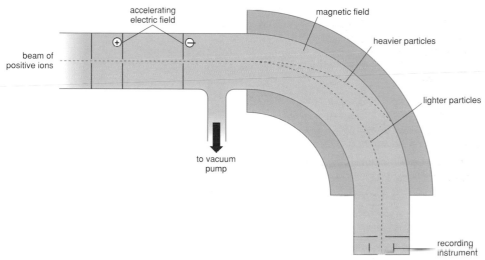

Figure 2 *A mass spectrometer. A beam of positive ions is accelerated by an electric field and then deflected by a magnetic field. The amount of deflection depends on the mass of the particles and the strength of the magnetic field. Lighter particles are deflected more than heavier particles. As the magnetic field is increased in strength, the heavier particles are deflected more and measured on the recording instrument*

Study Questions

1 Explain the following terms:
   (i) *atomic number*; (ii) *mass number*;
   (iii) *isotope*.
2 a) What is the atomic number of fluorine?
   b) How many protons, neutrons and electrons are there in one fluorine atom of mass number 19?
3 a) What do 16, 8, 2⁻ and O mean with reference to the symbol, $^{16}_{8}O^{2-}$?
   b) How many protons, neutrons and electrons are there in one $^{23}_{11}Na^+$ ion?
4 Why do some elements have relative atomic masses which are not close to whole numbers?

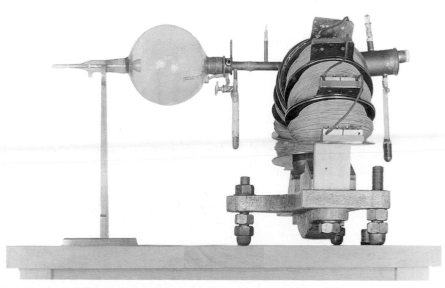

Aston's original spectrometer. Positive ions were accelerated from the glass bulb along the horizontal tube at the top of the instrument. The coils of the electromagnet produced a magnetic field which deflected the particles

4 Isotopes

Did you know?

Sometimes, chemists need to obtain just one isotope of an element. For example, natural uranium contains two isotopes, uranium-235 and uranium-238. Uranium-235 is needed for use in nuclear reactors, but natural uranium contains only about 0.7% of this isotope. Nuclear reactors need uranium with 3 or 4% of uranium-235.

Chemists can produce uranium with a higher percentage of uranium-235 because of the different physical properties of the two isotopes.

Natural uranium is converted to uranium hexafluoride (UF_6) which is very volatile. UF_6 is vapourised and diffused through a series of porous barriers. Particles of $^{235}UF_6$ are slightly lighter than those of $^{238}UF_6$. So they move faster and diffuse easier than those of $^{238}UF_6$. After several diffusions through the porous barriers, the uranium hexafluoride contains 3 or 4% $^{235}UF_6$. This can be converted back to uranium and used as nuclear fuel.

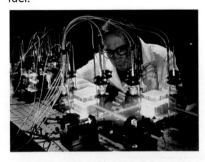

A technician researches the effect of lasers on isotopes of uranium

Isotopes are atoms of the same element with different masses. All the isotopes of one element have the same number of protons. Therefore, they have the same atomic number. As isotopes have the same number of protons, they must also have the same number of electrons. This gives them the same chemical properties because chemical properties depend upon the number of electrons in an atom.

Isotopes do, however, contain different numbers of neutrons. This means that:

> Isotopes have the *same* **atomic number** but *different* **mass numbers**.

For example, neon has two isotopes (Figure 1). Each isotope has 10 protons and 10 electrons and therefore an atomic number of 10. But one of these isotopes has 10 neutrons and the other has 12 neutrons. Their mass numbers are therefore 20 and 22. They are sometimes called neon-20 and neon-22.

These two isotopes of neon have the same chemical properties because they have the same number of electrons. But they have different physical properties because they have different masses. Samples of $^{20}_{10}Ne$ and $^{22}_{10}Ne$ have different densities, different melting points and different boiling points.

Isotopes have the same:	Isotopes have different:
● number of protons,	● numbers of neutrons,
● number of electrons,	● mass numbers,
● atomic number,	● physical properties.
● chemical properties.	

neon-20   **neon-22**

$^{20}_{10}Ne$ $^{22}_{10}Ne$

	neon-20	neon-22
number of protons	10	10
number of electrons	10	10
atomic number	10	10
number of neutrons	10	12
mass number	20	22

Figure 1 *The two isotopes of neon*

Relative atomic mass

Most elements contain a mixture of isotopes. This explains why their relative atomic masses are *not* whole numbers.

> The relative atomic mass of an element is the average mass of one atom, taking account of its isotopes and their relative proportions.

Gamma rays from unstable (radioactive) isotopes can penetrate body tissues and kill cancer cells

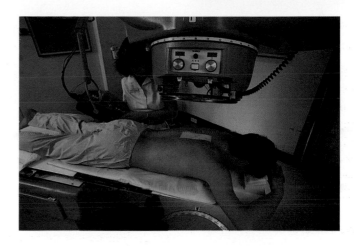

Look at the mass spectrometer trace for chlorine in Figure 2. This shows that chlorine consists of two isotopes with mass numbers of 35 and 37. These isotopes can be written as $^{35}_{17}Cl$ and $^{37}_{17}Cl$.

If chlorine contained 100% $^{35}_{17}Cl$, then its relative atomic mass would be 35. If it contained 100% $^{37}_{17}Cl$, then its relative atomic mass would be 37. A 50:50 mixture of $^{35}_{17}Cl$ and $^{37}_{17}Cl$ would have a relative atomic mass of 36.

Figure 2 shows that naturally-occurring chlorine contains three times as much $^{35}_{17}Cl$ as $^{37}_{17}Cl$, i.e. 75% to 25%. This gives a relative atomic mass of 35.5, as shown in Table 1.

The relative atomic mass can also be calculated as:

$$75\% \text{ chlorine-35} + 25\% \text{ chlorine-37}$$

$$= \frac{75}{100} \times 35 + \frac{25}{100} \times 37 = 26.25 + 9.25 = 35.5$$

Study Questions

1 There are three isotopes of hydrogen with mass numbers of one, two and three. (Naturally-occurring hydrogen is almost 100% $^{1}_{1}H$.) How many protons, neutrons and electrons do each of the three isotopes have?

2 Neon has two isotopes, with mass numbers of 20 and 22.
   a) How do you think the boiling point of $^{20}_{10}Ne$ will compare with that of $^{22}_{10}Ne$? Explain your answer.
   b) Suppose a sample of neon contains equal numbers of the two isotopes. What is the relative atomic mass of neon in this sample?
   c) Neon in the air contains 90% of $^{20}_{10}Ne$ and 10% of $^{22}_{10}Ne$. What is the relative atomic mass of neon in the air?

3 Discuss the following questions with two or three others.
   a) Why do isotopes have the same chemical properties, but different physical properties?
   b) Why do samples of natural uranium from different parts of the world have slightly different relative atomic masses?
   c) Why can chlorine form molecules with three different relative molecular masses?

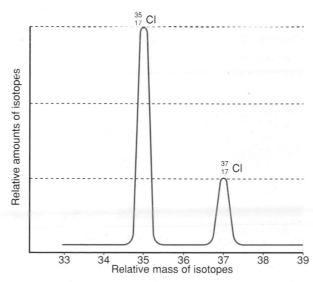

Figure 2 *A mass spectrometer trace for chlorine*

Table 1 *The relative atomic mass of chlorine for different mixtures of its isotopes*

Percentage of $^{35}_{17}Cl$	100	75	50	25	0
Percentage of $^{37}_{17}Cl$	0	25	50	75	100
Relative atomic mass	35	35.5	36	36.5	37

Further ideas about electrons

In 1911, Rutherford put forward some key ideas about atomic structure. He said that atoms had a small positive nucleus containing protons surrounded by lots of empty space. Tiny negative electrons orbit the nucleus through this empty space like planets orbiting the Sun.

In 1913, the Danish scientist Niels Bohr suggested a more accurate model for the arrangement of electrons in atoms.

Bohr said that the orbiting electrons were grouped together in layers or **shells**. Each shell could only hold a limited number of electrons (Figure 1).

Niels Bohr developed Rutherford's early ideas about atomic structure

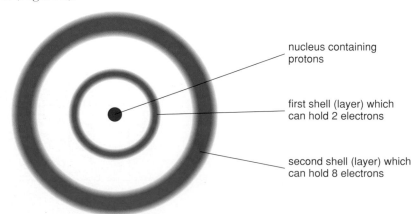

Figure 1 *Filling shells with electrons is like filling shelves in a shop. The lowest shells (shelves) are filled first. Each shell (shelf) only holds a limited number of electrons (items)*

Filling the shells

The first shell is nearest the nucleus. The electrons in it are strongly attracted to the nucleus and it is the first shell to be filled. It can hold only two electrons. When the first shell contains two electrons, it is full and the electrons in it are stable (Figure 2).

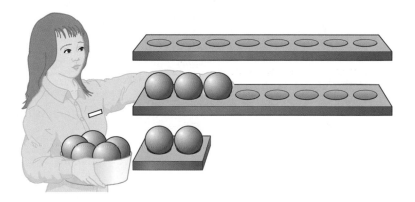

nucleus containing protons

first shell (layer) which can hold 2 electrons

second shell (layer) which can hold 8 electrons

Figure 2 *Niels Bohr's model for the arrangement of electrons in the first and second shells*

When the first shell is full, the second shell starts to fill. This shell is further from the nucleus and the electrons in it have more energy. The second shell can hold a maximum of eight electrons. When the second shell contains eight electrons it is full and the electrons in it are stable. Once the second shell is full, the third shell starts filling. This shell is further from the nucleus again. The third shell is also very stable when it contains eight electrons.

Electron structures and the noble gases

Bohr's ideas about electrons in shells have helped us to understand why the noble gases are so unreactive. The first shell is full and the electrons in it are stable when it contains two electrons. This corresponds exactly with helium. Helium has two electrons. They both go into the first shell, which is then full and stable.

The second shell is full and the electrons in it are stable when it contains eight electrons. So the next element to be very unreactive like helium will have two electrons filling the first shell and then eight electrons filling the second shell. This corresponds to neon, the tenth element in the periodic table with ten electrons in total. Because neon has two electrons in the first shell and eight electrons in the second shell, we say its electron structure is 2,8 (Figure 3).

The third shell is also stable when it contains eight electrons. So, the next element to be very unreactive will have two electrons filling the first shell, eight filling the second shell and eight in the third shell. This corresponds to argon, the eighteenth element in the periodic table with 18 electrons in total. So, the electron structure of argon is written as 2,8,8 (Figure 3).

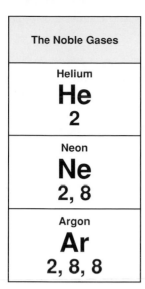

The Noble Gases
Helium
He
2
Neon
Ne
2, 8
Argon
Ar
2, 8, 8

Figure 3 *Electron structures of the noble gases*

Electron structures of the elements

Figure 4 shows the first 20 elements in periodic table order. The atomic number and electron structure of each element is written below its symbol. When the first shell is full at helium, further electrons go into the second shell. So the electron structure of lithium is 2,1; beryllium is 2,2; boron is 2,3; etc. When the second shell is full at neon, electrons start to fill the third shell and so on.

Period 1 Atomic No.				H 1				He 2
Electron structure				1				2
Period 2 Atomic No.	Li 3	Be 4	B 5	C 6	N 7	O 8	F 9	Ne 10
Electron structure	2, 1	2, 2	2, 3	2, 4	2, 5	2, 6	2, 7	2, 8
Period 3 Atomic No.	Na 11	Mg 12	Al 13	Si 14	P 15	S 16	Cl 17	Ar 18
Electron structure	2, 8, 1	2, 8, 2	2, 8, 3	2, 8, 4	2, 8, 5	2, 8, 6	2, 8, 7	2, 8, 8
Period 4 Atomic No.	K 19	Ca 20						
Electron structure	2, 8, 8, 1	2, 8, 8, 2						

Figure 4 *The electron structures of the first 20 elements in the periodic table*

Electron structures help us to explain why elements in the same group have similar properties.

Group 1: the alkali metals

Look at Figure 5. Notice that each of the alkali metals has one electron in its outer shell. Alkali metals can lose this outer electron very easily to form ions with one positive charge (Li^+, Na^+, K^+). These ions are very stable because they have an electron structure like a noble gas. For example, the electron structure of Na^+ is 2,8 which is like neon. The electron structure of K^+ is 2,8,8 like argon. Alkali metals have similar properties because they have similar electron structures.

- They are very reactive because they lose their single outer electron so easily.

- They form ions with a charge of 1+. So, the formulas of their compounds are similar.

As the atomic number of the alkali metals increases, the outer electron is further from the positive nucleus. This means that the electron is held less strongly by the nucleus. So, the electron is lost more readily and this explains why the alkali metals become more reactive as their atomic number increases.

Group 7: the halogens

All the halogen atoms have seven electrons in their outer shell (Figure 6). By gaining one electron, they form negative ions (F^-, Cl^-, Br^-). These ions have stable electron structures like the next noble gas.
Halogens have similar properties because they have the same number of electrons in their outer shell.

- They are reactive because they easily gain one electron.

- They form ions with a charge of 1–. So, the formulas of their compounds are similar.

As the atomic number of the halogens increases, the outer shell is further from the nucleus. This means that an electron is attracted less readily into the outer shell. So, halogens get less reactive as their atomic number increases.

Elements in the same group of the periodic table have similar properties because they have the same number of electrons in their outer shell.

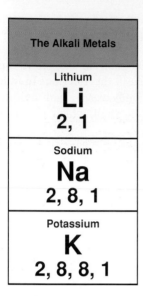

The Alkali Metals
Lithium **Li** 2, 1
Sodium **Na** 2, 8, 1
Potassium **K** 2, 8, 8, 1

Figure 5 *Electron structures of the alkali metals*

The Halogens
Fluorine **F** 2, 7
Chlorine **Cl** 2, 8, 7
Bromine **Br** 2, 8, 18, 7

Figure 6 *Electron structures of the halogens*

Chlorine is the most useful and most common halogen. It is added in very small quantities to water in swimming pools to kill bacteria and other micro-organisms

Atoms, ions and the periodic table

Look at Table 1. This shows the electron structures of the atoms and ions of elements in period 3 of the periodic table.

Table I *Electron structures of the atoms and ions of elements in period 3*

Group ➤	1	2	3	4	5	6	7	8
Elements in period 3	Na	Mg	Al	Si	P	S	Cl	Ar
Electron structure	2,8,1	2,8,2	2,8,3	2,8,4	2,8,5	2,8,6	2,8,7	2,8,8
No. of electrons in outer shell	1	2	3	4	5	6	7	8
Common Ion	Na^+	Mg^{2+}	Al^{3+}	–	–	S^{2-}	Cl^-	–
Electron structure of ion	2,8	2,8	2,8	–	–	2,8,8	2,8,8	–

- The elements in groups 1, 2 and 3, like sodium, magnesium and aluminium, have only 1, 2 or 3 electrons in their outer shell. These elements at the beginning of the period *lose* electrons to form positive ions (Na^+, Mg^{2+}, Al^{3+}). Their ions have an electron structure like the previous noble gas.

- The elements in groups 6 and 7, like sulphur and chlorine, have outer shells that are nearly full. These elements near the end of the period *gain* electrons to form negative ions (S^{2-}, Cl^-). Their ions have an electron structure like the next noble gas, argon.

- Elements in groups 4 and 5, like silicon and phosphorus, have outer shells which are roughly half full of electrons. These elements in the middle of the period do not usually form ions. Instead, they form chemical bonds by *sharing* electrons. We shall study this further in the next unit.

- The elements in group O, like argon, have outer shells of electrons that are very stable. These elements, at the end of a period, do not usually form compounds.

Study Questions

1 Why are the noble gases so unreactive?

2 a) Write down the electron structures of magnesium and calcium.
   b) How many electrons are there in the outer shell of an atom of an element in group 2?
   c) What charge will stable ions of group 2 elements have?

3 How many protons, neutrons and electrons are there in: (i) one N atom, (ii) one N^{3-} ion?

4 Write the electron structure for:
   (i) Li,
   (ii) Li^+,
   (iii) O,
   (iv) O^{2-}.

Electric light bulbs are filled with argon or krypton. These inert gases are so unreactive and their electron structures are so stable that the metal filament can be above 1000°C without reacting with them

In the last unit, we discovered that:

- Metal atoms, like sodium, magnesium and aluminium, *lose electrons* from their outer shell and form positive ions when they react.

- Non-metal atoms, like sulphur and chlorine, *gain electrons* and form negative ions when they react.

- Non-metals can also *share electrons* when they react to form compounds.

These ideas form the basis of the **electronic theory of chemical bonding**. When atoms react, they lose, gain or share electrons in order to get a stable electron structure like a noble gas.

Two kinds of bond are formed when atoms react with each other – ionic bonds and covalent bonds.

Ionic bonds are formed when metals react with non-metals. Metals form positive ions and non-metals form negative ions. The attraction between ions of opposite charge forms the ionic bond. Ionic bonds are sometimes called electrovalent bonds.

Covalent bonds are formed when non-metals react with each other. Covalent bonds involve a sharing of electrons. The positive nucleus of each non-metal attracts the shared negative electrons and this forms the covalent bond.

Ionic bonding: transfer of electrons

Figure 1 shows what happens when sodium chloride (Na^+Cl^-) is formed. Electron structures are shown for the sodium and chlorine atoms and for their respective ions.

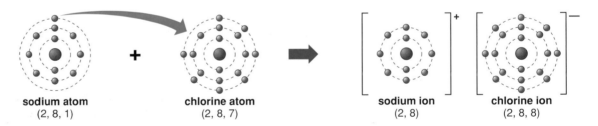

sodium atom   chlorine atom   sodium ion   chlorine ion
(2, 8, 1)   (2, 8, 7)   (2, 8)   (2, 8, 8)

Figure 1 *Electron transfer during the formation of sodium chloride*

The sodium atom has one electron in its outer shell and chlorine has seven. During the reaction, the sodium *transfers* its one outer electron into the outer shell of the chlorine atom. This produces:

- a sodium ion (Na^+) with the same stable electron structure as the noble gas neon and

- a chloride ion (Cl^-) with the same stable electron structure as the noble gas argon.

So, the formation of sodium chloride involves the *complete transfer* of an electron from a sodium atom to a chlorine atom forming Na^+ and Cl^- ions.

Ionic (electrovalent) bonds result from the electrical attraction between oppositely charged ions.

The formation of sodium chloride in Figure 1 can be summarised by showing only the outer shell electrons.

$$\text{Na}^{\bullet} \quad + \quad {}^{\times}_{\times}\overset{\times\times}{\underset{\times\times}{\text{Cl}}}{}^{\times} \quad \Longrightarrow \quad \left[\text{Na}\right]^{+} \quad \left[{}^{\bullet}_{\times}\overset{\times\times}{\underset{\times\times}{\text{Cl}}}{}^{\times}_{\times}\right]^{-}$$

(2, 8, 1) (2, 8, 7) (2, 8) (2, 8, 8)

This is called a 'dot-cross' diagram because the electrons of the different atoms are shown as either dots or crosses. Remember though that all electrons are identical.

Compounds containing ions with ionic bonds are called **ionic compounds**. The structure, bonding and properties of ionic compounds are discussed in Unit H6.

Figure 2 shows two more examples of electron transfer and ionic bonding.

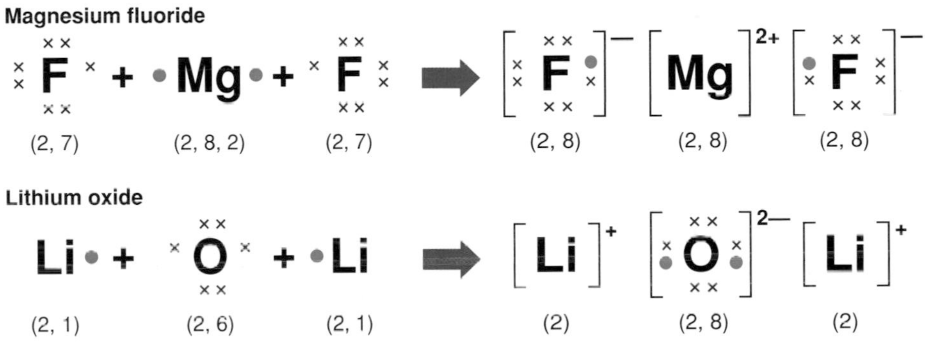

Magnesium fluoride

$${}^{\times}_{\times}\overset{\times\times}{\underset{\times\times}{\text{F}}}{}^{\times} + {}^{\bullet}\text{Mg}^{\bullet} + {}^{\times}\overset{\times\times}{\underset{\times\times}{\text{F}}}{}^{\times}_{\times} \Longrightarrow \left[{}^{\times}_{\times}\overset{\times\times}{\underset{\times\times}{\text{F}}}{}^{\bullet}_{\times}\right]^{-} \left[\text{Mg}\right]^{2+} \left[{}^{\bullet}_{\times}\overset{\times\times}{\underset{\times\times}{\text{F}}}{}^{\times}_{\times}\right]^{-}$$

(2, 7) (2, 8, 2) (2, 7) (2, 8) (2, 8) (2, 8)

Lithium oxide

$$\text{Li}^{\bullet} + {}^{\times}\overset{\times\times}{\underset{\times\times}{\text{O}}}{}^{\times} + {}^{\bullet}\text{Li} \Longrightarrow \left[\text{Li}\right]^{+} \left[{}^{\bullet}_{\times}\overset{\times\times}{\underset{\times\times}{\text{O}}}{}^{\times}_{\bullet}\right]^{2-} \left[\text{Li}\right]^{+}$$

(2, 1) (2, 6) (2, 1) (2) (2, 8) (2)

Figure 2 *Electron transfers in the formation of magnesium fluoride and lithium oxide*

Notice the following points in these 'dot-cross' diagrams.

- Transfer of electrons to form ionic bonds is typical of the reactions between metals and non-metals.

- Atoms tend to form ions with electron structures like noble gases, e.g. helium (2), neon (2,8) and argon (2,8,8). This makes them stable.

- One magnesium atom has two electrons in its outer shell (Figure 2). It reacts with two fluorine atoms, each of which takes one electron. The Mg^{2+} ion and the two F^- ions all finish with an electron structure like neon.

Two Li atoms react with one O atom to form lithium oxide (Figure 2). In this case, the two Li^+ ions have an electron structure like helium and the O^{2-} ion has an electron structure like neon.

Covalent bonds: sharing electrons

A chlorine atom is very unstable. Its outer shell contains seven electrons. At normal temperatures, chlorine atoms join up in pairs to form Cl_2 molecules. Why is this? If two chlorine atoms come close together, the electrons in their outer shells can overlap. Each chlorine atom can share one of its electrons with the other atom (Figure 3). The two atoms share a pair of electrons and get a stable electron structure like argon.

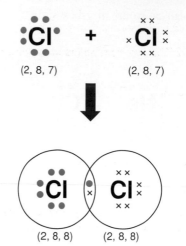

Figure 3 *Electron sharing in the covalent bond in a chlorine molecule*

The shared electrons attract the positive nuclei of both atoms and this holds the atoms together. This attraction forms a **covalent bond.**
Notice in Figure 3 that:

● the shared pair of electrons contribute to the outer shell of both chlorine atoms.

● circles are used to enclose the electrons in the outer shell of each chlorine atom.

● the chlorine atoms have bonded together forming an uncharged molecule.

> A covalent bond is formed by the sharing of a pair of electrons between two atoms. Each atom contributes one electron to the bond.

When non-metal atoms react, they form molecules. In these molecules, the atoms are joined by covalent bonds. The covalent bonding and electron structures of some common molecules are shown in Figure 4. Check the following points in Figure 4.

1 All the atoms have an electron structure like a noble gas.

2 The electron structures of these molecular compounds can be related to the displayed formulas shown on the left hand side of each dot-cross diagram. In the displayed formulas, each covalent bond is shown as a line between atoms (e.g. H—O—H for water).

3 H atoms always have one bond. Cl atoms always have one bond. Oxygen atoms have two bonds, nitrogen atoms have three bonds and carbon atoms have four bonds.

4 Double covalent bonds result from the sharing of two pairs of electrons as in oxygen and carbon dioxide.

Study Questions

1 Look at Figure 2.
   a) How many electrons do lithium and oxygen atoms lose or gain in forming lithium oxide, Li_2O?
   b) Which noble gases have electron structures like the ions in lithium oxide?
   c) Why do two lithium atoms react with one oxygen atom in forming lithium oxide?

2 Draw a diagram similar to those in Figure 2 to show what happens when potassium reacts with fluorine to form potassium fluoride, KF. Show the dot and cross structures and electronic structures.

3 Draw a 'dot-cross' diagram to show the bonding in a hydrogen molecule, H_2.

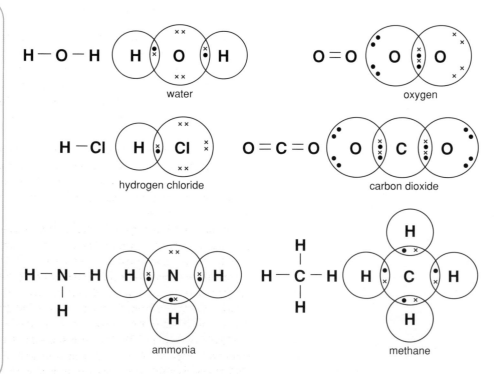

Figure 4 *The covalent bonding and electron structures of some common molecules*

1 Checking Dalton's Ideas about Atoms

John Dalton put forward his Atomic Theory in 1807. The five main points in his theory are listed below.

- All matter is made up of tiny particles, called atoms.

- Atoms cannot be made or broken apart.

- All the atoms of one element are exactly alike.

- Atoms of one element are different from those of all other elements.

- Atoms combine in small numbers to form molecules.

Dalton's ideas are still very helpful to scientists. But, modern knowledge about atoms, molecules and atomic structure has shown that four of these five main points are inaccurate.

1 We now know that matter is composed of smaller particles than atoms. What are these smaller particles called?

2 (i) Use a periodic table to name three elements that have been made (synthesised) by chemists.
(ii) Where do these synthesised elements lie in the periodic table?

3 What type of element breaks apart naturally?

4 (i) What name is given to atoms of the same element which are *not* exactly alike?
(ii) How do these atoms differ?

5 How do atoms of one element always differ in atomic structure from those of all other elements?

6 Give examples of two substances in which atoms have combined in very large numbers to form one molecule.

John Dalton was born in Cumbria in 1766. For most of his life he taught at the Presbyterian College in Manchester. Dalton was colour-blind and he did research into this condition. Because of this, colour blindness is sometimes called 'Daltonism'

2 Marie Curie discovers Radium

In 1896, the Frenchman, Henri Becquerel was studying the reactions of uranium compounds. Becquerel left one of his uranium compounds in the dark near some photographic plates. When Becquerel came to use the photographic plates, he was surprised to discover that they had been affected in the area near the uranium salts. The affect was similar to that caused by light. Because of this, Becquerel suggested that the uranium compound was giving off radiation. He said the radiation was a form of energy like light.

Marie Curie's interest was fired by Becquerel's ideas. Her husband, Pierre, gave up his own research and the two of them began to study uranium compounds in more detail. They found that all uranium salts gave off some kind of radiation and affected photographic plates. They called the process **radioactivity** and described the uranium salts as **radioactive**.

During their investigations, the Curies noticed that pitchblende (impure uranium sulphide) was much more radioactive than pure uranium. This led them to think that the pitchblende contained another element more radioactive than uranium.

Starting in 1898, Marie and Pierre worked for four years in an old shed in Paris trying to extract the more radioactive substance. By 1902, they had obtained one gram of radium chloride from 8 tonnes (8 000 000 grams) of pitchblende. The radium was two million times more radioactive than uranium.

In 1903, Pierre and Marie Curie shared the Nobel Prize for Physics with Henri Becquerel. Tragically, Pierre was run over and killed by a horse-drawn cart in Paris in 1906. Marie carried on working with radioactive materials and in 1911, she was awarded the Nobel Chemistry Prize. She was the first person to win two Nobel Prizes.

Pierre and Marie Curie spent four years isolating radium chloride from pitchblende. The radium in this was two million times more radioactive than uranium.

Marie Curie kept on working until 1934 when she died of leukaemia which had been caused by radioactivity.

1 Scientists sometimes need to use their imagination to explain their results. How did Becquerel do this?

2 How did Pierre and Marie Curie test Becquerel's ideas?

3 Why were the ideas about radioactivity accepted so readily?

4 What led the Curies to search for radium in pitchblende?

5 Look at the periodic table on page 94.
   (i) Which group is radium in?
   (ii) What is the formula of radium chloride?

6 Scientific discoveries can provide great benefits but they can also create hazards and problems. State one benefit and one hazard from radioactivity.

Did you know?

Marie Curie's laboratory notebooks are still highly radioactive. Anyone touching them has to wear protective gloves and clothing.

3 Using *PowerPoint* to illustrate the formation of an ionic and a covalently-bonded compound

a) Produce a *PowerPoint* presentation showing the formation of an ionic compound of your choice. Your slides should demonstrate:
   (i) The changes which occur in the electronic structures of the two elements as they form the compound,
   (ii) How the elements are held together in the compound.

b) Repeat the *PowerPoint* presentation but this time for the formation of a covalently-bonded compound of your choice.

4 Using Publisher to design a poster

Using *Publisher*, design a poster relating the atomic structure, electronic structure and bonding of an element of your choice to its properties, reactions or uses.
Your poster should include a picture relevant to the element and a few short sentences to highlight the important information.

Section K   Summary

1 Atomic structure
All atoms are built up from three tiny particles – **protons**, **neutrons** and **electrons**.
- The proton and the neutron are both assigned a relative mass of one. An electron has a mass of $\frac{1}{1840}$ of this.
- Protons have a positive charge of $+1$. Neutrons have no charge. Electrons have a negative charge of -1.
- Protons and neutrons occupy the **nucleus** at the centre of an atom. Electrons occupy layers or **shells** at different distances from the nucleus.

2 Protons, neutrons and electrons are the building blocks for all atoms.
- All atoms of a particular element have the same number of protons.
  e.g. Hydrogen atoms have one proton, helium atoms have two protons, carbon atoms have six protons and iron atoms have 26 protons.
- In any **atom**, the number of electrons is equal to the number of protons, so that overall the atom is neutral.

3 The **atomic number** of an atom (Z) = the number of its protons
$$= \text{the order of the element in the periodic table}$$
(e.g. Sodium is the eleventh element in the periodic table, with eleven protons, Z = 11.)

4 The **mass number** of an atom (A) = number of protons + number of neutrons.
So, sodium atoms with 11 protons and 12 neutrons have a mass number of 23, A = 23.

5 Isotopes are atoms of the same element with the same atomic number but different mass numbers.

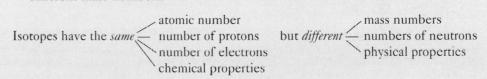

Isotopes have the *same* — atomic number / number of protons / number of electrons / chemical properties   but *different* — mass numbers / numbers of neutrons / physical properties

6 The relative atomic mass of an element (A_r) is the average mass of one atom taking account of its isotopes and their relative proportions.
e.g. Boron contains 20% boron-10 and 80% boron-11.
$$\therefore A_r(B) = \frac{20}{100} \times 10 + \frac{80}{100} \times 11 = 2.0 + 8.8 = 10.8$$

7 Electron structure
- The electrons in an atom determine its chemical properties.
- Electrons occupy layers or shells at different distances from the nucleus. When these shells are filled, the atoms or ions become stable.
- The first shell nearest the nucleus is full and stable when it contains two electrons. This is the case for helium atoms, so they are very stable and unreactive.
- The second shell is full and stable when it contains eight electrons. This is the case for neon. Neon has a filled first shell with 2 electrons and a filled second shell with 8 electrons. So, its electron structure is written as 2,8.
- Elements in the same group have similar electron structures. This gives them similar chemical properties.
  e.g. All the elements in group 1 have one electron in their outer shell.
  Li 2,1; Na 2,8,1; K 2,8,8,1.
  They lose this outer electron easily. So they are reactive and they form similar ions with one positive charge, Li^+, Na^+, K^+.

8 The electronic theory of chemical bonding

When atoms react, they lose, gain or share electrons in order to get a stable electron structure like a noble gas.

- **Ionic bonds** are formed when metals react with non-metals. Electron transfer occurs. Metal atoms lose electrons to form positive ions. Non-metals gain these electrons to form negative ions.

e.g.

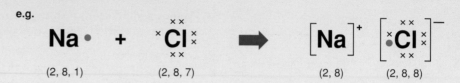

(2, 8, 1)   (2, 8, 7)   (2, 8)   (2, 8, 8)

The ionic bond results from the electrical attraction between oppositely charged ions.

- **Covalent bonds** are formed when non-metals react with each other. The non-metal atoms share electrons.

e.g.

(2, 8, 7)   (2, 8, 7)   (2, 8, 8)   (2, 8, 8)

The positive nucleus of each atom attracts the shared negative electrons and this forms the covalent bond.

Section K   Exam Questions

1

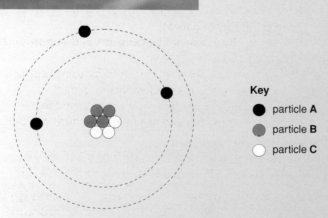

Key
- ● particle **A**
- ● particle **B**
- ○ particle **C**

(a) The diagram shows the arrangement of particles in an atom of the element lithium.

(i) Identify the particles **A**, **B**, and **C**.

(ii) What is the mass number of the atom in the diagram?

(iii) Use the diagram to explain why this element is in group 1 of the periodic table.

(b) Another element in group 1 is sodium.
Sodium reacts with chlorine (Cl_2) to form sodium chloride (NaCl).
Write a balanced equation for this reaction.

Edexcel (specimen paper, 2003)

2 The flow chart gives an outline of the extraction of aluminium.

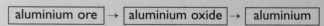

aluminium ore → aluminium oxide → aluminium

(a) (i) Name the aluminium ore used.

(ii) Name the type of process used to extract aluminium from aluminium oxide.

(b) The word equation for the extraction of aluminium is:

aluminium oxide → aluminium + oxygen

The reaction is endothermic.

(i) Explain what is meant by **endothermic**.

(ii) Suggest why this reaction is endothermic.

(c) Aluminium oxide contains aluminium ions (Al^{3+}).
The atomic number of aluminium is 13.
The mass number of aluminium is 27.

(i) Copy and complete the table to show the number of protons, neutrons and electrons in an aluminium atom (Al) and an aluminium ion (Al^{3+}).

Formula of particle	Number of protons	Number of neutrons	Number of electrons
Al			
Al^{3+}			

(ii) Name the type of bonding present in aluminium oxide.
(iii) State ONE physical property you would expect aluminium oxide to have.

Edexcel 2000

3   The elements in Mendeléev's periodic table were arranged in order of increasing atomic mass. Part of the modern periodic table is shown.

(a) Copy and complete the sentence by writing in the missing words.

The modern periodic table is arranged in order of increasing ....

(b) (i) Name a metal in the same group as lithium.
(ii) Name a non-metal in the same period as magnesium.

(c) The table contains some information about **two** elements.

Element	Symbol	Number of		
		protons	neutrons	electrons
fluorine	F	9	10	9
chlorine	Cl	17	18	17
chlorine	Cl	17	20	17

(i) In terms of atomic structure, give **one** feature that both these elements have in common.
(ii) There are two *isotopes* of chlorine shown in the table. Explain what *isotope* means.
(iii) Explain, in terms of electron arrangement, why fluorine is more reactive than chlorine.

(d) Sodium reacts with chlorine to form the compound sodium chloride.
$$2Na + Cl_2 \rightarrow 2NaCl$$
Describe, in terms of electron arrangement, the type of bonding in:
(i) a molecule of chlorine;
(ii) the compound sodium chloride.

AQA 2000

4   The table below show some information about the isotopes of chlorine.
(a) Copy the table and use information from the periodic table to help you complete the table.

Isotope	Mass Number	Abundance	Number of protons in one atom	Number of electrons in one atom	Number of neutrons in one atom
chlorine-35		75%			
chlorine-37		25%			

(b) (i) Show why the relative atomic mass of chlorine is given as 35.5.
(ii) What is the relative molecular mass of a chlorine molecule?
(c) Draw a dot and cross diagram for a molecule of chlorine, showing outer electrons only.
(d) State ONE use of chlorine, apart from water purification.   **Edexcel 1998**

5   Use the periodic table to help you answer these questions.
(a) A Russian chemist named Mendeleev produced a periodic table.

His periodic table had the elements in order of increasing atomic mass.

Find the elements **potassium** and **argon** in the periodic table.
(i) What problem is caused by using atomic mass to place these elements in order?
(ii) Show how this problem is solved for potassium and argon in a modern periodic table.

The table below gives information about some elements in the third period of the periodic table.

element	symbol	electron arrangement	formulae of chlorides
sodium	Na		NaCl
magnesium	Mg	2,8,2	
aluminium	Al		$AlCl_3$
silicon	Si		$SiCl_4$
phosphorus	P		PCl_5
sulphur	S		S_2Cl_2
chlorine	Cl		——

(b) There is a pattern in the electron arrangements of atoms of elements in this period.
(i) Copy and complete the missing electron arrangements in the table.
(ii) What is the connection between electron arrangement and the position of the element in the periodic table?
(c) There is a pattern in the formulae of chlorides in this period.
Suggest the formula for magnesium chloride.
(d) Sodium reacts with cold water.
(i) Write down the names of the products of this reaction.
(ii) Write a balanced equation for this reaction.
(e) Potassium is in the same group of the periodic table as sodium.
(i) Write down the electron arrangement in a potassium atom.
(ii) Explain why potassium reacts faster than sodium with cold water.

OCR 1999

6 In some nuclear reactors sodium metal is used to transfer heat. The sodium is heated to about 500°C by the reactor. The heat is transferred to water to produce steam.
(a) What property of metals makes sodium very good for use in heat transfer?
(b) Is sodium a solid, a liquid or a gas when it has been heated by the nuclear reactor?
(c) What happens when a small piece of sodium reacts with water?
You should describe what you would see and state what substances are formed.
(d) When sodium reacts with water it forms sodium ions.
The diagrams below represent the electron arrangements of some atoms and ions.

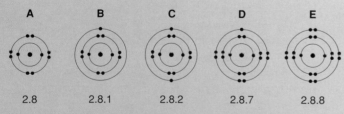

A	B	C	D	E
2.8	2.8.1	2.8.2	2.8.7	2.8.8

Which of the diagrams, **A** to **E**, represents the electron arrangement of each of the following?
(i) A sodium atom, Na; (ii) A sodium ion, Na$^+$.

(e) Scientists have been able to make new elements in nuclear reactors. One of these new elements is fermium. An atom of fermium is represented by the symbol below.

$$^{257}_{100}\text{Fm}$$

(i) How many protons does this atom contain?
(ii) How many neutrons does this atom contain?

AQA 1999

7 (a) Magnesium, atomic number 12, reacts with oxygen, atomic number 8, to form magnesium oxide.
(i) Give the electronic structures of the two elements magnesium and oxygen.
(ii) Explain, by means of a diagram or otherwise, the electronic changes that take place during the formation of magnesium oxide. Include the charges on the ions.
(iii) Explain why the bonding in magnesium oxide produces a solid with a high melting point.
(b) Hydrogen, atomic number 1, forms hydrogen molecules, H_2.
By means of a diagram show the bonding in a hydrogen molecule.

WJEC 2001

8 Uranium metal can be produced by reacting uranium hexafluoride with calcium.
$$UF_6 + 3Ca \rightarrow 3CaF_2 + U$$
(a) Describe how calcium and fluorine bond together to form calcium fluoride. The electron arrangement of each atom is shown.

(b) Uranium has two main isotopes, $^{235}_{92}U$ and $^{238}_{92}U$. Use these as examples to explain what is meant by the word isotope.
(c) At the start of a reaction there was 174.5 g of uranium hexafluoride, UF_6.
Relative atomic masses: F=19; U=235
(i) Calculate the relative formula mass of uranium hexafluoride, UF_6.
(ii) Calculate the mass of uranium that would be produced from 174.5 g of uranium hexafluoride.

AQA 1999

Earth and Atmosphere

The Earth's surface is continually being changed and weathered by temperature changes and the action of water

By the end of this section you should:
- Know how the Earth's atmosphere and oceans have changed over time.
- Understand how processes in the carbon cycle, nitrogen cycle and water cycle help to maintain the composition of the atmosphere and oceans.
- Be able to describe the structure and formation of igneous, sedimentary and metamorphic rocks.
- Appreciate how evidence for the formation and deformation of rocks can be obtained from the rock record.
- Know that the Earth's crust is composed of gigantic plates in relative motion.
- Understand how plate tectonics results in the folding, faulting, formation and deformation of rocks.

Layers of the Earth

The Earth is a ball of rock and iron. Its radius is about 6400 km. 4500 million years ago, the Earth was a mass of molten rock. Gradually, it cooled down over millions of years. During this period, heavier metals sank to the centre of the Earth forming a **core** of very dense molten iron at about 4000°C (Figure 1). This core is surrounded by a thick layer of moderately dense solid and molten rock in the **mantle**. Temperatures in the mantle range from 1500 to 3500°C.

Less dense material collected on the surface of the Earth. This formed a thin **crust** about 50 km thick. Where the crust is thickest, its surface is above sea level.

Outside and above the Earth is the **atmosphere** – a layer of gases about 100 km deep.

Did you know?

At 6 km above sea level, the air becomes so thin that most living things cannot survive. Moving in the other direction, oceans are about 6 km deep. So, almost all life on Earth exists in a thin layer about 12 km thick.

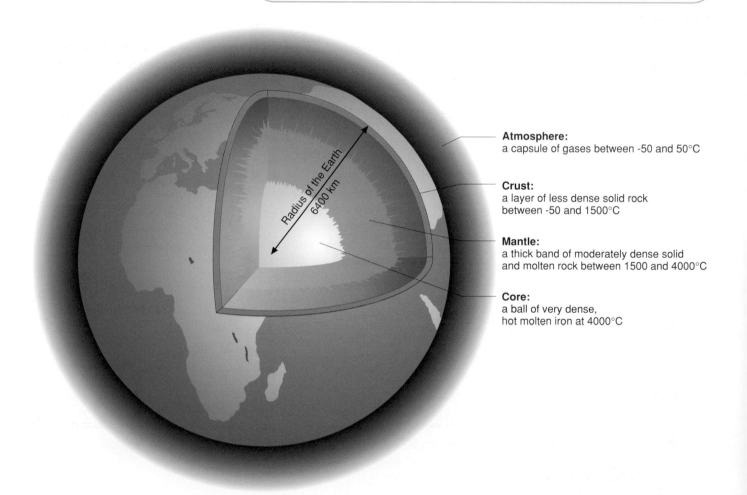

Atmosphere:
a capsule of gases between -50 and 50°C

Crust:
a layer of less dense solid rock between -50 and 1500°C

Mantle:
a thick band of moderately dense solid and molten rock between 1500 and 4000°C

Core:
a ball of very dense, hot molten iron at 4000°C

Radius of the Earth 6400 km

Figure 1 *Layers of the Earth. Notice how the temperature and density of the layers increase towards the centre of the Earth*

Water vapour in the atmosphere condenses to form clouds as the air is forced to higher and colder zones by high mountains

How did the atmosphere and oceans form?

a) While the Earth was still forming, the gases above its surface were mainly hydrogen and helium. These gases had such small molecules that they escaped from the Earth's gravitational attraction into outer space (Figure 2a).

Figure 2a

b) As molten rocks on the Earth's surface cooled, there was intense volcanic activity. Rocks decomposed, elements reacted and gases were released to form the first atmosphere (Figure 2b).

This early atmosphere was mainly carbon dioxide and water vapour with smaller amounts of methane (CH_4) and ammonia (NH_3).

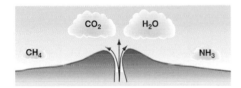

Figure 2b

c) As the temperature dropped still further, water vapour condensed to form rivers, lakes and oceans (Figure 2c).

Figure 2c

Plants appear and further changes occur

d) Plants appeared on the Earth 3 500 million years ago and this caused further changes in the atmosphere. Plants used water and carbon dioxide for photosynthesis and this added oxygen to the atmosphere (Figure 2d).

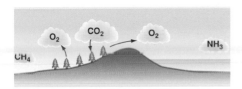

Figure 2d

e) Flammable gases, like methane and ammonia, burnt in this oxygen producing more water, more carbon dioxide and nitrogen (Figure 2e).

Figure 2e

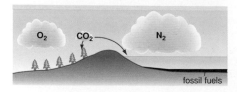

Figure 2f

Ammonia in the early atmosphere was also removed by two other processes:

- nitrifying bacteria which changed the ammonia into nitrates and
- denitrifying bacteria which converted the ammonia to nitrogen.

f) At the same time, carbon dioxide in the early atmosphere was also decreasing. There were three main reasons for this (Figure 2f):

- the removal of carbon dioxide by photosynthesis,
- the slow formation of fossil fuels from carbon compounds in plants and sea creatures,
- carbon dioxide dissolving in oceans, lakes and rivers.

So, the early atmosphere containing carbon dioxide, water vapour, methane and ammonia gradually changed over 4 000 million years to form:

- oceans, lakes and rivers containing liquid water and
- an atmosphere containing mainly nitrogen and oxygen.

> The atmosphere has remained more or less the same for the last 200 million years. Its composition is:
>
> - about four fifths nitrogen,
> - about one fifth oxygen,
> - plus small amounts of carbon dioxide, water vapour and noble gases.

Accurate percentages of these gases in dry air are shown in Table 1. The Earth is the only planet in our solar system with oxygen in its atmosphere and abundant surface water in rivers, lakes and oceans. Other planets, such as Mars do, however, have some water vapour and polar ice caps.

Keeping the atmosphere in balance

The composition of the atmosphere has stayed constant for the last 200 million years. This is due to processes in the carbon cycle, the nitrogen cycle (Unit J9) and the water cycle (Unit B7) which keep things in balance.

In the carbon cycle:

- carbon dioxide and water vapour are removed from the atmosphere by photosynthesis but returned to the atmosphere when animals and plants respire and during the combustion of carbon compounds.

In the nitrogen cycle:

- nitrogen is removed from the air by nitrogen-fixing bacteria in plants and during the Haber Process, but returned to the air when animal and plant matter dies and decays.

Did you know?

When oxygen appeared in the atmosphere 3 500 million years ago:

- micro-organisms which could not tolerate oxygen began to disappear,
- an ozone layer started to form. This absorbed harmful ultraviolet radiation from the sun and allowed new organisms to evolve.

Table I *The percentages of gases in dry air*

Gas	Percentage
Nitrogen	78.1
Oxygen	20.9
Argon	0.9
Carbon dioxide	
Neon	less
Krypton	than
Xenon	0.1

A fossilised ichthyosaurus in sedimentary rock

In the water cycle:

● water vapour is continually being added to and removed from the atmosphere by processes of evaporation and condensation respectively.

The solubility of gases in the water of rivers and oceans also helps to maintain a balance of gases in the atmosphere.

The solubilities of oxygen and nitrogen are very low, but there are massive amounts of carbon dioxide dissolved in the oceans. This is used by aquatic organisms for photosynthesis and to produce shells containing calcium carbonate. These shells eventually end up as sedimentary carbonate rocks which release carbon dioxide during volcanic activity thousands, if not millions, of years later.

Keeping the oceans in balance

The composition of the oceans is also kept in balance by a combination of processes.

● During the water cycle, water vapour is lost by evaporation but replaced when it rains, hails or snows.

● Solid materials are added to the oceans when soluble substances, like rock salt (sodium chloride) dissolve and during the weathering of rocks, like chalk and limestone. At the same time, dissolved solids are removed from the oceans when marine organisms form shells and bones and when salt deposits crystallise from seawater.

Coral deposits form from calcium and carbonate ions in sea water. These ions are also needed for the formation of bones in fish and shells in crustaceans

Study Questions

1 a) What are the main layers in the structure of the Earth?
   b) What is:
      (i) the radius of the Earth,
      (ii) the distance around the Earth from the North Pole to the South Pole?

2 a) What two substances do the Earth's surface and atmosphere contain which are essential for living things?
   b) How did these substances get into the atmosphere and on the Earth's surface?
   c) Why do you think there are no living things on:
      (i) the planet, Mercury,
      (ii) the planet, Pluto?

3 a) State three major activities of humans which have begun to affect the composition of the atmosphere during the last 150 years.
   b) Why are changes in the composition of the atmosphere causing concern?

4 Unit G10 will help you with this question.
   a) Why does rain water wear away limestone? Write equations for the reactions involved.
   b) Why are there dry valleys in limestone areas?

Wherever you go, rocks are below your feet. The Earth formed 4.5 billion years ago from a huge ball of hot, molten material. As this cooled, the molten mixture set to form layers with a solid crust of rock on the surface of the Earth.

Rocks are very important. They provide important building materials and ores from which metals are extracted.

Rocks in the Earth are usually mixtures of different substances. When the Earth first cooled, its solid crust was composed of **igneous rocks**. At first, there were no other types of rock. Over millions of years, two other types of rock were created – **sedimentary rocks** and **metamorphic rocks**. Figure 1 shows how these three types of rock are being formed today.

Igneous rocks

Igneous rocks are formed when hot, molten magma cools and solidifies.

The magma comes from the Earth's mantle or from other rocks which have melted close to the mantle. As the molten magma cools, it solidifies as a mixture of different substances with interlocking crystals. The size of crystals in the igneous rock depends on the rate at which the magma has cooled and crystallised.

Some igneous rocks are produced when volcanoes erupt and the lava cools quickly in a matter of days or weeks. This produces rocks, such as basalt, with small crystals which are usually dark in colour. These igneous rocks which form quickly at or near the Earth's surface are described as **extrusive.**

Other igneous rocks are formed deep in the Earth's crust close to the mantle. Here, the magma cools very slowly, possibly over centuries. This produces rocks with much larger crystals such as granite and quartz which are usually light in colour. These igneous rocks which form slowly below the Earth's surface are described as **intrusive.**

This is a smoothly polished sample of granite – an igneous rock. 'Igneous' means formed by fire. Igneous rocks are formed from the cooling of very hot, molten rock. Granite forms when molten rocks cool slowly below the Earth's surface so the crystals in it are large

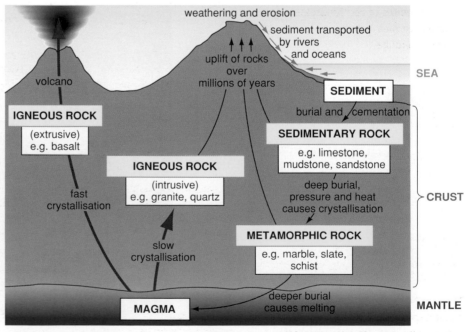

Figure 1 *The formation of igneous, sedimentary and metamorphic rocks*

The tors on Dartmoor and most of the Scottish Highlands are composed of granite – an intrusive igneous rock

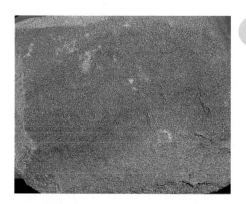

This is a sample of red sandstone – a sedimentary rock. It has formed from the erosion of granite

Sedimentary rocks

Sedimentary rocks are formed from particles and sediment of eroded rocks. These sediments build up and become buried. As more sediment collects it is compressed and compacted, eventually becoming rocks.

Sediments, such as sand and gravel may be carried by rivers or ocean currents and deposited elsewhere. As the sediment builds up, the material below is pressed down and compacted. Water is squeezed out and the sediment gets cemented together by salts crystallising out of the water. Eventually, new, soft rocks such as mudstone, sandstone and shale are formed. Other sedimentary rocks, such as coal, chalk and rock salt, have formed after the decay of living things or after crystallisation from sea water. If the sediments are buried deeper, the soft rock, such as chalk, gets converted to harder rocks like limestone.

All of these rocks are known as **sedimentary rocks** because they are formed by compacting and cementing sediments.

This is a polished sample of marble, a metamorphic rock. It has formed from sedimentary rocks at high temperature and presure

Metamorphic rocks

Sedimentary rocks can be changed into harder rocks by enormous pressure or very high temperatures. The new rock has a different structure from the original rock. It is therefore called 'metamorphic rock' from a Greek word meaning 'change of shape'. Slate and marble are good examples of metamorphic rocks. Slate and schist are formed when mudstone (shale) is subjected to very high temperatures. Marble is formed when limestone comes into contact with very hot igneous rock or molten magma.

Metamorphic rocks are formed by the action of heat and pressure on existing rocks.

Table 1 *Identifying igneous, sedimentary and metamorphic rocks*

Property	Igneous	Sedimentary	Metamorphic
● Is the rock hard or soft?	hard	soft (grains can be rubbed off)	usually hard
● What is the structure?	interlocking crystals	separate grains	grains or crystals
● Might the rock have layers?	no	yes	yes
● Might the rock have fossils?	no	yes	yes
● Might the rock fizz (give off CO_2) with dilute HCl?	no	yes	yes

Evidence in the rocks

Table 1 summarises the properties of igneous, sedimentary and metamorphic rocks. It will help you to decide whether a rock is igneous, sedimentary or metamorphic.

By looking at rocks carefully, we can obtain evidence about their structure, their formation and their age.

Igneous rocks

● Igneous rocks are hard and crystalline. The size of their crystals give us evidence of their formation either from intrusions below the Earth's surface or from the lava flows of molten magma.

● Igneous rocks never contain fossils because they would be decomposed at the temperatures of hot molten magma.

● Igneous rocks don't contain any carbonates, like the calcium carbonate in the bones of some fossils. These carbonates are decomposed at the temperatures of hot magma.

$$\text{calcium carbonate} \xrightarrow{\text{heat}} \text{calcium oxide} + \text{carbon dioxide}$$
$$CaCO_3(s) \rightarrow CaO(s) + CO_2(g)$$

So, igneous rocks don't give off carbon dioxide with dilute hydrochloric acid.

Sedimentary rocks

● Sedimentary rocks are usually soft. Their structure is composed of grains or small fragments of material.

● Sedimentary rocks often show evidence of the conditions under which the sediments were deposited. Often, they are formed in layers indicating clearly defined periods during which different sediments have been deposited. Sometimes, they show ripple marks from river currents or waves.

● Sedimentary rocks, particularly in the UK are often composed of chalk or limestone. These contain calcium carbonate which fizzes with dilute hydrochloric acid as carbon dioxide is produced.

Limestone cliffs at West Bay in Dorset, UK, show clearly defined layers

$$\text{calcium carbonate} + \text{hydrochloric acid} \rightarrow \text{calcium chloride} + \text{water} + \text{carbon dioxide}$$
$$CaCO_3(s) + 2HCl(aq) \rightarrow CaCl_2(aq) + H_2O(l) + CO_2(g)$$

Metamorphic rocks

Metamorphic rocks have a mixture of the properties of igneous and sedimentary rocks.

- Metamorphic rocks are usually harder than sedimentary rocks but softer than igneous rocks.

- Metamorphic rocks may have grains or crystals.

- Metamorphic rocks can have layers or fossils. Marble (containing calcium carbonate) will fizz with dilute HCl.

- Some metamorphic rocks have the same composition as sedimentary rocks and this is strong evidence for their formation from the latter. For example, marble and limestone are both forms of calcium carbonate ($CaCO_3$).

The rock record

Sedimentary rocks often contain fossils of plants and animals which died when the sediments were being deposited.

These fossils provide evidence that a rock is sedimentary and give us clues to the age of the rock. Some of the clues which we get from fossils are shown in Figure 2.

Age of the rock	Typical fossils in the rock	
up to 2 million years ago	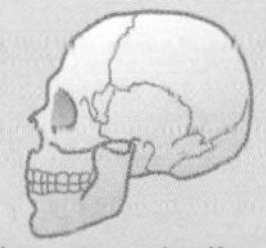 human skulls	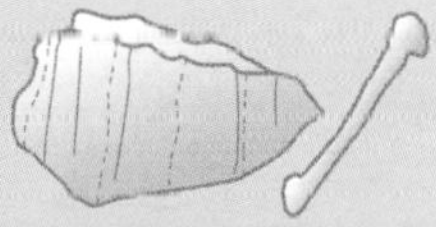 mammoth tooth & bones
up to 65 million years ago	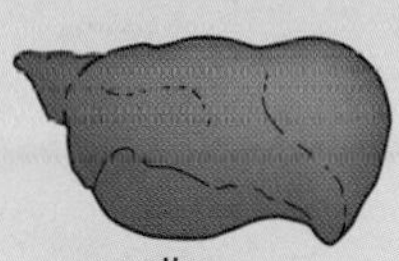 snails	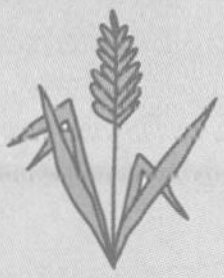 grasses
up to 225 million years ago	 ammonites	 two sided shells
up to 600 million years ago	 trilobites	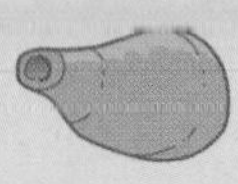 lampshells

Figure 2 *Clues from fossils about the age of rocks*

Different types of fossils help us to date rocks and this evidence and dating from rocks is called the **rock record**. In general, the older fossils appear in the deeper rocks and the deepest rocks are usually the oldest. Very often, there are relatively young sedimentary rocks near the surface of the Earth and these lie on top of older rocks.

The rock cycle

Figure 3 summarises the stages in the rock cycle. The complete cycle lasts hundreds of millions of years and there are short cuts to the full cycle. Notice how stages in the rock cycle relate to processes in the formation of rocks in Figure 1.

Sediments form as a result of the weathering and erosion of rocks. These sediments are compressed to form sedimentary rocks which form metamorphic rocks under the effects of heat and pressure.

At very high temperatures, metamorphic rocks and igneous rocks melt to form magma.

As magma cools and crystallises, it forms igneous rocks.

Finally, all three rock types (igneous, metamorphic and sedimentary) are eroded and weathered to form sediments and the cycle begins once again.

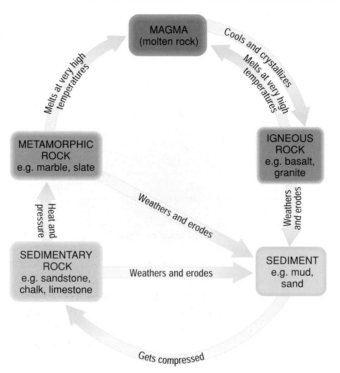

Figure 3 *The rock cycle*

Study Questions

1   Look closely at the rock cycle in Figure 3 and explain the following statement. 'One rock is the raw material for another'.

2   a)   When the Earth was first formed, there were only igneous rocks. Why was this?

   b)   Are the following rocks igneous, sedimentary or metamorphic: (i) coal, (ii) diamond, (iii) slate, (iv) mudstone?

3   a)   How are sediments turned into sedimentary rocks?

   b)   How are sedimentary rocks turned into metamorphic rocks?

   c)   What happens to sediments during the processes in a) and then b)?

4   You are given three pieces of rock by a friend who wants to know more about them. Rock A is made of rounded pebbles held together by a hard, sandy layer. Rock B is white in colour and contains several small fossils which look like shells you have seen at the seaside. Rock C is very hard and is made of large crystals which you can see quite clearly.
What could you tell your friend about the rocks?

The Earth's structure

The Earth's *shape* is like an orange – spherical but slightly flattened at the poles. Its *structure* is like a badly cracked egg. The 'cracked shell' is like the Earth's thin crust, the 'egg white' is the mantle and the 'yolk' is the core (Figure 1).

Evidence for the Earth's structure comes from various sources including the study of rocks, mines, volcanoes, earthquakes and the Earth's magnetic field.

Notice in Figure 1 that the three concentric layers of crust, mantle and core increase in thickness, in density and in temperature towards the centre.

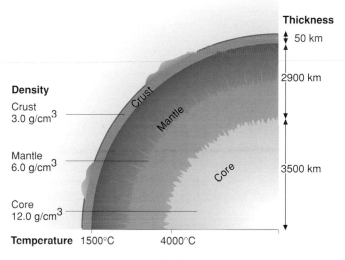

Figure I *A cross section of the Earth showing the thicknesses, densities and temperatures in its internal structure*

The deepest mines in the Earth go to a depth of about 3 km. The temperature here is about 50°C.

Below the crust, temperatures in the outer mantle are about 1500°C. This is hot enough to soften the rocks so they behave like plasticine. Within the mantle, temperatures are between 2000 and 3000°C and the material is liquid. In the Earth's core, the temperatures are even higher, reaching 4000°C.

Why is the Earth's core so hot?

There are two reasons for this.

1 When the Earth first formed, the temperatures inside were very high. Since then, the outer layers of the Earth have helped to insulate the core.

2 Some rocks in the Earth, particularly granite, contain radioactive isotopes of elements such as uranium, thorium and potassium. As the nuclei of these elements decay (break up), energy is released as heat and electromagnetic radiation. This energy helps to maintain temperatures inside the Earth.

Earth movements

The Earth's crust is not one continuous shell of rock, but cracked and broken into massive sections called **plates**. These vast plates float on the denser mantle below. The Earth's core is as hot as the surface of the Sun. This causes slow convection currents in the liquid mantle and slow movements of the plates in the Earth's crust. Figure 2 shows a map of the world with the main plates and their direction of movement.

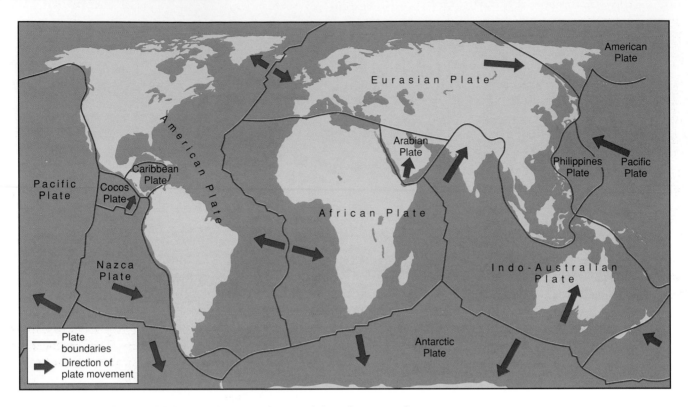

Figure 2 *A map of the world showing the main plates and their directions of movement*

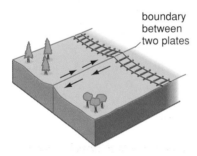

(a) Plates in the Earth's crust are bent as they slide past each other in opposite directions. The earth and rocks are displaced sideways

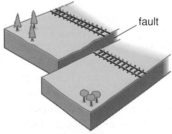

(b) Stresses in the bent plates are suddenly released as a break appears in the earth. The ground shakes (an earthquake) and a fault has formed

Figure 3 *How an earthquake occurs*

The study of the movement and interaction of the giant plates on the Earth's surface is called **plate tectonics**.

Plate tectonics explain many of the geological features on the Earth including the burial of rocks, volcanoes, earthquakes and even the formation of mountain ranges.

Measurements from space satellites have shown that the American Plate is moving away from the Eurasian and African Plates by 5cm each year. Over thousands and millions of years, movements such as this can cause massive changes on the Earth.

In order to appreciate the importance of plate tectonics, it is helpful to study what happens when plates slide past each other, when they move apart and when they move towards each other.

What happens when plates slide past each other?

When two plates slide past each other, stresses and strains build up in the Earth's crust. Massive forces are involved which come from the internal energy of the Earth. This energy drives the convection currents in the mantle and the movements of the plates. The forces are so great that they cause the plates to bend. In some cases, the stresses and strains are released suddenly. The Earth moves, the ground shakes violently in an **earthquake** and breaks appear in the ground. These breaks in the ground, when plates slide past each other horizontally are called **tear faults** (Figure 3(b)). The San Andreas Fault in California and the Great Glen Fault in Scotland are examples of tear faults. In fact, the map of Scotland would look very different if the Great Glen tear fault had not occurred (Figure 4).

There is severe damage and often loss of life when an earthquake occurs. Buildings collapse and roads are torn apart

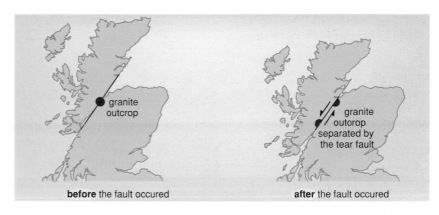

before the fault occured   **after** the fault occured

Figure 4 *The map of Scotland before and after the Great Glen Fault*

What happens when plates move apart?

When plates move apart, the crust is stretched and cracks sometimes appear in the Earth's surface. In some cases, hot molten rock escapes through the cracks and erupts as a **volcano** (unit L2). As the plates move further apart, surface rocks sink and may get buried. This results in vertical faults. These faults produced by stretching (tension) forces are called **normal faults**. When two vertical faults occur alongside each other, rift valleys are formed (Figure 5).

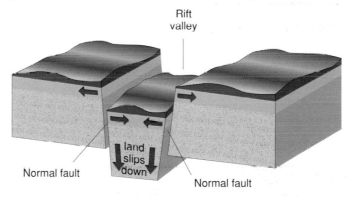

Figure 5 *As plates move apart, the land on one side may sink into the crack. If there are two normal (vertical) faults near each other, a rift valley may form*

What happens when plates move towards each other and collide?

The Earth's crust that lies under the continents is called **continental crust**. The crust that lies under the oceans is called **oceanic crust**. The continental crust is thicker and contains less dense rocks such as granite. The oceanic crust is thinner but contains denser rocks like basalt. If a continental plate and an oceanic plate move towards each other, then the denser oceanic plate will sink under the lighter continental plate (Figure 6). This causes the burial of rocks and parts of the oceanic crust may be forced into the mantle where it melts to form magma. At the same time, the continental crust gets squashed and lifted up into folds.

Folds in the Earth's crust at Stair Hole, Lulworth Cove in Dorset. Folds like this have been created in the UK even though we are more than 1000 km from the collision of the American Plate and the Eurasian Plate

Figure 6 *A continental plate and an oceanic plate moving towards each other*

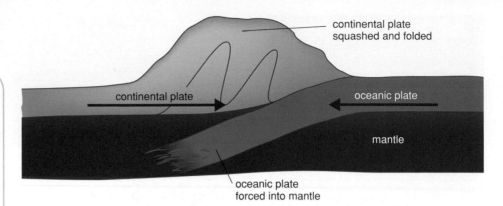

continental plate squashed and folded

continental plate

oceanic plate

mantle

oceanic plate forced into mantle

Study Questions

1 The crust of the Earth is thought to account for only 1% of the total volume of the Earth. The mantle accounts for about 82%. Using these figures, construct a pie chart for the major layers of the Earth.

2 Suppose the photo of the folds in the Earth's crust at Stair Hole, Lulworth is taken facing east.
  a) Which directions did the forces which created the fold come from?
  b) Was the force a compression or a tension?
  c) Draw a sketch map of the fold and explain how it formed.

3 In California, most of the orange groves have trees growing in straight lines. In some groves, however, the lines of trees are kinked, although they were not planted like this.
  a) Explain why the lines of trees are now kinked.
  b) In what interesting geological area are these orange groves?

4 The diagram below shows an oceanic plate approaching a land mass. Redraw the diagram and on it write:

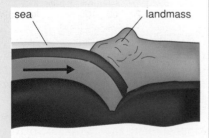

sea   landmass

  (i) O on the oceanic plate,
  (ii) C on the continental plate,
  (iii) M where solid rock is melting,
  (iv) S where sediment is depositing.
  Explain how Earth movements can lead to an earthquake.

Over millions of years, this results in the formation of mountain ranges. This is what has happened and continues to happen in South America as the Nazca Plate collides with the American Plate to create the Andes Mountains (see Figure 2). As these new mountain ranges form, they replace older mountain ranges worn down by weathering and erosion.

If two continental plates or two oceanic plates move towards each other and collide, rocks are pushed and squeezed together. When this happens, sedimentary layers of the Earth's crust become tilted, folded and even turned upside down (Figure 7). If this process continues for millions of years, then mountain ranges will form. The Alps, the Pyrenees and the Himalayas all formed in this way.

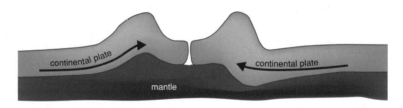

continental plate   continental plate

mantle

Figure 7 *Continental plates moving towards each other. This causes tilting and folding*

Sometimes, cracks appear when plates move towards and push against each other. Land on one side of the crack is then forced upwards whilst that on the other side gets buried (Figure 8). This is called a **reverse fault**.

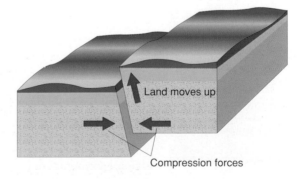

Land moves up

Compression forces

Figure 8 *As plates move towards each other, the Earth may crack forming a reverse fault*

Every year, there are reports of earthquakes and volcanoes somewhere in the world. All of these, together with folding, faulting (fracturing) and mountain formation show that the Earth's crust is unstable when subjected to powerful tectonic forces.

1 Rock on the map

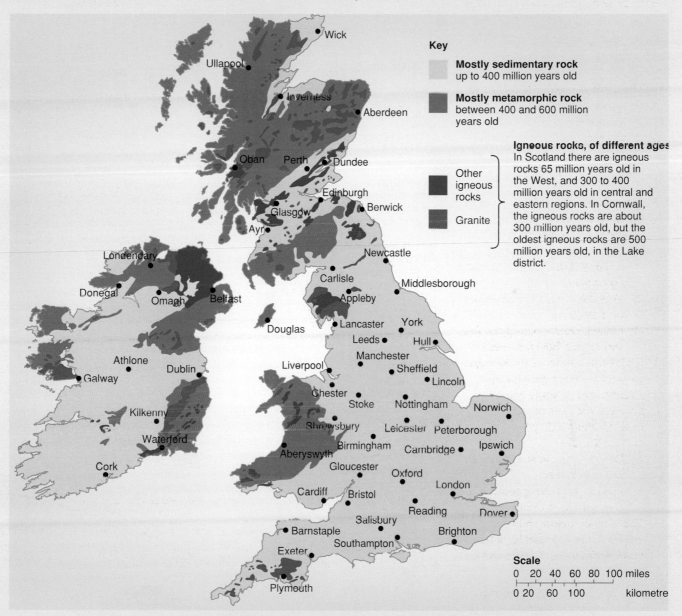

Key

Mostly sedimentary rock
up to 400 million years old

Mostly metamorphic rock
between 400 and 600 million
years old

Igneous rocks, of different ages
In Scotland there are igneous
rocks 65 million years old in
the West, and 300 to 400
million years old in central and
eastern regions. In Cornwall,
the igneous rocks are about
300 million years old, but the
oldest igneous rocks are 500
million years old, in the Lake
district.

Other
igneous
rocks

Granite

Scale
0 20 40 60 80 100 miles

0 20   60   100   kilometre

This map shows the types of rock that lie at or just beneath the surface in the British
Isles. Using the map, the key and perhaps an atlas, answer the following questions.

1 About how old is the rock upon which these places are built?
   a) Liverpool b) Aberystwyth c) Aberdeen d) your home

2 What type of rock are these places built upon?
   a) Plymouth b) Oban c) Belfast d) your home

3 How far away are the nearest igneous rocks to
   a) London b) Edinburgh c) Newcastle d) your home?

4 How long ago were the most recent volcanoes active in the British Isles?

5 About 400 million years ago, part of the British Isles was a huge mountain range,
   similar to the Himalayas today. This mountain range contained metamorphic rocks
   and granite. Which part of the British Isles do you think this was?

2 Weathering of Gravestones

The table below shows data obtained by school children doing a project on the weathering of gravestones.

Dates on gravestones	Type of rock		
	Sandstone	Marble	Granite
1720–1770	extremely badly weathered	very badly weathered	moderately weathered
1771–1819	very badly weathered	badly weathered	moderately weathered
1820–1870	badly weathered	moderately weathered	slightly weathered
1871–1919	moderately weathered	slightly weathered	unweathered
1920–1980	slightly weathered	unweathered	unweathered
1981–2002	unweathered	unweathered	unweathered

a) Why do you think they chose a graveyard for this study?
b) What do the results show?

3 River Erosion

The graph below shows the velocity of flow of a stream of water needed to pick up and transport particles of different sizes (Curve A). Curve B of the graph shows the velocity of flow at which particles of different sizes come out of suspension and are deposited. Use the graph to answer the following questions.

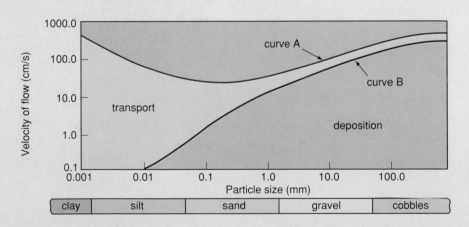

a) Which type of material is most easily transported?
b) At approximately what velocity will clay particles be picked up?
c) At approximately what velocity will coarse gravel be picked up?
d) In a stream flowing at a velocity below 50 cm per second, what type of material is most likely to be picked up?
e) Explain the shape of Curve B.

4 Looking at rocks

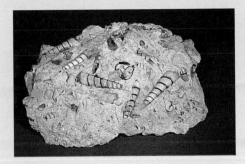
Rock X

Rock Y

Look at the photos of the two rocks above labelled X and Y.

a) Describe the appearance of (i) X, (ii) Y.
b) What type of rock is (i) X, (ii) Y?
c) Describe fully how you think rock X was formed.
d) Describe fully how you think rock Y was formed.
e) What tests could you carry out to check your answers in part b)?

5 Using the Web to identify ores

Match the ores on the left of the table below with the chemical names on the right.
If you need help with this, log onto www.periodic.lanl.gov/ or minerals.galleries.com

Ores	Chemical names
Anhydrite	barium sulphate
Argentite	copper carbonate
Barite	calcium carbonate
Bauxite	calcium magnesium carbonate
Chalcopyrite	calcium sulphate
Cassiterite	copper iron sulphide
Cinnabar	copper(I) oxide
Cuprite	hydrated aluminium oxide
Dolomite	iron(III) oxide
Galena	lead sulphide
Haematite	mercury sulphide
Halite	silver sulphide
Limestone	sodium chloride
Malachite	tin oxide
Rutile	titanium oxide

Section L   Summary

I The Earth's Structure

The Earth has four distinct layers. The temperature and density of these layers increases from the atmosphere to the core.

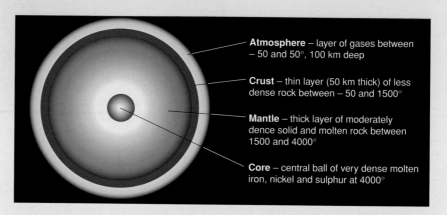

Atmosphere – layer of gases between – 50 and 50°, 100 km deep

Crust – thin layer (50 km thick) of less dense rock between – 50 and 1500°

Mantle – thick layer of moderately dence solid and molten rock between 1500 and 4000°

Core – central ball of very dense molten iron, nickel and sulphur at 4000°

2 The Earth's Atmosphere

The Earth's early atmosphere was mainly carbon dioxide and water vapour with smaller amounts of methane and ammonia. When plants appeared $3\frac{1}{2}$ million years ago, they used carbon dioxide and water for photosynthesis and produced oxygen. Methane and ammonia burnt in the oxygen to produce more water, carbon dioxide and nitrogen. Ammonia was also removed from the early atmosphere by bacteria. Large amounts of carbon dioxide were gradually removed from the atmosphere by photosynthesis, by the slow formation of fossil fuels and by carbon dioxide dissolving in the water of oceans, lakes and rivers.

The composition of the atmosphere has remained more or less the same for the last 200 million years with:

- about $\frac{4}{5}$ths nitrogen,

- about $\frac{1}{5}$th oxygen,

- small amounts of carbon dioxide, water vapour and noble gases.

The composition of the atmosphere and oceans is kept in balance by processes in the carbon cycle, the nitrogen cycle and the water cycle.

3 Rock types

There are three different rock types:

	Igneous	Sedimentary	Metamorphic
Formed from →	cooling and crystallisation of magma	compacting and cementing sediments	heat and exposure on existing rocks
Structure →	interlocking crystals	grains or fragments of rock	grains or small crystals
Examples →	granite, basalt	mudstone, limestone, sandstone	slate, marble

4 Evidence from rocks

By looking carefully at rocks we can get evidence about their structure, formation and age. For example:

- the size of crystals in igneous rocks gives evidence of their formation either intrusively or extrusively.

- the absence of fossils and carbonates in igneous rocks gives evidence of formation from materials exposed to very high temperatures.

- ripple marks or layers in sedimentary rocks provide evidence of the conditions under which they formed.

- fossils in sedimentary rocks provide evidence of the age of the rocks with younger rocks lying on top of older rocks.

- some metamorphic rocks have the same composition as sedimentary rocks which is strong evidence for their formation from the latter.

5 Earth movements

The Earth's crust is cracked and divided into vast sections called **plates** which float on the dense liquid mantle. The continents and oceans lie on top of these plates which move very, very slowly due to convection currents in the mantle. The study of the movement and interaction of the gigantic plates is called **plate tectonics**.

- *When plates slide past each other*, tear faults and earthquakes occur.

- *When plates move apart*, normal faults, volcanoes and rift valleys can occur.

- *When plates move towards each other*, folds and reverse faults can occur. Some rocks may be buried, others get uplifted and this can result over millions of years, in the formation of mountains.

Section L   Exam Questions

1 (a) Choose the correct formula for each of the following gases.

water vapour	HO	H_2O	HO_2
nitrogen	N	N_2	N_3
carbon monoxide	CO	C_2O	CO_2

(b) Millions of years ago, the atmosphere contained:

> **carbon dioxide**   **carbon monoxide**
> **hydrogen**   **nitrogen**   **water vapour**

  (i) What originally produced these gases?
  (ii) The amounts of these gases have changed over millions of years. State **two** of these gases which have decreased.
  (iii) Name the gas, **not** on the list, which now makes up about 20% of the atmosphere.

(c) Describe the test for carbon dioxide.

(d) Photosynthesis changes the amount of oxygen and carbon dioxide in the atmosphere. How does photosynthesis change the amount of:
  (i) oxygen,   (ii) carbon dioxide?

Edexcel, specimen paper 2003

2 This question is about different types of rocks.
(a) The lists show the names of some rocks and descriptions of them.
Copy the list and draw a line from each name to the correct description.
Each name must be joined to a different description. One has been done for you.

name of rock	description of rock
basalt	grains arranged in layers of dark and light bands
conglomerate	crystals smaller then 0.5 mm, mainly dark in colour
gneiss	small stones bound together by cementing material
granite	hard, brittle, grey rock that splits into sheets
slate	crystals bigger than 0.5 mm, mainly light in colour

(b) Write down the name of an example of each of the following rock types. Choose your answers from this list:

basalt, conglomerate, gneiss, granite, slate.

  (i) a sedimentary rock
  (ii) a metamorphic rock
  (iii) an extrusive igneous rock
  (iv) an intrusive igneous rock

OCR 1999

3 For 200 million years the proportions of the different gases in the atmosphere have been much the same as today. Over the past 150 years the amount of carbon dioxide in the atmosphere has increased from 0.03% to 0.04%.
(a) Describe how carbon dioxide is released into the atmosphere:
  (i) by human and industrial activity;
  (ii) from carbonate rocks by geological activity.
(b) Explain how the seas and oceans can decrease the amount of carbon dioxide in the atmosphere.
(c) (i) Give **one** reason why the amount of carbon dioxide in the atmosphere is increasing gradually.
  (ii) Give **one** effect that increasing levels of carbon dioxide in the atmosphere may have on the environment.

AQA 1999

4 The diagrams below show what three types of rock look like under the microscope.

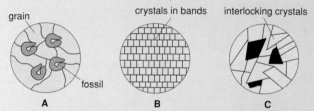

Using the words in the box below copy and complete the table that follows:

> **granite   igneous   limestone   marble
> metamorphic   sedimentary**

Rock	Type of rock	Name of rock
A	sedimentary	limestone
B	....	....
C	....	....

(b) The Earth's lithosphere is cracked into a large number of pieces which are moving very slowly.
  (i) Give the name for these large pieces.
  (ii) State the result of these large pieces slowly moving
    I. apart,   II. towards each other.

WJEC, specimen paper 2003

5 The diagram represents the layers of the Earth.

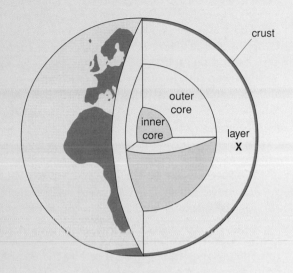

(a) (i) Give the name of layer **X**.
(ii) The inner core is smaller and nearer to the centre of the Earth than the outer core. Give **one** other difference between the inner and outer parts of the core.

(b) A student was shown two igneous rocks **A** and **B**. Rock **A** had large crystals. Rock **B** had small crystals.
(i) Describe how igneous rocks are formed.
(ii) Explain fully why the crystals in rock **A** are larger than the crystals in rock **B**.

(c) Explain why most igneous rocks form near the boundaries of tectonic plates.

AQA 2000

6 The diagram shows how rocks are broken down and new rocks formed in the rock cycle.

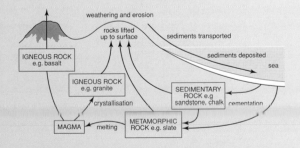

(a) There are four processes involved in forming sedimentary rocks.
They are in the wrong order below.

A depositing sediments
B cementation
C transporting sediments
D weathering and erosion

Copy out and then fill in the following boxes to show the correct order. Use the diagram to help you.

(b) Write down **two** processes taking place when **metamorphic** rocks turn into **igneous** rocks.
(c) What conditions of temperature and pressure are needed to turn **sedimentary** rocks into **metamorphic** rocks?
(d) This table shows some information about slate, chalk and granite.

rock	is the rock crystalline?	can the rock contain fossils?
slate	*no*	*yes*
chalk		
granite		

Copy and finish the table by putting '*yes*' or '*no*' in each of the four spaces. The diagram may help you.
(e) Igneous rocks can be described as **extrusive** or **intrusive**. Basalt is an extrusive rock. Granite is an intrusive rock. Describe how extrusive rocks and intrusive rocks are formed from magma.

OCR 2000

7 The diagram below shows one of the plates under the Pacific Ocean. It is always moving, very slowly, towards and under the South American land mass.

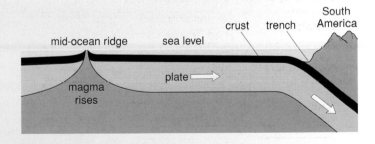

(a) Copy the diagram and on it write:
(i) **S** where molten rock is solidifying;
(ii) **M** where solid rock is melting.
(b) Sedimentary rock forms on top of the plate. Describe how sedimentary rock is formed.

Edexcel 2000

8 (a) The main components of the *original* Earth's atmosphere were carbon dioxide and water. The pie chart below shows the approximate composition of dry air in the atmosphere *today*.

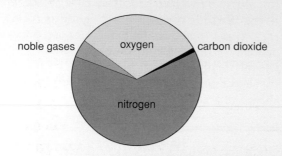

(i) State the **source** of the original Earth's atmosphere.

(ii) Name the gas in the pie chart which is entirely biological in origin.

(iii) There has been a drastic reduction in the amount of water vapour in the air over geological time. Explain how this decrease occurred.

(b) The Earth's atmosphere is surrounded by a layer of ozone. State the importance of the ozone layer to our health.

(c) Give one use to which oxygen is put.

(d) The Carbon Cycle helps to maintain atmospheric composition. Name **two** processes which have the opposite effect to photosynthesis in the Carbon Cycle.

WJEC 2000

9 The diagram shows a cross section through layers of different rocks in the Earth's crust.

Use the diagram to help you answer the questions that follow.

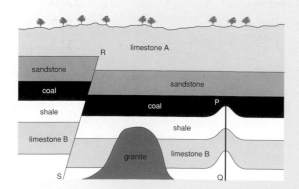

(a) From the diagram choose
(i) an igneous rock.
(ii) the oldest sedimentary rock.

(b) The granite crystallised from magma.
Describe and explain the likely appearance of the crystals in the granite.
Your answer should refer to the size of the crystals and the conditions resulting in their formation.

(c) Marble is a metamorphic rock formed from limestone.
(i) Where on the diagram is marble likely to form?
(ii) Suggest why both limestone and marble react in the same way with dilute hydrochloric acid.

(d) On the diagram **P–Q** is a fold and **R–S** is a fault. How can you tell that the fold **P–Q** occurred earlier in geological time than the fault **R–S**?

(e) Folding and faulting are caused by the Earth's crust experiencing huge pressures.
What process causes the crust to experience such pressures?

OCR 2001

10 Two samples of rock from different parts of a volcanic island had the same chemical composition but different crystal size.

(a) Name this type of rock and describe how it was formed, accounting for the difference between the samples.

(b) Analysis of another rock showed that it contained an oxide of tin in which 3.57 g of tin was combined with 0.96 g of oxygen.
(i) Calculate the empirical formula of the tin oxide present in the rock.
(Relative atomic masses; $O = 16$, $Sn = 119$)
(ii) The melting point of the tin oxide was found to be over 1000°C.
Explain why tin oxide has a high melting point and suggest the type of structure it has.

Edexcel 1999

Relative Atomic Masses

Element	Symbol	A_r	Element	Symbol	A_r
Aluminium	Al	26.9	Magnesium	Mg	24.3
Antimony	Sb	121.8	Manganese	Mn	54.9
Argon	Ar	39.9	Mercury	Hg	200.6
Arsenic	As	74.9	Molybdenum	Mo	95.9
Barium	Ba	137.3	Neon	Ne	20.2
Beryllium	Be	9.0	Nickel	Ni	58.7
Bismuth	Bi	209.0	Nitrogen	N	14.0
Boron	B	10.8	Oxygen	O	16.0
Bromine	Br	79.9	Phosphorus	P	31.0
Cadmium	Cd	112.4	Platinum	Pt	195.1
Caesium	Cs	132.9	Potassium	K	39.1
Calcium	Ca	40.1	Rubidium	Rb	85.5
Carbon	C	12.0	Scandium	Sc	45.0
Chlorine	Cl	35.5	Selenium	Se	79.0
Chromium	Cr	52.0	Silicon	Si	28.1
Cobalt	Co	58.9	Silver	Ag	107.9
Copper	Cu	63.5	Sodium	Na	23.0
Fluorine	F	19.0	Strontium	Sr	87.6
Gallium	Ga	69.7	Sulphur	S	32.1
Germanium	Ge	72.6	Tellurium	Te	127.6
Gold	Au	197.0	Thorium	Th	232.0
Helium	He	4.0	Tin	Sn	118.7
Hydrogen	H	1.0	Titanium	Ti	47.9
Iodine	I	126.9	Tungsten	W	183.9
Iridium	Ir	192.2	Uranium	U	238.0
Iron	Fe	55.8	Vanadium	V	50.9
Krypton	Kr	83.8	Xenon	Xe	131.3
Lead	Pb	207.2	Zinc	Zn	65.4
Lithium	Li	6.9			

Index

A *see* ampere
acetic acid *see* ethanoic acid
acid rain 32–3, 140, 141
acidic oxides 25
acids 138–49, 150–1
    carboxylic 215–16
    concentrated/dilute 143
    everyday life 140–1
    ions 142
    making 138–9
    neutralisation 145–7
    pH 143
    properties 142–4
    reactions 118–19, 120, 121, 142, 149
    salts preparation 154
    strong/weak 143–4
    sulphuric acid 148–9
activities
    acids, bases and salts 162–3
    air and water 40–1
    atomic structure and bonding 273–4
    Earth and atmosphere 293–5
    metals 132–3
    oil products 220–1
    particles, reactions and equations
        62–3
    patterns and properties 108–9
    raw materials to pure substances
        16–18
    reaction rates 250–2
    structure of materials 188–9
addition reactions 204–5, 206, 213
air 2–3
    acids 140
    breathing 23, 26–7
    burning 26
    composition 22–3, 282
    oxygen 22–5
    pollution 32–4
    redox reactions 30–1
    rusting 28–9
    separation 23
alchemy 16–17
alcohols 213–14
    see also ethanol
alkali metals 90–1, 94, 96–7, 268
alkaline oxides 25
alkaline-earth metals 94
alkalis 130–1, 145–7, 150–2, 184–5
alkanes 199–201, 205
alkenes 202–3, 204–5, 206–8
allotropes 174
alloys 8, 9, 29, 98, 116–17, 236
    see also steel

alpha particles 258–9
aluminium 80–1, 83, 84–5
AMMChem plant, Oakbridge 251
ammeters 72, 77
ammonia
    atmospheric 281–2
    fertilisers manufacture 245–7
    formation 241
    Haber process 61, 233, 237, 241–7, 282
    molecule 53
    moles 56
    nitric acid manufacture 245–6
    properties 245
    test for 129
ammonites 287
ammonium nitrate 145, 245, 246–7
ammonium phosphate fertiliser 163
ammonium sulphate 245, 247
ampere (A) 76
amylase 238
anions 76, 79, 128–9
anodes 72, 74–5, 76–7, 80–1, 83, 185
anodising 82–3, 84–5
aqueous solutions 72, 74
argon 23
Arrhenius, Svante 150, 151
Aston, F. W. 262–3
atmosphere 280, 281–3
'Atomic Theory of Matter' 51
atoms 51–7
    bonding 270–2, 274
    electron sharing 178–9
    isotopes 262–5
    mass 55, 56–7
    number 94, 262–5
    particles 258–61
    periodic table 269
    shells 266–8
    structure 257–78
Avogadro, Amedeo 56
Avogadro's constant 56

bacteria 282
balanced chemical equations 58–9
bases 141, 142, 145–7, 149, 150–1
basic oxides 25
batteries 71, 144
bauxite 80, 84
Becquerel, Henri 273–4
biodegradable plastics 208
biological catalysts *see* enzymes
birth control 249
blast furnaces 126–7
bleaching agents 102, 103, 104

body *see* human body
Bohr, Niels 266
boiling point 14, 50
    alkali metals 91, 96–7
    halogens 101
    metals 114
    noble gases 107
    periodic table 108
    simple molecular substances 178
    water 161
bonds
    breaking and making 218–19
    covalent 174–9, 270–2, 274
    electron structure 269
    intermolecular 177–9
    ionic 182–3, 270–1, 274
Boyle, Robert 5
bread-making 239
breathing 22, 24, 26–7
brine 184
bronze 116
Brown, Robert 48
Brownian motion 48–9
burning
    alkanes 201
    energy change measurement 217–18
    fire fighting 41, 180
    flammable substances 15
    importance 26
    oxy-acetylene 233
    oxygen 233
    plastic waste 210

C *see* coulomb
calcium carbonate 159, 160, 230–1
calcium fluoride 152
calcium hydroxide 151–2, 156
calcium ions 183
calcium oxide 156
calorimetry 217–18
carbohydrate 149
carbon 55, 117, 127, 174–6, 188, 282
carbon dioxide
    alkane combustion 201
    atmospheric 32, 33, 281–2
    making 180
    properties/preparation 180–1
    test for 129
carbon fibre 188
carbon monoxide 201
carbonates 128–9, 142, 149, 154–5, 286
carbonic acid 142, 143, 159, 228
carboxylic acids 215–16
catalase 237, 238

catalysis 99, 229, 236–9
  biological *see* enzymes
  catalytic converters 237
  catalytic cracking 202–3, 204
  catalytic hydrogenation 205, 221
cathode rays 258
cathodes 72, 74–7, 80, 81, 83, 185
cations 76, 79, 130–1
cement 156
centrifuging 11
ceramics 4
CFCs *see* chlorofluorocarbons
Chadwick, James 260
chalk 157
changes of state 4, 49–50
charge, electric 76–9, 261
chemical bonds 218–19
chemical equations 58–9, 60–1
chemical properties *see* reactivity
chlor-alkali process 184–5
chlorine 102–3, 104–5, 218–19, 265, 271–2
chlorofluorocarbons (CFCs) 32, 34, 105
chromatography 13
classification 4
clay 172
Clean Air Act 34
clean water 10, 35, 41
climate change *see* global warming
close packing 114
coal 194–5
coins 117
coloured compounds 99
combining power *see* valency
combustion *see* burning
composites 157, 188
compounds 5, 8–9, 52, 73, 178–9
concentrated acids 143, 148, 149
concentration 233
concrete 157
condensation 12, 197–8
conduction 71, 72–3, 115, 176
contact process 138–9
continental crust 291, 292
copper 8
  compounds 79
  electrolysis 85
  ions 76–8
  mining 132–3
  oxide 59, 63
  wires 71
coral 283
core (Earth's) 280, 284, 289
corrosive substances 15

coulomb (C) 76
covalent bonds 174–9, 270, 271–2, 274
cracking, catalytic 202–3, 204
cross-linked plastics 208, 209–10
crude oil 3, 196–8, 199–201, 202–3
crust (Earth's) 280, 284, 291, 292
crystals 11, 29, 152, 170–1, 286–8
cubic crystals 170–1
Curie, Marie 7, 273–4
Curie, Pierre 273–4

Dalton, John 7, 45, 51, 273
decomposition 6, 128
dehydrating agents 149
denaturation 238
density 114
dental care 145, 163
detergents 36
diamond 174–5
diatomic molecules 53, 101
diffraction patterns 171
diffusion 48
dilute acids 143
dilution 47
disinfectants 104
displacement reactions 103
displayed formulas 177, 199, 200, 202
dissolved oxygen 37, 39
dissolving sugar 46
distillation 12–13, 161, 196–8, 212
Döbereiner, Johann Wolfgang 90–1
Döbereiner's triads 90–1
double covalent bonds 272
dynamic equilibrium 241

Earth 279–301
  atmosphere 280, 281–3
  crust 9, 280, 284, 291, 292
  movements 289–92
  oceans 281–2, 283
  rocks 284–8, 293, 295
  structure 280, 289
earthquakes 289, 290, 291
electricity 69–88
  acid solutions 142
  conduction 72–3
  currents 70–1
  everyday life 70–1
  light bulbs 107, 269
  measurement 76–8
electrodes 72, 74–5
electrolysis 69–88
  copper 76–7, 85
  industry 80–1
  ion charges 78–9

ions 75
metals 124–5
products 74
purification 81
recycling 81, 84
electrolytes 72
electrons 258–60, 266–72
  electron sharing *see* covalent bonds
  electron transfer *see* ionic bonds
electroplating 82–3
electrovalent bonding *see* ionic bonding
elements 5–9
  abundance 9
  atoms and molecules 53
  electricity conduction 73
  patterns 90–5
  periodic table 92–5, 108, 262, 267–9
  symbols 51–2
emission spectroscopy 130
end point 146
endothermic reactions 194, 217–19
energy 194–5, 217–19, 235
energy level diagrams 217, 219
environment 21–44, 108–9
enzymes 229, 237, 238, 239
equations 58–9, 60–1
equilibrium 241
erosion 288, 294
esterification 216
ethanoic acid 142, 143, 144, 215–16
ethanol 212–14
ethene 204–5, 206, 213
eutrophication 247
evaporation 11, 12, 50
exam questions
  acids, bases and salts 166–8
  air and water 43–4
  atomic structure and bonding 276–8
  Earth and atmosphere 298–300
  electricity and electrolysis 87–8
  metal compounds 135–6
  oil products 224–6
  particles, reactions and equations 66–8
  patterns and properties 111–12
  raw materials to pure substances 20
  reaction rates 253–6
  structure of materials 191–2
exothermic reactions 26, 31, 194, 201, 217–19
explosives 242, 245
extraction 11, 122–7
extrusion 208

Index

extrusive rock 284
eye protection 57, 146, 148, 150, 154, 180

Faraday constant (F) 78
Faraday, Michael 73
farming methods 249
faults 290–2
fermentation 12, 212, 213, 239
fertilisers 36–7, 163, 245–7, 248
fibres 4
filtrates 10
filtration 10–11
fire extinguishers 180
fire triangle 27, 41
flame tests 130
flammable substances 15
   see also burning
fluorescent lights 107
food 140, 145, 163, 228, 246, 249
formic acid 144
formulas 60–1
   displayed 177, 199, 200, 202
   finding 56–7, 63
   ionic compounds 183
   molecular 53, 179, 199, 200
fossils 194–5, 286, 287, 295
fractional distillation 12–13, 196–8, 212
freezing 50
fuels 26, 32–3
   natural gas 194–5, 199–201, 242
   oil 1, 3, 36–7, 194–5, 196–8, 202–3

galvanizing 29
gamma radiation 265
gases 4, 49, 61, 194–5
Geiger, Hans 258–60
giant covalent (molecular) structures 173, 174–6
giant ionic structures 173, 182–3
giant metallic structures 173
glass 4, 186, 187
global warming 33–4
gold 122, 132
granite 284–5, 294
graphite 174, 175–6
Great Glen Fault 290–1
Greek thought 16–17
'greenhouse effect' 33–4

Haber, Fritz 7, 242
Haber process 61, 233, 237, 241–7, 282
halides, test for 129
halogens 94, 100–5, 268
hard water 158–61
hardness, diamond 175
harmful substances 15

hazard symbols 14–15
heat 37, 194, 217–19
helium atom 260–1
hexagonal crystals 170–1
homologous series 199–200, 213, 215
human body 140, 229
   see also enzymes
hydrates 28–9, 152
hydration 213
hydrocarbons 199–201
hydrochloric acid 139, 142, 143, 184–5, 230–2
hydrogen 6, 218–19, 228, 241–7, 260–1
hydrogen chloride 53, 218–19
hydrogen peroxide 236, 237, 238
hydrogenation, catalytic 205, 221
hydroxides 150

ice formation 240
identification *see* tests
igneous rock 284–5, 286, 288, 293
'immobilised' enzymes 239
impurities, metals 125, 127
incineration 210
indicator *see* universal indicator
industry
   alkalis 151
   ammonia 61, 241–7, 282
   chlor-alkali process 184–5
   electricity 70
   electrolysis 80
   enzymes 239
   fertilisers from ammonia 245–7
   Haber process 242–7, 282
   hydrochloric acid 139
   iron ore to steel 126–7
   limestone 156–7
   reaction rates 229
   redox reactions 30–1
   sulphuric acid 138–9
inert gases *see* noble gases
insect stings 145
insoluble salts 152–4
insulators 70–1
intermolecular bonding 177–9
intrusive rock 284
ion-exchange, water softening 161
ionic bonds 182, 270–1, 274
ionic compounds 182–3
ionic structures, giant 182–3
ions 53
   acids 142
   charges 76–9
   electrolysis 75
   electron structure 269

hard water 158
   neutralisation 147, 150–1
   transition metals 99
iron extraction 126–7
irreversible reactions 240
irritant substances 15, 16
isomerases 239
isomerism, alkanes 200
isotopes 262–5

kinetic theory of matter 49

labels, hazard 15–16
landfill 210
lasers 107, 264
lattice arrangements 170–1
Law of Conservation of Mass 7, 59
Law of octaves 92
lead chromate 60
legumes 248
light bulbs 107, 269
lime 79
limestone 127, 156–9, 162–3, 228, 286, 287
limewater 181
lipases 239
liquids 4, 10–13, 49, 72–3, 74–5
litmus 138
locating agents 13
lubricants 175–6

magma 284, 286, 288
magnesium oxide 57, 58
malleability 115
man-made materials 2
manganese dioxide 236
mantle 280, 284, 289, 292
manufacture *see* industry
marble 157, 230–2, 285, 287, 294
margarine 205, 221
Marsden, Ernest 258–9
marsh gas 45
mass 7, 55, 60–1, 62
mass number 262–5
mass spectrometry 55, 263, 265
materials, structure 169–92
matter, kinetic theory of 49
measurement 76, 230–1
melting point 14, 50
   alkali metals 91, 96–7
   diamond 175
   graphite 176
   halogens 101
   metals 114
   noble gases 107
   periodic table 108

simple molecular substances 178
Mendeléev, Dmitri 7, 92
Mendeléev's periodic table 92–3
metalloids 90, 94
metals 3, 113–36
  see also alloys
  acid reactions 118–19, 120, 121, 142, 149
  alkali metals 90–1, 94, 96–7, 268
  alkaline-earth metals 94
  compounds of 128–31
  electricity conduction 73
  extracting 122–7
  halides 102–3
  ionic compounds 182
  manufacture by electrolysis 80–1
  ores 2–3, 122–5, 295
  oxides 24–5, 119–20
  patterns 90–1
  properties 90–1, 96–9, 114–15
  reactions 118–21, 123–4
  redox reactions 30–1
  transition metals 94, 98–9
metamorphic rock 284, 285–6, 287, 288, 293
methane 199
mica 169
mining 97, 108–9, 122–3, 132–3
miscible liquids 12
mixtures 8–9, 10–13
molar volume 61
molecules 51–7, 178–9, 199, 200
moles 56, 60
molten aluminium oxide 80–1
molten sodium chloride 74–5
motion, particles 48–50
mountain ranges 292
M_r *see* relative formula masses

names, salts 147, 183
naphtha 242
natural gas 194–5, 199–201, 242
naturally occurring materials *see* raw materials
negative ions *see* anions
neon isotopes 264
neutral point 146
neutralisation 142, 145–7, 150–1, 245
neutrons 258, 260
Newlands, John 92
Newlands' octaves 92
nitrate, test for 129
nitric acid 142, 143, 245–6
nitrogen 23, 241–7, 248–9, 282
Nitrogen Cycle Game 250–1

noble gases 94–5, 106–7, 267, 269
non-metals 94–5
  bonding 270, 272
  electricity conduction 73
  ionic compounds 182
  oxides 138–9, 181
normal faults 291
nuclei 178–9, 258–60, 266

oceanic crust 291, 292
oceans 281–2, 283
octaves, Law of 92
oil 1, 3, 36–7, 194–8, 202–3
optimum temperature 238
ores 2–3, 80, 84, 122–5, 295
organic fertilisers 248
oxidation 30–1, 83, 103, 119, 120–1, 214
oxides 24–5, 32–4
oxidising substances 15
oxy-acteylene torches 233
oxygen 22–5, 37, 39, 233
ozone 105

panning for gold 132
paper industry 151
particles 45–68, 235
  see also atoms
patterns and properties 89–112
periodic table 92–5, 108, 262, 267–9
permanent hardness 161
pesticides 36–7
petrol 202–3
pH 138, 140, 143, 145, 163, 238
photosynthesis 282
physical properties *see* properties
pig-iron 125–7
plants 145, 246, 248
plastics 4, 206–11, 220
plate tectonics 289–90, 292
platinum alloy 236
pollution 21, 32–4, 36–7, 40
polymerisation 206–8
polypropene 207
polythene 206–7
polyvinyl chloride (PVC) 104, 105, 207
'pop' test for hydrogen 6
positive ions *see* cations
potassium chloride 155
potassium manganate (VII) solution 47
precipitate tests 131
precipitation 153, 154, 234–5
preparation of salts 153–5
pressure 14, 242–4
products 5
properties 3–4

see also reactivity
alkali metals 90–1, 96–7
alloys 117
electron structure 267–8
halogens 100–1
metals 114–15
noble gases 106–7
patterns 89–112
periodic table 92–5, 108
relation to structure and use 172–3
transition metals 98–9
proteases 239
protons 258–60, 266
pure substances 2, 14–15
purification 81, 125, 127
PVC *see* polyvinyl chloride
pyrolysis 211

quicklime 156, 157

radiation 258–9, 265
radioactivity 273–4
radium 273–4
random movements 48
rates of reaction
  calculating 230–1
  catalysts 236–9
  concentration 233
  Haber process 243–4
  importance 229
  increasing 232–3
  surface area 232
  temperature 234–5
raw materials 1–4
rayon industry 151
reactions 5, 8–9
  alkane combustion 201
  displacement 103
  endothermic 194, 217–19
  equations 58–9
  exothermic 26, 31, 194, 201, 217–19
  halogens 102–3
  irreversible 240
  metals 118–21, 123–4
  rates 227–56
  redox 30–1, 83, 120–1
  reversible 240–1
reactivity
  see also rates of reaction
  alkali metals 96–7
  electron structure 267–8
  halogens 102–3
  metals 118–19, 123–4
  noble gases 106
  periodic table 95

series 119–20, 124
transition metals 99
recycling 81, 84, 187, 211
red copper oxide 63
redox reactions 30–1, 83, 120–1
reduction 30–1, 83, 120–1, 124–5, 126–7
refineries, oil 193, 203
refrigeration 180
relative atomic mass 56–7, 260–1, 264–5, 301
relative formula masses (Mr) 60–1, 62
residues 10
respiration 27
reverse faults 292
reversible reactions 240–1
rheostats 77
rift valleys 291
river erosion 294
rocks 284–8, 293, 295
rubber 188–9
rusting 28–9
Rutherford, Ernest 259–60, 266

sacrificial protection 29
salt *see* sodium chloride
salts 100, 147, 152–5, 183
San Andreas Fault 290
sandstone 285, 294
saturated compounds 199–203
saturated solutions 38
scum (soap) 158–9
seawater 3, 11, 281–2, 283
seaweed 100
sedimentary rock 284, 285–6, 288, 293
separation 10–13, 23, 196–8
sewage 36
shells 266–8
silicon dioxide glass 186
silver chloride 152
simple molecular structures 173, 177–9, 180
slag 127
slaked lime 156
slip 115
soap scum 158–9
soda glass 186
sodium 214
sodium carbonate 161
sodium chloride 3, 8, 11, 74–5, 97, 182–5
sodium hydroxide 130–1, 151–2, 184–5
softening water 160–1
soil 140–1, 248–9
solids 4, 49, 72–3, 173
solubility 21, 38–9, 41, 152–3
soluble aspirin 62

soluble salts 152–3, 154–5
solutes 11, 38
solution mining 97, 184
solutions 11, 12, 38, 46–7, 72, 73, 74
solvents 11, 12, 38–9
spectator ions 147
spectrometry, mass 263, 265
spectroscopy, emission 130
stalactites 160
stalagmites 160
standard pressure 14
state symbols 59
states of matter 4, 49–50
steel 2, 24, 30–1, 117, 127, 132
strong acids 143–4
structures
    carbon dioxide 180–1
    carbon fibre 188
    crystals 170–1
    diamond and graphite 174–6
    giant covalent (molecular) 173, 174–6
    giant ionic 173, 182–3
    giant metallic 173
    glass 186–7
    materials 169–92
    relation to properties and use 172–3
    rubber 188–9
    simple molecular 173, 177–9
    sodium chloride 184–5
    solids 173
sugar dissolving 46
sulphate, test for 129
sulphite, test for 129
sulphur 7, 139, 189
sulphur dioxide 138
sulphur trioxide 139
sulphuric acid
    contact process 138–9
    dehydrating agent 149
    molecular formula 53
    properties 142
    reaction with water 148–9
    strong acid 143
    sulphur mining 61
    uses 148
surface area, reaction rates 232
suspensions 11
symbols 51–2, 59
synthesis 6

tear faults 290
temperature 48–50, 234–5, 238
temporary hardness 161
tests
    ammonia 129

anions 128–9, 133
carbon dioxide 129
cations 130–1, 133
chlorine 102
halides 129
hydrogen 6
metals 130–1
tetrahedral bond arrangement 199
thermal decomposition 6, 128
thermosetting plastics 209–10, 211
thermosoftening plastics 209, 211
Thomson, J. J. 258
tin extraction 62
titration 146
TNT *see* trinitrotoluene
toxic substances 15, 102
transfer of electrons *see* ionic bonds
transition metals 94, 98–9
trilobites 287
trinitrotoluene (TNT) 242, 245

universal indicator 138, 146
unsaturated compounds 202–3
uranium 264
UV radiation 105

valency 179, 183
Van der Waals forces 177–9
volcanos 289, 291
volume, molar volume 61
vulcanisation 188

waste, plastics 210–11
water
    addition 213
    bonding 177
    of crystallisation 29, 152
    cycle 35–6, 283
    formation 59
    formula 57
    hard 158–61
    molecules 52, 53, 179
    pollution 36–7, 40
    properties 38–9
    purification 10, 41
    softening 160–1
    sulphuric acid 148, 149
weak acids 143–4
weathering 228, 288, 294
weight, atoms 55
wood 4
world food problem 249

X-rays 171

yeast 239